KU-490-264

Figures in a Wessex Landscape

For Bernard

and for Quentin, Phyllida,
Andrew, and Rowena

Figures in a Wessex Landscape

THOMAS HARDY's picture of English country life

Edited by Joanna Cullen Brown

Allison & Busby
Published by W.H. Allen & Co Plc

An Allison & Busby book
Published in 1987 by
W.H. Allen & Co Plc
44 Hill Street, London W1X 8LB

Printed and bound in Great Britain by
Adlard & Son Ltd, The Garden City Press

ISBN 0 85031 373 2

Contents

List of Illustrations

Black and white photographs

Watercolours by Henry Moule

Introduction

Of the fourteen novels Thomas Hardy wrote, the most well-known are those with rural characters and settings. We rightly think of Hardy as inseparable from Wessex, but this conclusion is often reached too superficially. We tend to forget that Hardy lived for five years in London, at an impressionable age and the outset of his career as an architect; and that he claimed to know "every street and alley west of St Paul's like a born Londoner, which he was often supposed to be".[1] It was only deteriorating health which took him back at this stage to Dorset; he tried subsequently to live again in London after his marriage, and spent a few weeks or months there almost every year until he was over seventy.

Yet London never really suited Hardy, physically, temperamentally, or creatively. Apart from the fact that he fell ill on almost every prolonged visit there, he frequently comments on its artificialities and damaging effect — "London, that *hotplate* of humanity, on which we first sing, then simmer, then boil, then dry away to dust and ashes!"[2] In those novels where he tried to portray cosmopolitan high society, somehow the spark of life often fails to kindle; and people like Lady Mabella Buttermead in *The Well-beloved* end up, as Lord David Cecil amusingly points out,[3] like characters out of *The Young Visiters*.

This comparative failure, in spite of Hardy's conscious observation and note-taking (in case, as he thought, he should be obliged to write "society" novels) is significant. It is plainly in contrast with his success in writing the country novels for which he is particularly remembered. It leads us to the realization that by the time Hardy's fame brought him friends in aristocratic circles, it was too late for his creative gift. Whether he would or no, it was his earliest experience, in deepest rural England, which made him a great poet and writer. It was that life as a child under the mysteries of "the full-starred heavens",[4] amid the multitudinous sounds and scents of the heath and the strange lights of the woods at evening, that generated and released in Thomas Hardy the extraordinary fires of his poetic imagination. To the end, Nature and the life of the country, with all the contradictions he came to see in them, remained for Hardy one of the mainsprings of his life and work.

In fourteen novels, about a thousand poems, two poetic dramas, articles such as "The Dorsetshire Labourer", and over forty not-so-short stories, Hardy has built up a picture of every aspect of nineteenth-century country life such as only the listener, watcher, and poet he was could perceive. His observation of the natural world is almost unparalleled. He also meditates, in a complex and often self-contradictory way, upon Nature and the universe, and their relationship to man both as an individual and in society.

With such an output, it is not surprising that only the dedicated Hardy student has the opportunity to form a rounded view of Hardy's understanding of Nature, the country, and the countryman. Yet this understanding should be of special interest to us. We live at a time when, in many parts of the world, global communication and travel have almost obliterated local and rural traditions; when the fashion in some circles to decry the past threatens to cut off twentieth-century men and women from all their roots — an unsound principle in husbandry; and when highly-populated countries need constant vigilance to ensure that there will even be any countryside left to enjoy.

Hardy the countryman has something of value to say on all these counts, and many more. This selection from his writings — poems and prose — has been made to illustrate how rich and deep is this vein, and how great are the rewards in reading more of him.

* *

When Thomas Hardy — third of that name — was born in 1840 in the cottage at Higher Bockhampton, on the rim of the heath he later immortalized, he was born into a country childhood and a deeply rural community which he never forgot, and which affected his whole life. On the south side, the cottage garden merged with a plantation where he could hear the winter birds roosting in the hollies, where weird lights and shadows at dusk caused strange visions among the trees. To the east, the two or three beeches whose long fingers brushed the cottage walls gave way at once to the upward slope of the great heath, rising to the ancient tumuli of Rainbarrows and the sudden drop from the ridge to the lush Frome Valley beyond. Even as an infant, when one hot day his mother found a snake curled peacefully on his breast as the two slept unheeding in his cradle, he was tied up with the living scene around him. Children brought up in solitary country places, he noted many years later, are "imaginative, dreamy, and credulous of vague mysteries. The Unknown comes within so short a radius from themselves by comparison with the city-bred".[5] Hardy was certainly all of these things, exceptionally sensitive to the beauty of words and music and the natural world around him. At the age of only four or five, he tells us, he had discovered the precise step where the setting sun flooded the Venetian-red stair of the cottage; and every evening he would sit there alone, reciting aloud Watt's hymn "And now another day is gone", as a kind of private incantation.

As a child, Hardy never wanted to grow up or leave his own community. As a man, he was always nostalgic about his country childhood, countless poems, stories, and jottings celebrating its joys and the surroundings that made him. "Logs on the Hearth"[6] shows him as an old man gazing at the burning wood on his fire, and remembering each fork and bough of the tree it had been when he climbed it with his sister. A diary note recalls how, full of curiosity one day, he had gone down on all fours in the eweleaze and pretended to eat grass, to see what the sheep would do: and when he looked up, they were all around him in a close ring, gazing with astonished faces. "Childhood Among the Ferns"[7] sums up his feelings then.

Yet it was not just natural beauty that formed him, but the warm consciousness of the community where he belonged. Although the "Mellstock Quire" of his grandfather, father, and uncle, justly famed in that part of Dorset, was disbanded only a year or two after he was born, it was still the life-breath of the family, and figures with affectionate pride in many poems and short stories besides *Under the Greenwood Tree*. His own part, singing in church and as an unpaid entertainer, fiddling with his father at many a wedding or village festivity until he was a young man, continued the family tradition and deepened his knowledge of the country community. (Hardy himself tells the story of how, as a boy of thirteen or fourteen playing at a dance, he was only stopped after a frenetic three-quarters of an hour of non-stop fiddling by the anxious hostess fearful for his blood-vessels. . . .) It also explains his unrivalled knowledge of hymn, psalm, and country-dance tunes (recognized by the Dorset Regiment when in 1907 they wrote from India, asking him for a suitable marching tune "with the required local affinity"[8]) and his endearing picture of the part played by music and dancing in the do-it-yourself entertainment of country life at this time.

Hardy's sense of the community, and its past, was widened too by others besides the Choir: his paternal grandmother, who lived with them until she died when he was seventeen, and

> With cap-framed face and long gaze into the embers —
> — We seated around her knees —[9]

told her tales of Buonaparte, and the beacon alarms of Dorset, the maypole dances, and the creaking gibbet under the lightning flash. There were the Mummers he pictured in *The Return of the Native*; the "girls resembling the three dairymaids in *Tess* [who] used to get me to write their love-letters for them when I was a little boy";[10] and Louie, the rich farmer's daughter loved from afar but discouraged from knowing him, to whom he only once murmured "Good evening" in the lane. When, in 1910, Hardy was given the freedom of Dorchester, it was characteristic of him that he asked: "Where is the Dorchester of my early recollection — I mean the human Dorchester — the kernel — of which the houses were but the shell?" And pointing to the cemetery he went on: "There is the Dorchester I know best."[11] People always came first. As a boy of nine he was taken, wide-eyed, to a harvest supper in the old barn at Kingston Maurward Manor (and met soldiers for the first time — invited by the squire as dancing partners for the farm girls). The scene never faded from his long memory: those young women in their light gowns sitting on benches against the wall, and the last of the traditional harvest-home ballads sung, before the railway and other new influences brought to Dorchester all the comic songs from London which were to swamp them for ever.

Country traditions and folklore were something Hardy felt passionately about. "At the dates represented in the various narrations things were like that in Wessex: the inhabitants lived in certain ways, engaged in certain occupations, kept alive certain customs, just as they are shown doing in these pages . . .".[12] Local papers gave accounts of wife-selling earlier in the century, and of skimmington rides even as Hardy was writing *The Mayor of Casterbridge.* One of his cousins was regarded as a witch, and cases similar to Susan Nunsuch's stabbing of Eustacia were being reported as late as 1883 and 1884. In *The Woodlanders*, Grace Melbury's horse was "hag-rid" and called forth more tales of equestrian witches; Tess imagined the pricking and ducking of witches as she walked by night along Blackmoor Vale; *The Return of the Native* is full of wax effigies and crooked sixpences and the hint of an evil eye through a side window. Ordinary superstitions abounded too. The bees swarming on Dick Dewy's wedding-day were an unlooked-for piece of luck; but if anyone died in the Hintocks, the hives had to be tapped to wake the bees, or they would pine away — and the cock that crowed on the afternoon that Tess was married was an ill-omen. Whether it be a whole story based on these "smouldering village beliefs",[13] like *The Withered Arm*, or a more incidental use, Hardy's stories are close-woven throughout with threads of country lore.

And his country people talked as they worked, their tales and chronicles passing on the traditions as their hands were busied with copse-work or milking. Hardy's knowledge of rural occupations was extensive and fundamental. He knew about the

"singular heart-shaped spade" used by the peat-cutters on the heath,[14] how furze was carted and stacked, and how in the long summer days a man could live by cutting faggots which sold at half a crown a hundred.[15] He knew the different sounds of the sheep bell, according to the activities of the sheep; the delicate operation needed to prick the wind from the clover-swollen flock; and how the turning of the wheel to grind the sheep shears brought leaden dizziness to the head. He knew all about lime-burning, and the curious aura of freshness it imparted to the lime-burner himself; about wimbling hay-bonds, the tear of the ripping-tool in the woodlanders' barking season, and the role of each hand in the making of spars for thatching. He knew the best recipes for mead, and the glories of cider-making in the "blue stagnant air of autumn" (an activity last shared by Hardy with his own father in 1873, and never by him forgotten), with all those richly-varied, mellow-countenanced apples and their ineffable "sweet smells and oozings".[16] He knew how the pails were hung in a dairy, and what time of the year "brought great changes to the world of kine"; and how the "squish-squash" of the milk rolling in the great churn changed when the butter came to a "decided flick-flack". He knew about the rigours of reed-drawing, how to thatch a rick, and about different kinds of thatch supports. He knew the changing sounds of a mill as it moved from one operation to another. Is there anything significant about these rural occupations that he did not know? It would be hard to find.

Yet it would be easy to stop at an idyllic picture full of local colour. Nothing could be further from what Charles Morgan saw in Hardy as "the passionate boldness of his mind".[17] For as he knew the country people of his native heath, so he knew how they lived and worked, and how many of them, in the agricultural depressions of the nineteenth century, suffered from poverty, injustice, and humiliation. A survey in 1837 showed that the agricultural labourers of Cheshire led the country with 13 shillings per week, while those in "the wretched villages of Dorsetshire . . . where the traveller sees the worst of houses and the poorest of labourers"[18] came last with seven shillings and sixpence or less. Tied cottages and insecurity of labour were the rule; even when conditions had somewhat improved, Hardy notes wryly in his diary (1884): "It is now spring; when, according to the poets, birds pipe, and (the householder adds) day-labourers get independent after their preternatural civility through the frost and snow."[19] Sadder still was the lot of lifeholders like Giles Winterborne and the Durbeyfields (and some who were driven, alas, to Casterbridge's notorious Mixen Lane), whose home only lasted three generations: at the third death their cottage was taken from them, often only for destruction. (Hardy's birthplace itself was held on these terms by his father.) The lifeholder system was one of the chief causes of the demise of the skilled craftsman — "the backbone of the village life"[20] — one of Hardy's special concerns; but at least it kept people at home, and helped to check the migration which was fatal, not only to cottage horticulture, but "to the preservation of local skills and traditions, close inter-social relations, and eccentric individualities".[21] Hardy could see the dilemma clearly enough, wanting that preservation, but passionately wanting wrongs to be righted and the countryside to share in general progress. When Farfrae's management methods improved Henchard's business,

> letters and ledgers took the place of "I'll do't," and "you shall hae 't"; and, as in all such cases of advance, the rugged picturesqueness of the old method disappeared with its inconveniences.[22]

Neither in his famous "The Dorsetshire Labourer" article of 1883, nor his letter to the enquiring Rider Haggard in 1902, did Hardy offer easy solutions. Yet he never forgot what he had known, or heard at first hand, in the past — the cholera epidemic in the Dorchester slums when he was fourteen, the sheep-keeping boy he knew who "to my horror, . . . died of want, the contents of his stomach at the autopsy being raw turnip only";[23] the two public hangings he had seen as a lad, and his father's story (retold in "The Withered Arm") of the youth who had been hanged after merely watching one of the many protest rick-burnings earlier in the century. And in his novels with characteristic compassion he showed how the loss of the Durbeyfield home caused Tess's final disaster, how Oak the skilled shepherd was forced to parade himself for hire as a general labourer at the Fair; how the old Maltster was only employed for eleven months of the year so that he might not become a charge on the parish; and how the dying Fanny Robin was reduced to the workhouse. Most moving perhaps are his glimpses of the sweated labour of young women: Marty South working at her sick father's rough spar-making far into the night for eighteen pence a thousand; and above all the "steam tyrant", the diabolical threshing-machine which nearly broke Tess.

In spite of such miseries, however, Hardy was convinced that life in the country was nobler, or produced a finer human being, then city life. "A pure atmosphere and a pastoral environment", he wrote in "The Dorsetshire Labourer", "are a very appreciable portion of that sustenance which tends to produce the sound mind and body". Nature has its own healing powers, and the solitude of less populated places is also creative. Marty South's face "had the usual fulness of expression which is developed by a life of solitude".[24] (Is this partly why many modern actors playing in Hardy films are often so unconvincing?) Gabriel Oak under the stars on Norcombe Hill experienced the supreme beauty of the scene and its "complete abstraction" from "the sights and sounds of man".[25] Natural, country living produces the right values, and shows up shoddy ones. Hardy once commented typically on the Assizes at Dorchester that "the Lord Chief Justice, eminent counsel etc. reveal more of their weaknesses and vanities here in the country than in London".[26] *Jude the Obscure* is full of the contrasts between town and country values. For Hardy too often the town was the home of "Men with a wintry sneer, and women with tart disparagings" where "I seem to be false to myself".[27] Too often "the smear of 'civilization'"[28] sullies human existence. "Rural low life," wrote Hardy, "may reveal coarseness of considerable leaven; but that libidinousness which makes the scum of cities so noxious is not usually there."[29]

Yet just as he was not blind to the injustices and squalor of some rural working conditions, so Hardy was not blind to the other face of solitude, and the grave drawbacks of living in sparse, inbred country communities. Though "isolation on a heath renders vulgarity well-nigh impossible",[30] it also produced the searing loneliness of Eustacia's tragedy. The village social hierarchies too could cause heartache, the intermarriages "of Hapsburgian frequency"[31] only increased the tightness of an ingrowing and inward-looking community where choice and opportunities were still further limited. Eustacia, her life now narrowed with a half-blind, furze-cutting husband to the empty shell of their isolated cottage on the heath, walks over to East Egdon to join in a village festivity on a grassy plateau. There among the fifteen or twenty dancing couples "a beholder might well have wondered how such a prepossessing set of young women of like size, age, and disposition, could have been collected together where there were only one or two villages to choose from."[32] But Hardy goes on to the heart of the problem, which he further developed in *The Woodlanders* and *Tess*. "A whole village-full of sensuous emotion, scattered abroad all the year long, surged here in focus for an hour."[33] In such rural situations as this, and the Hintocks, and the life of Tess and her workmates, "dramas of a grandeur and unity truly Sophoclean are enacted in the real, by virtue of the concentrated passions and closely-knit interdependence of the lives therein."[34] Where there were no urban distractions, no other places to escape to, love and friendship were everything in life. Feelings and sufferings were consequently the more intense, fatalism in this regard the natural thing, for what choice had they? "It was to be."

Shut in among themselves as they were, these country people at least communicated deeply and closely with each other. They never looked through people as Jude was looked through, serenely unnoticed, by the nonchalant undergraduates of Christminster. The countrymen who met near Dogbury Gate talked of "Life and Death at Sunrise"[35] in the most natural way. Even the silent trudge of two people along the heath track, which opens *The Return of the Native*, is, as Hardy points out, its own way of communication. More typical are the many scenes of general conversation in all the stories, from the ready acceptance of the first two Strangers at the christening party at Higher Crowstairs, to the priceless, ageless ruminations of Joseph Poorgrass and his fellows. Hardy's portrayal of country humour, with its incongruities, its wisdom, its eccentricities, and its simplicity, must rank him with the Immortals. It deserves a study longer than space allows here: the selections must speak for themselves.[36] Yet this is perhaps the moment to remind ourselves clearly that even in his humour Hardy rarely makes fools of his country folk. Writing to the *Cornhill Magazine* about the illustrations for his forthcoming serial *Far from the Madding Crowd*, Hardy underlined his "hope that the rustics, although *quaint*, may be made to appear intelligent and not boorish at all".[37] In "The Dorsetshire Labourer", and later in a famous passage in *Tess*,[38] Hardy discusses seriously the nature of the true countryman; and it is a recurrent theme, as these selections will show.

Hardy was quick to point out too why the Dorset country people, unlike the "strained, calculating, unromantic middle classes', were full of character. Descended from the Normans, from the local squires (and their wild oats), and even, visibly, from the Romans, "they are the representatives of antiquity.... I have seen faces here that are the duplicates of those fine faces I saw at Fiesole, where also I picked up Roman coins the counterpart of those we find here so often."[39]

The past was ever-present with Hardy. "We two kept house, the Past and I...."[40] He was constantly preoccupied with its visible remains and its invisible aura — the presence of old Rome in every Casterbridge street and alley, the ghost of the Lear-like King Ina on the heath; the now-neglected lane which "had been a highway to Queen Elizabeth's subjects and the cavalcades of the past";[41] the lonely track below High Stoy Hill haunted by the shades of all who have travelled it.[42] One of the things that makes Marygreen so depressing a setting for Jude is that

> the fresh harrow-lines seemed to stretch like the channellings in a piece of new corduroy, lending a meanly utilitarian air to the expanse, taking away its gradations, and depriving it of all history....[43]

This ever-present past was nearer to the country-dweller than to the citizen. "It is among such communities as these that happiness will find her last refuge on earth, since it is among them that a perfect insight into the conditions of existence will be longest postponed," wrote Hardy.[44] The "postponement" was because of the time lag between town and country life. "Samplers are out of date — horribly countrified," exclaims Bathsheba Troy.[45] For Clym Yeobright, turning his back on Paris to return to help his fellows on Egdon Heath, the discrepancy had unfortunate consequences: "the rural world was not ripe for him".[46] Hardy saw that in his particularly rural part of Wessex the past was still almost the present:

> The citizen's *Then* is the rustic's *Now*... In Weatherbury three or four score years were included in the mere present, and nothing less than a century set a mark on its face or tone.[47]

Though the past had its evils, yet its continuity with the present made for wholeness. Unlike the changing functions of city buildings, the great mediaeval barn used for the sheep-shearing was still fulfilling its original ancient purpose, still warm in its welcome to shearer and shorn, as it had been in the time of Shakespeare.

> Here at least the spirit of the ancient builders was at one with the spirit of the modern beholder.... So the barn was natural to the shearers, and the shearers were in harmony with the barn.[48]

It was natural that Hardy, a professional architect, should particularly observe and appreciate the great barn. He also painted country life in farm and cottage interiors: chimney corners, and chimney-crooks that had to be pushed up,[49] the significance of the placing of candles for a party, the twisting oak stairs and worm-eaten floorboards of Weatherbury Upper Farm, Grammer Oliver winding the spit in the Melburys' homely kitchen, Mrs Yeobright's party sitting-room with the broad old settle where "songs and old tales are drawn from the occupants by the comfortable heat, like fruit from melon-plants in a frame".[50] The simplicity of some of his interiors underlines the material simplicity, and sometimes the poverty, of his country people's lives. In Marty South's uncurtained cottage the chimney smokes and so the door must be kept ajar; she gets cold as she works into the small hours, and her only, and ingenious, protection against the draught is a large blue umbrella, and a cloth draped over the door-opening and the window. Simplicity in furnishings is of course echoed by simplicity in clothes: of Barber Percomb "it could be seen by a glance at his rather finical style of dress that he did not belong to the country proper".[51] Even in the "venerable one coat" of Egdon Heath "lay a certain vein of satire on human vanity in clothes".[52]

Perhaps Hardy was thinking of Marty South and her cottage when he wrote, the year after *The Woodlanders*, that "Countrymen . . . are born, as may be said, with only an open door between them and the four seasons".[53] Though the four seasons do appear in this book, they are not as well represented as those who know the country life would acknowledge to be necessary. I hope to complement this picture of Hardy and country life with a second volume about Hardy and Nature: his experience and knowledge of it, his use of imagery and symbolism relating to it, and his views on man, Nature, and God. This may explain certain omissions from this volume; lack of space probably explains most others. I should be rash to say that Hardy almost wrote everything about everything — except, often, the things that concerned him most deeply — though Hardy students collecting material must sometimes feel this. However not everything has been quoted here. I have been able to give only an impression, and not an exhaustive catalogue. Sometimes obvious passages are omitted in favour of less well known ones, and vice versa. Where I have been unable to quote a long passage or poem I have usually referred the reader to it.

I should like to acknowledge my general debt to the many Hardy scholars whose work has enriched my understanding of Hardy. My thanks are due to the Trustees of the Dorset County Museum, Dorchester, for permission to reproduce some of their Henry Moule watercolours. For permission to quote, I thank the following: the Trustees of the Thomas Hardy Memorial Collection in the Dorset County Museum, Dorchester, Dorset, for extracts from Hardy's notebooks; Oxford University Press and the Trustees of the Thomas Hardy Estate for lines from Hardy's letters; Jonathan Cape Ltd for extracts from *Friends of a Lifetime*. I should also like to thank my old friend and teacher Mrs Katharine Moore for encouraging me to compile this book at the outset, and for his never-failing support and wise counsel, my husband.

Afterwards

When the Present has latched its postern behind my tremulous stay,
  And the May month flaps its glad green leaves like wings,
Delicate-filmed as new-spun silk, will the neighbours say,
  "He was a man who used to notice such things"?

If it be in the dusk when, like an eyelid's soundless blink,
  The dewfall-hawk comes crossing the shades to alight
Upon the wind-warped upland thorn, a gazer may think,
  "To him this must have been a familiar sight."

If I pass during some nocturnal blackness, mothy and warm,
  When the hedgehog travels furtively over the lawn,
One may say, "He strove that such innocent creatures should come to no harm,
  But he could do little for them; and now he is gone."

If, when hearing that I have been stilled at last, they stand at the door,
  Watching the full-starred heavens that winter sees,
Will this thought rise on those who will meet my face no more,
  "He was one who had an eye for such mysteries"?

And will any say when my bell of quittance is heard in the gloom,
  And a crossing breeze cuts a pause in its outrollings,
Till they swell again, as they were a new bell's boom,
  "He hears it not now, but used to notice such things"?

I

HARDY'S COUNTRY ROOTS

1 Hardy's Places

Hardy's childhood memories stretched back to a remote and primitive Dorset. "I have seen with my own eyes things that many people believe to have been extinct for centuries",[54] *he told William Archer in 1901. They included, to quote his own words, "seeing men in the stocks, corn-law agitations, mail-coaches, road-waggons, tinder-boxes, and candle-snuffing"*[55] *– and mummers and maypoles. When he was only six or seven he was marching around the garden brandishing a little wooden sword dipped in a newly-killed pig's blood and crying: "Free Trade or blood!"*[56] *He also had a vivid memory of the No-Popery riots of 1850, when effigies of the Pope and the new and fervently-proselytizing Archbishop Wiseman of Westminster were burned in Dorchester's Roman amphitheatre; he was extremely bewildered when, in the lurid procession, the cowl of one of the monks blew aside to reveal one of his father's workmen.*

None of this however stimulated him to wish to be a man who could take his full part in such exciting events. An early experience stood out for him: when as a small boy he lay in the sun, straw hat over his face filtering the sun, and thought how useless he was, and how he never wanted to grow up. This was turned into a poem, "Childhood Among the Ferns" (and into a passage in Jude the Obscure *in which he added much of the grown man's philosophy about Nature and the Universe).*

Hardy's childhood influenced him almost beyond measure: the older he grew, the more he wrote of it and with it, an apparently inexhaustible fount of inspiration and imaginative energy. It may be significant that on his death-bed he asked for kettle-broth, and for a rasher of bacon to be cooked on the flame of his bedroom fire, as he must have seen it cooked so often in his childhood home at Bockhampton.

Childhood among the Ferns

I sat one sprinkling day upon the lea,
Where tall-stemmed ferns spread out luxuriantly,
And nothing but those tall ferns sheltered me.

The rain gained strength, and damped each lopping frond,
Ran down their stalks beside me and beyond,
And shaped slow-creeping rivulets as I conned,

With pride, my spray-roofed house. And though anon
Some drops pierced its green rafters, I sat on,
Making pretence I was not rained upon.

The sun then burst, and brought forth a sweet breath
From the limp ferns as they dried underneath:
I said: "I could live on here thus till death";

And queried in the green rays as I sate:
"Why should I have to grow to man's estate,
And this afar-noised World perambulate?"

Winter Words

Hardy's birthplace and the parish church of Stinsford, where the Hardy family provided the music for over one hundred years, Hardy himself singing in the choir and also for a time teaching in the Sunday School, were places which were primarily connected with people – people who, in their different ways, gave him his sense of community and folk-lore and the past.

The surrounding countryside of "Egdon" Heath and the Frome Valley were vitally important to him in a different way, which lies within the scope of another volume and is not therefore illustrated here.

THE BIRTHPLACE AT HIGHER BOCKHAMPTON

Hardy was born on 2 June 1840, in the long, low thatched cottage which his great-grandfather John had built for Hardy's grandfather (first of three Thomas Hardys) at the beginning of the century. It was in a hamlet of only eight houses; behind it rose the heath.

Domicilium

It faces west, and round the back and sides
High beeches, bending, hang a veil of boughs,
And sweep against the roof. Wild honeysucks
Climb on the walls, and seem to sprout a wish
(If we may fancy wish of trees and plants)
To overtop the apple-trees hard by.

Red roses, lilacs, variegated box
Are there in plenty, and such hardy flowers
As flourish best untrained. Adjoining these
Are herbs and esculents; and farther still
A field; then cottages with trees, and last
The distant hills and sky.

Behind, the scene is wilder. Heath and furze
Are everything that seems to grow and thrive
Upon the uneven ground. A stunted thorn
Stands here and there, indeed; and from a pit

An oak uprises, springing from a seed
Dropped by some bird a hundred years ago.

In days bygone —
Long gone — my father's mother, who is now
Blest with the blest, would take me out to walk.
At such a time I once inquired of her
How looked the spot when first she settled here.
The answer I remember. "Fifty years
Have passed since then, my child, and change has marked
The face of all things. Yonder garden-plots
And orchards were uncultivated slopes
O'ergrown with bramble bushes, furze and thorn:
That road a narrow path shut in by ferns,
Which, almost trees, obscured the passer-by.

"Our house stood quite alone, and those tall firs
And beeches were not planted. Snakes and efts
Swarmed in the summer days, and nightly bats
Would fly about our bedrooms. Heathcroppers
Lived on the hills, and were our only friends;
So wild it was when first we settled here."

These lines – the earliest surviving of Hardy's poetry – were written between 1857 and 1860, but not published until two private limited editions in 1916 and 1918. They were however chosen by Hardy to be included in the Early Life of Thomas Hardy, *which appeared under his wife's name shortly after his death in 1928.*

Christmas Eve at the Tranter's House[57]

It was a long low cottage with a hipped roof of thatch, having dormer windows breaking up into the eaves, a chimney standing in the middle of the ridge and another at each end. The window-shutters were not yet closed, and the fire- and candle-light within radiated forth upon the thick bushes of box and laurestinus growing in clumps outside, and upon the bare boughs of several codlin-trees hanging about in various distorted shapes, the result of early training as espaliers combined with careless climbing into their boughs in later years. The walls of the dwelling were for the most part covered with creepers, though these were rather beaten back from the doorway — a feature which was worn and scratched by much passing in and out, giving it by day the appearance of an old keyhole. Light streamed through the cracks and joints of outbuildings a little way from the cottage, a sight which nourished a fancy that the purpose of the erection must be rather to veil bright attractions than to shelter unsightly necessaries. The noise of a beetle[58] and wedges and the splintering of wood was periodically heard from this direction; and at some little distance further a steady regular munching and the occasional scurr of a rope betokened a stable, and horses feeding within it.

The choir stamped severally on the door-stone to shake from their boots any fragment of earth or leaf adhering thereto, then entered the house and looked around to survey the condition of things. Through the open doorway of a small inner room on the right hand, of a character between pantry and cellar, was Dick Dewy's father Reuben, by vocation a "tranter", or irregular carrier....

Being now occupied in bending over a hogshead that stood in the pantry ready horsed for the process of broaching, he did not take the trouble to turn or raise his eyes at the entry of his visitors, well knowing by their footsteps that they were the expected old comrades.

The main room, on the left, was decked with bunches of holly and other evergreens, and from the middle of the beam bisecting the ceiling hung the mistletoe, of a size out of all proportion to the room, and extending so low that it became necessary for a full-grown person to walk round it in passing, or run the risk of entangling his hair....

Mrs Dewy sat in a brown settle by the side of the glowing wood fire — so glowing that with a heedful compression of the lips she would now and then rise and put her hand upon the hams and flitches of bacon lining the chimney, to reassure herself that they were not being broiled instead of smoked — a misfortune that had been known to happen now and then at Christmas-time.

"Hullo, my sonnies, here you be, then!" said Reuben Dewy at length, standing up and blowing forth a vehement gust of breath. "How the blood do puff up in anybody's head, to be sure, a-stooping like that! I was just going out to gate to hark for ye." He then carefully began to wind a strip of brown paper round a brass tap he held in his hand. "This in the cask here is a drop o' the right sort" (tapping the cask); "'tis a real drop o' cordial from the best picked apples — Sansoms, Stubbards, Five-corners, and such-like — you d' mind the sort, Michael?" (Michael nodded.) "And there's a sprinkling of they that grow down by the orchard-rails — streaked ones — rail apples we d'call 'em, as 'tis by the rails they grow, and not knowing the right name. The water-cider[59] from 'em is as good as most people's best cider is."...

"Come in, come in, and draw up to the fire; never mind your shoes," said Mrs Dewy, seeing that all except Dick had paused to wipe them upon the doormat. "I am glad that you've stepped up-along at last; and, Susan, you run down to Grammer Kaytes's and see if you can borrow some larger candles than these fourteens.[60] Tommy Leaf, don't ye be afeard! Come and sit here in the settle."

Under the Greenwood Tree

Grammer Kaytes, who is also referred to in A Pair of Blue Eyes, *was a real person, Rachel Keats, who lived next door to the Hardys – the spelling reveals local pronunciation. Her son William, a tranter, and his family lived opposite, and were the Dewys of this novel.*

The House of Hospitalities

Here we broached the Christmas barrel,
   Pushed up the charred log-ends;
Here we sang the Christmas carol,
         And called in friends.

Time has tired me since we met here
   When the folk now dead were young.
Since the viands were outset here
         And quaint songs sung.

And the worm has bored the viol
   That used to lead the tune,
Rust eaten out the dial
         That struck night's noon.

Now no Christmas brings in neighbours,
   And the New Year comes unlit;
Where we sang the mole now labours,
         And spiders knit.

Yet at midnight if here walking,
   When the moon sheets wall and tree,
I see forms of old time talking,
         Who smile on me.

Time's Laughingstocks

This was not strictly the Hardy house – though it played such a part on many occasions – but probably "the house by the well", neighbouring in the lane, which also appears in a short story, "Enter a Dragoon".

Other things beside parties for the "Quire" happened at the Hardys' cottage:

[1871] *March 22nd.* Smuggling, etc. While superintending the church music from 1801 onwards to about 1805 my grandfather used to do a little in smuggling, his house being a lonely one, none of the others in Higher Bockhampton being then built, or only one other. He sometimes had as many as eighty "tubs" in a dark closet (afterwards destroyed in altering the staircase) — each tub containing four gallons. The spirits often smelt all over the house, being proof, and had to be lowered for drinking. The tubs, or little elongated barrels, were of thin staves with wooden hoops: I remember one of them which had been turned into a bucket by knocking out one head and putting a handle. They were brought at night by men on horseback, "slung", or in carts. A whiplash across the window-pane would wake my grandfather at two or three in the morning, and he would dress and go down. Not a soul was there, but a heap of tubs loomed up in front of the door. He would set to work and stow them away in the dark closet aforesaid, and nothing more would happen till dusk the following evening, when groups of dark long-bearded fellows would arrive, and carry off the tubs in two and fours slung over their shoulders.

The smugglers grew so bold at last that they would come by day, and my grandmother insisted to her husband that he should stop receiving the tubs, which he did about 1805, though not till at a christening of one of their children they had "a washing pan of pale brandy" left them by the smugglers to make merry with. Moreover the smugglers could not be got to leave off depositing the tubs for some while, but they did so when a second house was built about a hundred yards off.

Many years later, indeed, I think in my mother's time, a large woman used to call, and ask if any of "it" was wanted cheap. Her hugeness was caused by her having bullocks' bladders slung round her hips, in which she carried the spirits. She was known as "Mother Rogers".

Memoranda I

The isolation so useful to the smugglers also meant that Hardy's most formative years were based in very deep country. Staying there again in April 1868 he tried to take down the exact notes of the nightingales which sang outside the bedroom windows; by the time he and his wife came to write the Life, *he noted that the nightingales sang there no more.*

A Bird-Scene at a Rural Dwelling

When the inmate stirs, the birds retire discreetly
From the window-ledge, whereon they whistled sweetly
    And on the step of the door,
    In the misty morning hoar;
  But now the dweller is up they flee
  To the crooked neighbouring codlin-tree;
And when he comes fully forth they seek the garden,
And call from the lofty costard, as pleading pardon
    For shouting so near before
    In their joy at being alive:—
Meanwhile the hammering clock within goes five.

I know a domicile of brown and green,
Where for a hundred summers there have been
Just such enactments, just such daybreaks seen.

Human Shows

On the centenary of Trafalgar Day, 21 October 1905, Hardy wrote to his friend Mrs Henniker: "You may like me to tell you that my relations are the only people we can discover in this part of the county who are still living in the same house they occupied on the day of the battle 100 years ago (in the direct line of descent)."

The Self-Unseeing

Here is the ancient floor,
Footworn and hollowed and thin,
Here was the former door
Where the dead feet walked in.

She sat here in her chair,
Smiling into the fire;
He who played stood there,
Bowing it higher and higher.

Childlike, I danced in a dream;
Blessings emblazoned that day;
Everything glowed with a gleam;
Yet we were looking away!

Poems of the Past and Present

Hardy's birthplace, and his experiences there, recur frequently and significantly in his writings throughout his life. There, besides poetry, he wrote his first novel The Poor Man and the Lady, *which though never published was later dismembered and partly used in* Under the Greenwood Tree, Desperate Remedies, *and* An Indiscretion in the Life of an Heiress. *At Bockhampton he also wrote parts of* Desperate Remedies *and* A Pair of Blue Eyes, Under the Greenwood Tree, *and* Far from the Madding Crowd. *During his parents' lifetime he visited them there nearly every Sunday when he was living in Dorchester; after his mother's death in 1904 he continued to visit his brother and two sisters who returned to live there until they moved in 1912 to Talbothays, the house at West Stafford which Hardy designed for them. From 1913 to 1921 the writer Hermann Lea lived in the birthplace; after he left, Hardy still visited the empty house until shortly before his death, sometimes showing it to friends like J.M. Barrie (May 1921). Since 1948 the house has belonged to the National Trust. On a visit in May 1922 Hardy found the house and garden unkempt – and, as often, said he would never go there again.*

Concerning His Old Home

Mood I

I wish to see it never —
　　That dismal place
　　With cracks in its floor —
I would forget it ever!

Mood II
To see it once, that sad
And memoried place —
Yes, just once more —
I should be faintly glad!

Mood III
To see it often again —
That friendly place
With its green low door —
I'm willing anywhen!

Mood IV
I'll haunt it night and day —
That lovable place,
With its flowers' rich store
That drives regret away!

Winter Words

Max Gate, Dorchester *April 26th, 1924*

My dear Mr Cockerell,
The bulbs you gave us have made a most magnificent show this spring. The crown imperial lilies are a marvellous sight, and T.H. gave a cry of joy when he saw them the other day. He said he had not seen any since they grew in his old garden at Bockhampton. . . .

With our kindest regards and many thanks.

Yours sincerely,

Florence Hardy.

Silences

There is the silence of a copse or croft
When the wind sinks dumb,
And of a belfry-loft
When the tenor after tolling stops its hum.

And there's the silence of a lonely pond
Where a man was drowned,
Nor nigh nor yond
A newt, frog, toad, to make the merest sound.

But the rapt silence of an empty house
Where oneself was born,
Dwelt, held carouse
With friends, is of all silences most forlorn!

Past are remembered songs and music-strains
Once audible there:
Roof, rafters, panes
Look absent-thoughted, tranced, or locked in prayer.

It seems no power on earth can waken it
Or rouse its rooms,
Or its past permit
The present to stir a torpor like a tomb's.

Winter Words

STINSFORD ("MELLSTOCK") CHURCH

At the foot of an incline the church became visible through the north gate, or "church hatch", as it was called here. Seven agile figures in a clump were observable beyond, which proved to be the choristers waiting; sitting on an altar-tomb to pass the time, and letting their heels dangle against it. The musicians being now in sight the youthful party scampered off and rattled up the old wooden stairs of the gallery like a regiment of cavalry; the other boys of the parish waiting outside and observing birds, cats, and other creatures till the vicar entered, when they suddenly subsided into sober church-goers, and passed down the aisle with echoing heels.

The gallery of Mellstock Church had a status and sentiment of its own. A stranger there was regarded with a feeling altogether differing from that of the congregation below towards him. Banished from the nave as an intruder whom no originality could make interesting, he was received above as a curiosity that no unfitness could render dull. The gallery, too, looked down upon and knew the habits of the nave to its remotest peculiarity, and had an extensive stock of exclusive information about it; whilst the nave knew nothing of the gallery folk, as gallery folk, beyond their loud-sounding minims and chest notes. Such topics as that the clerk was always chewing tobacco except at the moment of crying amen; that he had a dust-hole in his pew; that during the sermon certain young daughters of the village had left off caring to read anything so mild as the marriage service for some years, and now regularly studied the one which chronologically follows it; that a pair of lovers touched fingers through a knot-hole between their pews in the manner ordained by their great exemplars, Pyramus and Thisbe; that Mrs Ledlow, the farmer's wife, counted her money and reckoned her week's marketing expenses during the first lesson — all news to those below — were stale subjects here.

Old William sat in the centre of the front row, his violoncello between his knees and two singers on each hand. Behind him, on the left, came the treble singers and Dick; and on the right the tranter and the tenors. Further back was old Mail with the altos and supernumeraries.

Under the Greenwood Tree

Apl. 1871. In Church. The sibilants in the responses of the congregation, who bend their heads like pine-trees in a wind.

Memoranda I

The congregation in Tollamore Church were singing the evening hymn, the people gently swaying backwards and forwards like trees in a soft breeze. The heads of the village children, who sat in the gallery, were inclined to one side as they uttered their shrill notes, their eyes listlessly tracing some crack in the old walls, or following the movement of a distant bough or bird, with features rapt almost to painfulness...

Afternoon service in Tollamore parish was later than in many others in that neighbourhood; and as the darkness deepened during the progress of the sermon, the rector's pulpit-candles shone to the remotest nooks of the building, till at length they became the sole lights of the congregation. The lady was the single person besides the preacher whose face was turned westwards, the pew that she occupied being the only one in the church in which the seat ran all around.... Over her head rose a vast marble monument, erected to the memory of her ancestors, male and female; for she was one of high standing in that parish. The design consisted of a winged skull and two cherubim, supporting a pair of tall Corinthian columns, between which spread a broad slab, containing the roll of ancient names, lineages, and deeds, and surmounted by a pediment, with the crest of the family at its apex.

As the youthful schoolmaster gazed, and all these details became dimmer, her face was modified in his fancy, till it seemed almost to resemble the carved marble skull immediately above her head. The thought was unpleasant enough to arouse him from his half-dreamy state....

An Indiscretion in the Life of an Heiress

The monument Hardy here mentions was erected in Stinsford church to the memory of some of the Grey family, lords of the manor of Kingston Maurward in the parish of Stinsford. (It was their daughter Lora who built the bridge into Dorchester, still known as Grey's Bridge, which figures in several of Hardy's novels.) He does not describe in detail the hideous grinning skull which so haunted him as a child when he sat beneath it in the neighbouring Hardy pew.

Afternoon Service at Mellstock

(Circa 1850)

On afternoons of drowsy calm
　We stood in the panelled pew,
Singing one-voiced a Tate-and-Brady psalm
　To the tune of "Cambridge New".

We watched the elms, we watched the rooks,
The clouds upon the breeze,
Between the whiles of glancing at our books,
And swaying like the trees.

So mindless were those outpourings! —
Though I am not aware
That I have gained by subtle thought on things
Since we stood psalming there.

Moments of Vision

2 Hardy's People

THE HARDYS

Anyone who reads the Life of Thomas Hardy, *ostensibly by his wife Florence, but in fact dictated to her by Thomas himself before he died, should also read (differing) correctives such as Michael Millgate's* Thomas Hardy *and Robert Gitting's two volumes* Young Thomas Hardy *and* The Older Hardy. *Hardy himself was so obsessed by fears about the lowly social status of his family that much of what he wrote about them was distorted, or so entirely suppressed as to amount to falsehood. In most cases however his poetry gives a truer impression.*

Grandmother: Mary (Head) Hardy, a fount of stories from the past:

Hardy's grandmother spent her early, orphaned, years at Fawley, a Berkshire village which gave Hardy Jude's surname and setting. Between them and marrying Thomas Hardy I, she lived through some terrible experiences which her grandson never admitted. (For a discussion of some possibilities see both Gittings's Older Hardy *and Millgate.) She continued to live at Bockhampton until her death, and was a powerful link with the past for her grandson, who records her remark one hot thundery summer that "It was like this in the French Revolution, I remember."*[61] *In* The Return of the Native *he adapted her memory of the news of the French Queen's execution reaching her while she was ironing her best muslin dress — whose pattern she was never afterwards to forget.*

One We Knew
(M. H. 1772–1857)

She told how they used to form for the country dances —
  "The Triumph", "The New-rigged Ship" —
To the light of the guttering wax in the panelled manses,
  And in cots to the blink of a dip.

She spoke of the wild "poussetting" and "allemanding"
  On carpet, on oak, and on sod;
And the two long rows of ladies and gentlemen standing,
  And the figures the couples trod.

She showed us the spot where the maypole was yearly planted,
   And where the bandsmen stood
While breeched and kerchiefed partners whirled, and panted
   To choose each other for good.

She told of that far-back day when they learnt astounded
   Of the death of the King of France:
Of the Terror; and then of Bonaparte's unbounded
   Ambition and arrogance.

Of how his threats woke warlike preparations
   Along the southern strand,
And how each night brought tremors and trepidations
   Lest morning should see him land.

She said she had often heard the gibbet creaking
   As it swayed in the lightning flash,
Had caught from the neighbouring town a small child's shrieking
   At the cart-tail under the lash....

With cap-framed face and long gaze into the embers —
   We seated around her knees —
She would dwell on such dead themes, not as one who remembers,
   But rather as one who sees.

She seemed one left behind of a band gone distant
   So far that no tongue could hail:
Past things retold were to her as things existent,
   Things present but as a tale.

20 May 1902 *Time's Laughingstocks*

Father:

Thomas Hardy II built up a flourishing master-mason's business from very little. He seems to have been the source of many of Thomas III's macabre stories of flogging, hangings, and transportation; he was also a great nature-lover, and a very capable and devoted musician, one of the celebrated Stinsford ("Mellstock") church band who was also much in demand as fiddler at local entertainments — where his young son often accompanied him.

[1892] *August 14th.* Mother described to-day the three Hardys[62] as they used to appear passing over the brow of the hill to Stinsford Church on a Sunday morning, three or four years before my birth. They were always hurrying, being rather late, their fiddles and violoncello in green baize bags under their left arms. They wore top hats, stick-up shirt collars, dark blue coats with great collars and gilt buttons, deep cuffs and black silk "stocks" or neckerchiefs. Had curly hair, and carried their heads to one side as they walked. My grandfather wore drab cloth breeches and buckled shoes, but his sons wore trousers and Wellington boots.

The Life of Thomas Hardy

Thomas Hardy II was also a handsome man with a reputation as something of a lady-killer.

A Church Romance
(Mellstock: Circa 1835)

She turned in the high pew, until her sight
Swept the west gallery, and caught its row
Of music-men with viol, book, and bow
Against the sinking sad tower-window light.

She turned again; and in her pride's despite
One strenuous viol's inspirer seemed to throw
A message from his string to her below,
Which said: "I claim thee as my own forthright!"

Thus their hearts' bond began, in due time signed.
And long years thence, when Age had scared Romance,
At some old attitude of his or glance
That gallery-scene would break upon her mind,
With him as minstrel, ardent, young, and trim,
Bowing "New Sabbath" or "Mount Ephraim".

Time's Laughingstocks

In July 1892, Thomas Hardy II died in the house where he had been born.

To My Father's Violin

Does he want you down there
In the Nether Glooms where
The hours may be a dragging load upon him,
As he hears the axle grind
Round and round
Of the great world, in the blind
Still profound
Of the night-time? He might liven at the sound
Of your string, revealing you had not forgone him.

In the gallery west the nave,
But a few yards from his grave,
Did you, tucked beneath his chin, to his bowing
Guide the homely harmony
Of the quire
Who for long years strenuously —
Son and sire —
Caught the strains that at his fingering low or higher
From your four thin threads and eff-holes came outflowing.

And, too, what merry tunes
He would bow at nights or noons
That chanced to find him bent to lute a measure.
When he made you speak his heart
As in dream,
Without book or music-chart,
On some theme
Elusive as a jack-o'-lanthorn's gleam,
And the psalm of duty shelved for trill of pleausre.

Well, you cannot, alas,
The barrier overpass
That screens him in those Mournful Meads hereunder,
Where no fiddling can be heard
In the glades
Of silentness, no bird
Thrills the shades;
Where no viol is touched for songs or serenades,
No bowing wakes a congregation's wonder.

He must do without you now,
Stir you no more anyhow
To yearning concords taught you in your glory;
While, your strings a tangled wreck,
Once smart drawn,
Ten worm-wounds in your neck,
Purflings wan
With dust-hoar, here alone I sadly con
Your present dumbness, shape your olden story.

Moments of Vision

Mother:

Jemima Hand, Hardy's mother, was a woman of immense vitality and probably the strongest influence of his life. Her traumatic early life is described elsewhere.[63]

The Roman Road

The Roman Road runs straight and bare
As the pale parting-line in hair
Across the heath. And thoughtful men
Contrast its day of Now and Then,
And delve, and measure, and compare;

Visioning on the vacant air
helmed legionaries, who proudly rear
The Eagle, as they pace again
The Roman Road.

But no tall brass-helmed legionnaire
Haunts it for me. Uprises there
A mother's form upon my ken,
Guiding my infant steps, as when
We walked that ancient thoroughfare,
The Roman Road.

Time's Laughingstocks

He tells of their early pranks together, walking over the heath in outlandish garb with cabbage-nets over their faces, to startle an aunt in Puddletown; of his mother's buoyant carriage, so that even when she was nearly seventy strangers overtaking her from behind thought she was a much younger woman; of her irrepressible gaiety when nearly ninety, defying her daughters and waving her handkerchief from her wheelcair to the members of a London literary club driving past the end of the lane to visit her famous son in Dorchester.

From a letter to Sydney Cockerell, 3 June 1917:

. . . The only one of my family, so far as I remember, who was active at 77 was my mother. I find from a note that she walked here from Bockhampton in that year of her life, and in slippery winter weather. On our asking her with alarm why she had ventured out she said coolly: "To enjoy the beauties of Nature of course: why shouldn't I?"

Viola Meynell, *Friends of a Lifetime*

It was Hardy's mother who gave him his first books and his love of reading, and who through many a firelit evening in the Bockhampton home filled his mind with folklore and old traditions. Her part in stimulating his sense of community, the supernatural, and the past, must be similar to the part played by the natural world in stimulating his poetic imagination.

After The Last Breath
(J. H. 1813–1904)

There's no more to be done, or feared, or hoped;
None now need watch, speak low, and list, and tire;
No irksome crease outsmoothed, no pillow sloped
    Does she require.

Blankly we gaze. We are free to go or stay;
Our morrow's anxious plans have missed their aim;
Whether we leave to-night or wait till day
    Counts as the same.

The lettered vessels of medicaments
Seem asking wherefore we have set them here;
Each palliative its silly face presents
    As useless gear.

And yet we feel that something savours well;
We note a numb relief withheld before;
Our well-beloved is prisoner in the cell
    Of Time no more.

We see by littles now the deft achievement
Whereby she has escaped the Wrongers all,
In view of which our momentary bereavement
    Outshapes but small.

1904 *Time's Laughingstocks*

Something of Jemima Hardy's powerful and determined character may have been enshrined in Mrs Yeobright of The Return of the Native; *but it is noteworthy that she appears less often in both Hardy's prose and poetry than, for example, his sister Mary. Yet even as a grown man the Bockhampton home and his mother were Hardy's refuge in stress, and there is no doubt of her deep influence with him. Could it be that in some way she was too close — or too dominating — for words?*

Mary Hardy, sister:

If there were in my kalendar
    No Emma, Florence, Mary,
What would be my existence now —
    A hermit's? — wanderer's weary? —
    How should I live, and how
    Near would be death, or far?

Mary, only a year younger than Hardy, and whom in this poem "Conjecture" he ranks with his two wives, was always extremely close to him in sympathy and shared interests. Letters from him to her, quoted in the Life, *contain discussions about art and literature and a reference to Mary's winning of a drawing prize; as well as a promise by Hardy that when he came home from London after Christmas they must "have a bit of a lark". An unusually self-effacing person, she is thought to be partially the model for Elizabeth-Jane in* The Mayor of Casterbridge, *for Cytherea in* Desperate Remedies, *and for Faith in* The Hand of Ethelberta. *Hardy drew on her experiences of the Salisbury teachers' training college to describe Sue's in* Jude the Obscure. *Mary's interest in art was lifelong, and even when over seventy she would still travel to London from Dorchester for the day to see Royal Academy exhibitions.*

Logs On The Hearth

A Memory of a Sister

The fire advances along the log
Of the tree we felled,
Which bloomed and bore striped apples by the peck
Till its last hour of bearing knelled.

The fork that first my hand would reach
And then my foot
In climbings upward inch by inch, lies now
Sawn, sapless, darkening with soot.

Where the bark chars is where, one year,
It was pruned, and bled —
Then overgrew the wound. But now, at last,
Its growings all have stagnated.

My fellow-climber rises dim
From her chilly grave —
Just as she was, her foot near mine on the bending limb,
Laughing, her young brown hand awave.

December 1915 *Moments of Vision*

"Sacred to the Memory" and several other poems are explicitly about Mary; "Molly Gone", written after her death in 1915, may also be.

Molly Gone

No more summer for Molly and me;
There is snow on the tree,
And the blackbirds plump large as the rooks are, almost,

And the water is hard
Where they used to dip bills at the dawn ere her figure was lost
To these coasts, now my prison close-barred.

No more planting by Molly and me
Where the beds used to be
Of sweet-william; no training the clambering rose
By the framework of fir
Now bowering the pathway, whereon it swings gaily and blows
As if calling commendment from her.

No more jauntings by Molly and me
To the town by the sea,
Or along over Whitesheet to Wynyard's green Gap,
Catching Montacute Crest
To the right against Sedgmoor, and Corton-Hill's far-distant cap,
And Pilsdon and Lewsdon to west.

No more singing by Molly to me
In the evenings when she
Was in mood and in voice, and the candles were lit,
And past the porch-quoin
The rays would spring out on the laurels; and dumbledores hit
On the pane, as if wishing to join.

Where, then, is Molly, who's no more with me?
— As I stand on this lea,
Thinking thus, there's a many-flamed star in the air,
That tosses a sign
That her glance is regarding its face from her home, so that there
Her eyes may have meetings with mine.

Moments of Vision

After Mary, born in 1841, a long gap separated these two from the next two Hardy children — Henry, born 1851, and Kate, born 1856. Although they remained in close contact all their lives, Henry and Kate seem to have had little influence on Hardy.

Hardy's family consciousness, part of his feeling for the past, became increasingly acute through his lifetime.

A Wet Night

I pace along, the rain-shafts riddling me,
Mile after mile out by the moorland way,

And up the hill, and through the ewe-leaze gray
Into the lane, and round the corner tree;

Where, as my clothing clams me, mire-bestarred,
And the enfeebled light dies out of day,
Leaving the liquid shades to reign, I say,
"This is a hardship to be calendared!"

Yet sires of mine now perished and forgot,
When worse beset, ere roads were shapen here,
And night and storm were foes indeed to fear,
Times numberless have trudged across this spot
In sturdy muteness on their strenuous lot,
And taking all such toils as trifles mere.

Time's Laughingstocks

Night In The Old Home

When the wasting embers redden the chimney-breast,
And Life's bare pathway looms like a desert track to me,
And from hall and parlour the living have gone to their rest,
My perished people who housed them here come back to me.

They come and seat them around in their mouldy places,
Now and then bending towards me a glance of wistfulness,
A strange upbraiding smile upon all their faces,
And in the bearing of each a passive tristfulness.

"Do you uphold me, lingering and languishing here,
A pale late plant of your once strong stock?" I say to them;
"A thinker of crooked thoughts upon Life in the sere,
And on That which consigns men to night after showing the day to them?"

"— O let be the Wherefore! We fevered our years not thus:
Take of Life what it grants, without question!" they answer me seemingly.
'Enjoy, suffer, wait: spread the table here freely like us,
And, satisfied, placid, unfretting, watch Time away beamingly!"

Time's Laughingstocks

In his story "The Duke's Reappearance" Hardy retells a tradition connecting his ancestors the Swetmans of Townsend with the Duke of Monmouth's rebellion. In this he refers to a clock he knew at Bockhampton as "Swetman's one-handed clock on the stairs, that is still preserved in the family". A note found after his death records that "the large blue-and-white jug which hung on the middle of the [Bockhampton] dresser was called Benjamin *and was always used for the singers when they came to practise in grandfather's time."*

Old Furniture

I know not how it may be with others
    Who sit amid relics of householdry
That date from the days of their mothers' mothers,
    But well I know how it is with me
        Continually.

I see the hands of the generations
    That owned each shiny familiar thing
In play on its knobs and indentations,
    And with its ancient fashioning
        Still dallying:

Hands behind hands, growing paler and paler,
    As in a mirror a candle-flame
Shows images of itself, each frailer
    As it recedes, though the eye may frame
        Its shape the same.

On the clock's dull dial a foggy finger,
    Moving to set the minutes right
With tentative touches that lift and linger
    In the wont of a moth on a summer night,
        Creeps to my sight.

On this old viol, too, fingers are dancing —
    As whilom — just over the strings by the nut,
The tip of a bow receding, advancing
    In airy quivers, as if it would cut
        The plaintive gut.

And I see a face by that box for tinder,
    Glowing forth in fits from the dark,
And fading again, as the linten cinder
    Kindles to red at the flinty spark,
        Or goes out stark.

Well, well. It is best to be up and doing,
    The world has no use for one to-day

Who eyes things thus — no aim pursuing!
He should not continue in this stay,
But sink away.

Moments of Vision

FRIENDS AND NEIGHBOURS

Hardy remembered his childhood community all his life. In 1888 he made a note[64] *on "Youthful recollections of four village beauties", with each one's distinguishing marks. One was the red-haired gamekeeper's daughter of the poem "To Lizbie Browne", one a girl whose artificial dimple-making reappeared in the Arabella of* Jude the Obscure. *At the end of 1889 he wrote the following poem:*

At Middle-Field Gate In February

The bars are thick with drops that show
As they gather themselves from the fog
Like silver buttons ranged in a row,
And as evenly spaced as if measured, although
They fall at the feeblest jog.

They load the leafless hedge hard by,
And the blades of last year's grass,
While the fallow ploughland turned up nigh
In raw rolls, clammy and clogging lie —
Too clogging for feet to pass.

How dry it was on a far-back day
When straws hung the hedge and around,
When amid the sheaves in amorous play
In curtained bonnets and light array
Bloomed a bevy now underground!

Bockhampton Lane *Moments of Vision*

When asked many years later, Hardy gave the names of at least eight of the "bevy now underground" he had been remembering.

Louisa Harding was worshipped from afar. (In a passage originally written in the Life *but subsequently expunged before publication, Hardy wrote of her grave: ". . . and a nameless green mound in the corner of Mellstock Churchyard was visited more than once by one to whom a boyish dream had never lost its radiance.")*[65]

Louie

I am forgetting Louie the buoyant;
Why not raise her phantom, too,
  Here in daylight
  With the elect one's?
She will never thrust the foremost figure out of view!

Mid this heat, in gauzy muslin
See I Louie's life-lit brow
  Here in daylight
By the elect one's. —
Long two strangers they and far apart; such neighbours now!

July 1913 *Human Shows*

"The elect one" is Emma Lavinia, Hardy's first wife, now buried as was Louisa Harding in Stinsford Churchyard. "To Louisa in the Lane" was written only a few months before Hardy's death, so important were these youthful memories.[66]

The Lady of the Manor:

Another stratum in the social hierarchy had a profound influence on Hardy's life and writing in the person of Mrs Julia Augusta Martin, lady of the Manor of Kingston Maurward in Hardy's parish. A childless philanthropist who started the school at Lower Bockhampton "for the education of children of the labouring classes", young Thomas "almost from his infancy" had been her especial favourite, whom she would "take into her lap and kiss until he was quite a big child". Hardy tells how "his feeling for her was almost that of a lover". The rather abrupt end to their relationship caused by his removal to school in Dorchester affected him deeply; he never forgot "the thrilling 'frou-frou' of her four grey silk flounces, when she had used to bend over him, and when they had brushed against the font as she entered church on Sundays".[67]

This experience of social barriers to love became a dominant theme in Hardy's writing. It was strengthened by his romantic fascination with the story of Lady Susan Strangways, whose elopement with the Irish actor William O'Brien caused a London scandal. They subsequently lived many happy and popular years at Stinsford House, ended only by death, when Hardy's grandfather himself constructed their vault in Stinsford Church; the long poem "The Noble Lady's Tale" tells of their difficulties.

In the following poem, published in 1917 and partly inspired, it seems, by the attractive young Mrs Hanbury who was now the lady of Kingston Maurward Manor, Hardy was probably reliving his childhood experiences of the place and its lady.

In Her Precincts

Her house looked cold from the foggy lea,
And the square of each window a dull black blur
        Where showed no stir:
Yes, her gloom within at the lack of me
Seemed matching mine at the lack of her.

The black squares grew to be squares of light
As the eveshade swathed the house and lawn,
        And viols gave tone;
There was glee within. And I found that night
The gloom of severance mine alone.

Kingston Maurward Park *Moments of Vision*

(Another poem in Moments of Vision, "An Anniversary", *is also to be associated with this experience.)*

The "Mellstock" Quire:

When Thomas Hardy I took over the improving of the Stinsford Church music in 1801 or 1802, later enrolling his two sons into what became a locally "celebrated... string-band", he began an association which lasted for almost forty years. (When his son James and granddaughter Theresa took over the playing, first of the succeeding barrel-organ, then the harmonium, the Hardy family was responsible for Stinsford Church's music for over a hundred years.) Although it was disbanded in about 1842, too soon after the birth of Thomas Hardy III for him to remember the Quire at first-hand, it always formed a most important strand in his life and appears constantly in his writings (e.g. the stories "The Fiddler of the Reels", "The Waiting Supper", "The Grave by the Handpost", the novel Under the Greenwood Tree *— originally titled* The Mellstock Quire *— and many poems, including "The Rash Bride", "The Paphian Ball", "The Choirmaster's Burial", "The Dead Quire" — most too long for inclusion here — and "A Church Romance" (on page 26)).*

Christmas Eve: Going the Rounds

Shortly after ten o'clock the singing-boys arrived at the tranter's house, which was invariably the place of meeting, and preparations were made for the start. The older men and musicians wore thick coats, with stiff perpendicular collars, and coloured handkerchiefs wound round and round the neck till the end came to hand, over all which they just showed their ears and noses, like people looking over a wall. The remainder, stalwart ruddy men and boys, were dressed mainly in snow-white smock-frocks, embroidered upon the shoulders and breasts in ornamental forms of hearts, diamonds, and zigzags. The cider-mug was emptied for the ninth time, the music-books were arranged, and the pieces finally decided upon. The boys in the meantime put the old horn-lanterns in order, cut candles into short lengths to fit the lanterns; and, a thin fleece of snow having fallen since the early part of the evening, those who had no leggings went to the stable and wound wisps of hay round their ankles to keep the insidious flakes from the interior of their boots.

Mellstock was a parish of considerable acreage, the hamlets composing it lying at a much greater distance from each other than is ordinarily the case. Hence several hours were consumed in playing and singing within hearing of every family, even if but a single air were bestowed on each. There was Lower Mellstock, the main village; half a mile from this were the church and vicarage, and a few other houses, the spot being rather lonely now, though in past centuries it had been the most thickly-populated quarter of the parish. A mile north-east lay the hamlet of Upper Mellstock, where the tranter lived; and at other points knots of cottages, besides solitary farmsteads and dairies.

Old William Dewy, with the violoncello, played the bass; his grandson Dick the treble violin; and Reuben and Michael Mail the tenor and second violins respectively. The singers consisted of four men and seven boys, upon whom devolved the task of carrying and attending to the lanterns, and holding the books open for the players. Directly music was the theme old William ever and instinctively came to the front.

"Now mind, neighbours," he said, as they all went out one by one at the door, he himself holding it ajar and regarding them with a critical face as they passed, like a shepherd counting out his sheep. "You two counterboys, keep your ears open to Michael's fingering, and don't ye go straying into the treble part along o' Dick and his set, as ye did last year; and mind this especially when we be in 'Arise, and hail'. Billy Chimlen, don't you sing quite so raving mad as you fain would; and, all o' ye, whatever ye do, keep from making a great scuffle on the ground when we go in at people's gates; but go quietly, so as to strike up all of a sudden, like spirits."

"Farmer Ledlow's first?"

"Farmer Ledlow's first, the rest as usual."

"And, Voss," said the tranter terminatively, "you keep house here till about half-past two; then heat the metheglin and cider in the warmer you'll find turned up upon the copper; and bring it wi' the victuals to church-hatch, as th'st know."

Just before the clock struck twelve they lighted the lanterns and started. The moon, in her third quarter, had risen since the snow-storm; but the dense accumulation of snow-cloud weakened her power to a faint twilight which was rather pervasive of the landscape than traceable to the sky. The breeze had gone down, and the rustle of their feet and tones of their speech echoed with an alert rebound from every post, boundary-stone, and ancient wall they passed, even where the distance of the echo's origin was less than a few yards. Beyond their own slight noises nothing was to be heard save the occasional bark of foxes in the direction of Yalbury Wood, or the brush of a rabbit among the grass now and then as it scampered out of their way.

Most of the outlying homesteads and hamlets had been visited by about two o'clock; they then passed across the outskirts of a wooded park toward the main village, nobody being at home at the Manor. Pursuing no recognized track, great care was necessary in walking lest their faces should come in contact with the low-hanging boughs of the old lime-trees, which in many spots formed dense overgrowths of interlaced branches.

"Times have changed from the times they used to be," said Mail, regarding nobody can tell what interesting old panoramas with an inward eye, and letting his outward glance rest on the ground because it was as convenient a position as any. "People don't care much about us now! I've been thinking we must be almost the last left in the country of the old string players? Barrel-organs, and the things next door to 'em that you blow wi' your foot, have come in terribly of late years."

"Ay!" said Bowman shaking his head; and old William on seeing him did the same thing.

"More's the pity," replied another. "Time was — long and merry ago now! — when not one of the varmits was to be heard of; but it served some of the quires right. They should have stuck to strings as we did, and kept out clarinets, and done away with serpents. If you'd thrive in musical religion, stick to strings, says I."

"Strings be safe soul-lifters, as far as that do go," said Mr Spinks.

"Yet there's worse things than serpents," said Mr Penny. "Old things pass away, 'tis true; but a serpent was a good old note: a deep rich note was the serpent."

"Clar'nets, however, be bad at all times," said Michael Mail. "One Christmas — years agone now, years — I went the rounds wi' the Weatherbury quire. 'Twas a hard frosty night, and the keys of all the clar'nets froze — ah, they did freeze! — so that 'twas like drawing a cork every time a key was opened; and the players o' 'em had to go into a hedger-and-ditcher's chimley-corner, and thaw their clar'nets every now and then. An icicle o' spet hung down from the end of every man's clar'net a span long; and as to fingers — well, there, if ye'll believe me, we had no fingers at all, to our knowing."

"I can well bring back to my mind," said Mr Penny, "what I said to poor Joseph Ryme (who took the treble part in Chalk-Newton Church for two-and-forty year) when they thought of having clar'nets there. 'Joseph,' I said says I, 'depend upon't, if so be you have them tooting clar'nets you'll spoil the whole set-out. Clar'nets were not made for the service of the Lard; you can see it by looking at 'em,' I said. And what came o't? Why, souls, the parson set up a barrel-organ on his own account within two years o' the time I spoke, and the old quire went to nothing."

"As far as look is concerned," said the tranter, "I don't for my part see that a fiddle is much nearer heaven than a clar'net. 'Tis further off. There's always a rakish, scampish twist about a fiddle's looks that seems to say the Wicked One had a hand in making o'en; while angels be supposed to play clar'nets in heaven, or som'at like 'em if ye may believe picters."

"Robert Penny, you was in the right," broke in the eldest Dewy. "They should ha' stuck to strings. Your brass-man is a rafting dog — well and good; your reed-man is a dab at stirring ye — well and good; your drumman is a rare bowel-shaker — good again. But I don't care who hears me say it, nothing will spak to your heart wi' the sweetness o' the man of strings!"

"Strings for ever!" said little Jimmy.

"Strings alone would have held their ground against all the newcomers in creation." ("True, true!" said Bowman.) "But clarinets was death." ("Death they was!" said Mr Penny.) "And harmonions," William continued in a louder voice, and getting excited by these signs of approval, "harmonions and barrel-organs" ("Ah!" and groans from Spinks) "be miserable — what shall I call 'em? — miserable —"

"Sinners," suggested Jimmy, who made large strides like the men and did not lag behind with the other little boys.

"Miserable dumbledores!"

"Right, William, and so they be — miserable dumbledores!" said the choir with unanimity.

By this time they were crossing to a gate in the direction of the school which, standing on a slight eminence at the junction of three ways, now rose in unvarying and dark flatness against the sky. The instruments were retuned, and all the band entered the school enclosure, enjoined by old William to keep upon the grass.

"Number seventy-eight," he softly gave out as they formed round in a semicircle, the boys opening the lanterns to get a clearer light, and directing their rays on the books.

Then passed forth into the quiet night an ancient and time-worn hymn, embodying a quaint Christianity in words orally transmitted from father to son through several generations down to the present characters, who sang them out right earnestly:

"Remember Adam's fall,
O thou Man:
.............................."

Having concluded the last note they listened for a minute or two, but found that no sound issued from the schoolhouse.

"Four breaths, and then, 'O, what unbounded goodness!' number fifty-nine," said William.

This was duly gone through, and no notice whatever seemed to be taken of the performance.

"Good guide us, surely 'tisn't a' empty house, as befell us in the year thirty-nine and forty-three!" said old Dewy.

"Perhaps she's just come from some musical city, and sneers at our doings?" the tranter whispered.

"'Od rabbit her!" said Mr Penny, with an annihilating look at a corner of the school chimney, "I don't quite stomach her, if this is it. Your plain music well done is as worthy as your other sort done bad, a'b'lieve, souls; so say I."

"Four breaths, and then the last," said the leader authoritatively. "'Rejoice, ye Tenants of the Earth', number sixty-four."

At the close, waiting yet another minute, he said in a clear loud voice, as he had said in the village at that hour and season for the previous forty years —

"A merry Christmas to ye!"

Under the Greenwood Tree

Hardy wrote to his friend Mrs Henniker that the "Mellstock Choir" were the characters he liked best in his own novels.

ABSENT-MINDEDNESS IN A PARISH CHOIR

"It happened on Sunday after Christmas — the last Sunday ever they played in Longpuddle church gallery, as it turned out, though they didn't know it then. As you may know, sir, the players formed a very good band — almost as good as the Mellstock parish players that were led by the Dewys; and that's saying a great deal... — all sound and powerful musicians, and strong-winded men — they that blowed. For that reason they were very much in demand Christmas week for little reels and dancing parties: for they could turn a jig or a hornpipe out of hand as well as ever they could turn out a psalm, and perhaps better, not to speak irreverent. In short, one half-hour they could be playing a Christmas carol in the Squire's hall to the ladies and gentlemen, and drinking tay and coffee with 'em as modest as saints; and the next, at The Tinker's Arms, blazing away like wild horses with the 'Dashing White Sergeant' to nine couple of dancers and more, and swallowing rum-and-cider hot as flame.

"Well, this Christmas they'd been out to one rattling randy after another every night, and had got next to no sleep at all. Then came the Sunday after Christmas, their fatal day. 'Twas so mortal cold that year that they could hardly sit in the gallery; for though the congregation down in the body of the Church had a stove to keep off the frost, the players in the gallery had nothing at all. So Nicholas said at morning service, when 'twas freezing an inch an hour, 'Please the Lord I won't stand this numbing weather no longer: this afternoon we'll have something in our insides to make us warm, if it cost a king's ransom.'

"So he brought a gallon of hot brandy and beer, ready mixed, to church with him in the afternoon, and by keeping the jar well wrapped up in Timothy Thomas's bass-viol bag it kept drinkably warm till they wanted it, which was just a thimbleful in the Absolution, and another after the Creed, and the remainder at the beginning o' the sermon. When they'd had the last pull they felt quite comfortable and warm, and as the sermon went on — most unfortunately for 'em it was a long one that afternoon — they fell asleep, every man jack of 'em; and there they slept on as sound as rocks.

" 'Twas a very dark afternoon, and by the end of the sermon all you could see of the inside of the church were the pa'son's two candles alongside of him in the pulpit, and his spaking face behind 'em. The sermon being ended at last, the pa'son gie'd out the Evening Hymn. But no quire set about sounding up the tune, and the people began to turn their heads to learn the reason why, and then Levi Limpet, a boy who sat in the gallery, nudged Timothy and Nicholas, and said, 'Begin! begin!'

"'Hey? what?' says Nicholas, starting up; and the church being so dark and his head so muddled he thought he was at the party they had played at all the night before, and away he went, bow and fiddle, at 'The Devil among the Tailors', the favourite jig of our neighbourhood at that time. The rest of the band, being in the same state of mind and nothing doubting, followed their leader with all their strength, according to custom. They poured out that there tune till the lower bass notes of 'The Devil among the Tailors' made the cobwebs in the roof shiver like ghosts; then Nicholas, seeing nobody moved, shouted out as he scraped (in his usual commanding way at dances when folk didn't know the figures), 'Top couples cross hands! And when I make the fiddle squeak at the end, every man kiss his pardner under the mistletoe!'

"The boy Levi was so frightened that he bolted down the gallery stairs and out homeward like lightning. The pa'son's hair fairly stood on end when he heard the evil tune raging through the church, and thinking the quire had gone crazy he held up his hand and said: 'Stop, stop, stop! Stop, stop! What's this?' But they didn't hear'n for the noise of their own playing, and the more he called the louder they played.

"Then the folks came out of their pews, wondering down to the ground, and saying: 'What do they mean by such wickedness! We shall be consumed like Sodom and Gomorrah!'

"And the Squire, too, came out of his pew lined wi' green baize, where lots of lords and ladies visiting at the house were worshipping along with him, and went and stood in front of the gallery, and shook his fist in the musicians' face, saying, 'What! In this reverent edifice! What!'

"And at last they heard'n through their playing, and stopped.

"'Never such an insulting, disgraceful thing — never!' says the Squire, who couldn't rule his passion.

"'Never!' says the pa'son, who had come down and stood beside him.

"'Not if the Angels of Heaven,' says the Squire (he was a wickedish man, the Squire was, though now for once he happened to be on the Lord's side) — 'not if the Angels of Heaven come down,' he says, 'shall one of you villainous players ever sound a note in this church again; for the insult of me, and my family, and my visitors, and the pa'son, and God Almighty, that you've a-perpetrated this afternoon!'

"Then the unfortunate church band came to their senses, and remembered where they were; and 'twas a sight to see Nicholas Puddingcome and Timothy Thomas and John Biles creep down the gallery stairs with their fiddles under their arms, and poor Dan'l Hornhead with his serpent, and Robert Dowdle with his clarionet, all looking as little as ninepins; and out they went. The pa'son might have forgi'ed 'em when he learned the truth o't, but the Squire would not. That very week he sent for a barrel-organ that would play two-and-twenty new psalm-tunes, so exact and particular that, however sinful inclined you was, you could play nothing but psalm-tunes whatsomever. He had a really respectable man to turn the winch, as I said, and the old players played no more."

Life's Little Ironies

"William Dewy, Tranter Reuben, Farmer Ledlow late at plough,
Robert's kin, and John's, and Ned's,
And the Squire, and Lady Susan, lie in Mellstock churchyard now!"[68]

EPILOGUE

Winter Night In Woodland
(Old Time)

The bark of a fox rings, sonorous and long:—
Three barks, and then silentness; "wong, wong, wong!"
In quality horn-like, yet melancholy,
As from teachings of years; for an old one is he.
The hand of all men is against him, he knows; and yet, why?
That he knows not, — will never know, down to his death-halloo cry.

With clap-nets and lanterns off start the bird-baiters,
In trim to make raids on the roosts in the copse,
Where they beat the boughs artfully, while their awaiters
Grow heavy at home over divers warm drops.
The poachers, with swingels, and matches of brimstone, outcreep
To steal upon pheasants and drowse them a-perch and asleep.

Out there, on the verge, where a path wavers through,
Dark figures, filed singly, thrid quickly the view,
Yet heavily laden: land-carriers are they
In the hire of the smugglers from some nearest bay.
Each bears his two 'tubs', slung across, one in front, one behind,
To a further snug hiding, which none but themselves are to find.

And then, when the night has turned twelve the air brings
From dim distance, a rhythm of voices and strings:
'Tis the quire, just afoot on their long yearly rounds,
To rouse by worn carols each house in their bounds;
Robert Penny, the Dewys, Mail, Voss, and the rest; till anon
Tired and thirsty, but cheerful, they home to their beds in the dawn.

Human Shows

II
RURAL LIFE IN WESSEX

1 Folklore

This is a vast subject, and one that was constantly in both the forefront and, one might say, the subconscious part of Hardy's mind. It has been studied in Ruth Firor's Folkways in Thomas Hardy *(New York, 1962). I have tried to group together some examples of what he reveals under the following headings, though there is much that overlaps such distinctions: superstitious beliefs and practices, paganism and fatalism; legends and traditions; and customs.*

SUPERSTITIONS AND THE SUPERNATURAL

In 1901 Hardy had the following conversation with William Archer:

W. A. Now tell me, as to rural superstitions — belief in witchcraft, and so forth — are they dying out?
Mr Hardy. On the surface, yes; in reality, no. People smile and say, "Of course we don't believe in these things" — but their scepticism is only skin deep. You will find women to this day who will make an image of some enemy and either melt it before the fire or stick pins into it. The belief in the evil eye subsists in full force; also such ideas as that which I have introduced into one of my stories — that if you can draw blood from a witch, you render her powerless.

W. Archer, *Real Conversations*

Superstition was widespread and endemic:

Henchard, like all his kind, was superstitious.

The Mayor of Casterbridge

The movement of his mind seemed to tend to the thought that some power was working against him.

"I wonder," he asked himself with eerie misgiving; "I wonder if it can be that somebody has been roasting a waxen image of me, or stirring an unholy brew to confound me! I don't believe in such power; and yet — what if they should ha' been doing it?"

The Mayor of Casterbridge

[Tess] fell to reflecting again, and in looking downwards a thorn of the rose remaining in her breast accidentally pricked her chin. Like all the cottagers in Blackmoor Vale, Tess was steeped in fancies and prefigurative superstitions; she thought this an ill-omen — the first she had noticed that day.

Tess of the d'Urbervilles

The winding road downwards became just visible to her under the wan starlight as she followed it, and soon she paced a soil so contrasting with that above it that the difference was perceptible to the tread and to the smell. It was the heavy clay land of Blackmoor Vale, and a part of the Vale to which turnpike-roads had never penetrated. Superstitions linger longest on these heavy soils. Having once been forest, at this shadowy time it seemed to assert something of its old character, the far and the near being blended, and every tree and tall hedge making the most of its presence. The harts that had been hunted here, the witches that had been pricked and ducked, the green-spangled fairies that "whickered" at you as you passed; the place teemed with beliefs in them still, and they formed an impish multitude now.

Tess of the d'Urbervilles

The peninsula carved by Time out of a single stone, whereon most of the following scenes are laid, has been for centuries immemorial the home of a curious and well-nigh distinct people, cherishing strange beliefs and singular customs, now for the most part obsolescent. Fancies, like certain soft-wooded plants which cannot bear the silent inland frosts, but thrive by the sea in the roughest of weather, seem to grow naturally here.

1912 Preface to *The Well-Beloved*

"These Smouldering Village Beliefs"....

Some evil omens were connected with natural phenomena:

"And what do this comet mean?" asked Haymoss. "That some great tumult is going to happen, or that we shall die of a famine?"

"Famine — no!" said Nat Chapman. "That only touches such as we, and the Lord only concerns himself with born gentlemen. It isn't to be supposed that a strange fiery lantern like that would be lighted up for folks with ten or a dozen shillings a week and their gristing, and a load of thorn faggots when we can get 'em. If 'tis a token that he's getting hot about the ways of anybody in this parish, 'tis about my Lady Constantine's, since she is the only one of a figure worth such a hint.[69]

Two on a Tower

It was the universal custom thereabout to wake the bees by tapping at their hives whenever a death occurred in the household, under the belief that if this were not done the bees themselves would pine and perish during the ensuing year.

Interlopers at the Knap

On Tess's wedding day:

It was interrupted by the crowing of a cock....

"Oh?" said Mrs Crick. "An afternoon crow!"

Two men were standing by the yard gate, holding it open.

"That's bad," one murmured to the other, not thinking that the words could be heard by the group at the door-wicket.

The cock crew again — straight towards Clare.

"Well!" said the dairyman.

"I don't like to hear him!" said Tess to her husband. "Tell the man to drive on. Goodbye, goodbye!"

The cock crew again.

"Hoosh! Just you be off, sir, or I'll twist your neck!" said the dairyman with some irritation, turning to the bird and driving him away. And to his wife as they went indoors: "Now, to think o' that just today! I've not heard his crow of an afternoon all the year afore."

"It only means a change in the weather," said she; "not what you think: 'tis impossible!"

Tess of the d'Urbervilles

(It was a Dorset superstition that a cock crowing in the afternoon boded sickness or death.)

Horses were often good indicators of supernatural presences. A note of 1883 tells how Hardy, passing an old house once an inn, was shown the stable. Here in a quarrel one night one of a group of smugglers who frequented the inn was killed, in the furthest stall; any horse put there on certain nights would cry "like a child" at the hour the smuggler died, and be found bathed in sweat.[70] *Another note (1902) tells of the strange woolpack sometimes seen in the middle of the road at Vagg Hollow in Somerset — where horses would not move on without whipping. When a waggoner once struck it with his whip, it burst open, emitting smoke and a hoofed figure.*

*Vagg Hollow**

"What do you see in Vagg Hollow,
Little boy, when you go
In the morning at five on your lonely drive?"
"— I see men's souls, who follow
Till we've passed where the road lies low,
When they vanish at our creaking!

"They are like white faces speaking
Beside and behind the waggon —
One just as father's was when here.
The waggoner drinks from his flagon,

(Or he'd flinch when the Hollow is near)
But he does not give me any.

"Sometimes the faces are many;
But I walk along by the horses,
He asleep on the straw as we jog;
And I hear the loud water-courses,
And the drops from the trees in the fog,
And watch till the day is breaking,

"And the wind out by Tintinhull waking;
I hear in it father's call
As he called when I saw him dying,
And he sat by the fire last Fall,
And mother stood by sighing;
But I'm not afraid at all!"

*Vagg Hollow is a marshy spot on the old Roman Road near Ilchester, where "things" are seen. Merchandise was formerly fetched inland from the canal-boats at Load-Bridge by waggons this way.

Late Lyrics and Earlier

The Devil also figures in The Woodlanders, *where the local folk think Dr Fitzpiers has "sold his soul to the wicked one"; and in* Jude the Obscure:

"I've heard strange tales o' husbands in my time," observed the widow in a lowered voice. "They say that when the saints were upon earth devils used to take husbands' forms o' nights, and get poor women into all sorts of trouble. But I don't know why that should come into my head, for it is only a tale . . . What a wind and rain it is to-night!"

Jude the Obscure

Some omens were good. Because Eustacia gave Johnny Nunsuch a crooked sixpence (thought to be a charm against evil) he was not afraid to go home alone through the heath. Christian Cantle was "born wi' a caul" (a remnant of membrane like a cap found on some new-born babies), which was held to be a charm particularly against drowning; and

"That my bees should ha' swarmed just then, of all times and seasons!" [i.e. on his wedding-day] continued Dick, throwing a comprehensive glance like a net over the whole auditory. "And 'tis a fine swarm, too: I haven't seen such a fine swarm for these ten years."

"A' excellent sign," said Mrs Penny, from the depths of experience. "A' excellent sign."

"I am glad everything seems so right," said Fancy with a breath of relief.

Under the Greenwood Tree

But many everyday objects could bode sickness and death — keys breaking, clocks falling, and particularly the church bell going suddenly heavy in the ringer's hand, or even tolling without visible human action.

"I hope nothing is wrong about mistress," said Maryann, who with some other women was tying the bundles (oats being always sheaved on this farm), "but an unlucky token came to me indoors this morning. I went to unlock the door and dropped the key, and it fell upon the stone floor and broke into two pieces. Breaking a key is a dreadful bodement. I wish mis'ess was home."

Far from the Madding Crowd

Without any warning, the clock slowly inclined forward and fell at full length upon the floor.

The crash brought the farmer's wife rushing into the room. Christine had wellnigh sprung out of her shoes.... Assisted by Mrs Wake, she lifted the clock.... They propped it up temporarily, though it would not go again.

Christine had soon recovered her composure, but she saw that Mrs Wake was gloomy. "What does it mean, Mrs Wake?" she said. "Is is ominous?"

"It is a sign of a violent death in the family."

The Waiting Supper

She saw Him, She Said

"Why, I saw you with the sexton, outside the church-door,
So I did not hurry me home,
Thinking you'd not be come,
Having something to him to say. —
Yes: 'twas you, Dear, though you seemed sad, heart-sore;
How fast you've got therefrom!"

"I've not been out. I've watched the moon through the birch,
And heard the bell toll. Yes,
Like a passing soul in distress!"
"— But no bell's tolled to-day?"...
His face looked strange, like the face of him seen by the church,
And she sank to musefulness.

Human Shows

Premonitions

"The bell went heavy to-day
At afternoon service, they say,
And a screech owl cried in the boughs,

And a raven flew over the house,
And Betty's old clock with one hand,
That's worn out, as I understand,
And never goes now, never will,
Struck twelve when the night was dead still,
Just as when my last loss came to me....
Ah! I wonder who next it will be!"

Human Shows

"Well, one Sunday, at a time that William was in very good health to all appearance, the bell that was ringing for church went very heavy all of a sudden; the sexton, who told me o't, said he'd not known the bell go so heavy in his hand for years — and he feared it meant a death in the parish....

"On Midsummer Night it is believed hereabout that the faint shapes of all the folk in the parish who are going to be at death's door within the year can be seen entering the church. Those who get over their illness come out again after a while; those that are doomed to die do not return.

"'What did you see?' asked William's wife.

"'Well,' says Nancy, backwardly — 'we needn't tell what we saw, or who we saw.'

"'You saw my husband,' says Betty Privett, in a quiet way....

"Nancy did not answer yes or no to that, and no more was said. But three days after, William Privett was mowing with John Chiles in Mr Hardcombe's meadow, and in the heat of the day they sat down to eat their bit o' nunch under a tree, and empty their flagon. Afterwards both of 'em fell asleep as they sat. John Chiles was the first to wake, and as he looked towards his fellow-mower he saw one of those great white miller's-souls as we call 'em — that is to say, a miller-moth — come from Willam's open mouth while he slept, and fly straight away. John thought it odd enough, as William had worked in a mill for several years when he was a boy. He then looked at the sun, and found by the place o't that they had slept a long while, and as William did not wake, John called to him and said it was high time to begin work again. He took no notice, and then John went up and shook him, and found he was dead.

"Now on that very day old Philip Hookhorn was down at Longpuddle Spring dipping up a pitcher of water; and as he turned away, who should he see coming down to the spring on the other side but William, looking very pale and odd. This surprised Philip Hookhorn very much, for years before that time William's little son — his only child — had been drowned in that spring while at play there, and this had so preyed upon William's mind that he'd never been seen near the spring afterwards, and had been known to go half a mile out of his way to avoid the place. On inquiry, it was found that William in body could not have stood by the spring, being in the mead two miles off; and it also came out that the time at which he was seen at the spring was the very time when he died."

"The Superstitious Man's Story", *A Few Crusted Characters*

A letter of 1 April, 1894 from Hardy to his friend Edward Clodd makes an important postscript to this:

Certainly, all that about the "miller's-soul" is, or was till lately, an actual belief down here. It was told me years ago by an old woman. I may say, once for all, that every superstition, custom, etc., described in my novels may be depended on as true records of the same, whatever merit in folklorists' eyes they may have as such — and not inventions of mine.[71]

"The Withered Arm", one of the most interesting of Hardy's stories, is firmly rooted in Dorset folklore, and indeed, according to him, in fact. When he was a boy . . . there was still living an old woman who, for the cure of some eating disease, had been taken in her youth to have her "blood turned" by a convict's corpse, in the manner described in *The Withered Arm.*

Since writing this story some years ago [in 1888] I have been reminded by an aged friend who knew "Rhoda Brook" that, in relating her dream, my forgetfulness has weakened the facts out of which the tale grew. . . .

Preface to *Wessex Tales*

A blight has apparently been cast, unwittingly in her sleep, by the milkmaid Rhoda Brook on the arm of her former lover's new wife, Gertrude Lodge:

What the impress resembled seemed to have struck Gertrude herself since their last meeting. "It looks almost like finger-marks," she said; adding with a faint laugh, "My husband says it is as if some witch, or the devil himself, had taken hold of me there, and blasted the flesh."

Rhoda shivered, "That's fancy," she said hurriedly. "I wouldn't mind it, if I were you." . . .

And so the milkwoman's mind was chained anew to the subject by a horrid sort of spell as she returned home. The sense of having been guilty of an act of malignity increased, affect as she might to ridicule her superstition.

The Withered Arm

Mrs Lodge persuades Rhoda to lead her to Conjuror Trendle, a wise man or "exorcist" who lives in the heart of Egdon Heath:

He did not profess his remedial practices openly, or care anything about their continuance, his direct interests being those of a dealer in furze, turf, "sharp sand", and other local products. Indeed, he affected not to believe largely in his own powers, and when warts that had been shown him for cure miraculously disappeared — which it must be owned they infallibly did — he would say lightly, "O, I only drink a glass of grog upon 'em at your expense — perhaps it's all chance," and immediately turn the subject.

The Withered Arm

He examined her arm.

"Medicine can't cure it," he said promptly. "'Tis the work of an enemy."

Rhoda shrank into herself, and drew back.

"An enemy? What enemy?" asked Mrs Lodge.

He shook his head. "That's best known to yourself," he said. "If you like, I can show the person to you, though I shall not myself know who it is. I can do no more; and don't wish to do that."

She pressed him; on which he told Rhoda to wait outside where she stood, and took Mrs Lodge into the room. It opened immediately from the door; and, as the latter remained ajar, Rhoda Brook could see the proceedings without taking part in them. He brought a tumbler from the dresser, nearly filled it with water, and fetching an egg, prepared it in some private way; after which he broke it on the edge of the glass, so that the white went in and the yolk remained. As it was getting gloomy, he took the glass and its contents to the window, and told Gertrude to watch the mixture closely. They leant over the table together, and the milkwoman could see the opaline hue of the egg-fluid changing form as it sank in the water, but she was not near enough to define the shape that is assumed.

"Do you catch the likeness of any face or figure as you look?" demanded the conjuror of the young woman.

She murmured a reply, in tones so low as to be inaudible to Rhoda, and continued to gaze intently into the glass. Rhoda turned, and walked a few steps away.

The Withered Arm

In a short memoir, Some Recollections, *which Hardy's first wife Emma wrote the year before her death, but which lay undiscovered until after it, she tells how on Midsummer day, 1858, an old servant correctly prophesied the occupation of three people's future husbands — Emma's included — by letting them drop an egg-white similarly into a tumbler of water. Everyone there agreed that Emma's "shape" was a "large inkbottle and an immense quill pen", and that she would therefore marry a writer.*[72]

Gertrude Lodge tries a "hundred medicaments and spells" to cure her withered arm — in vain. After several years she visits the ageing conjuror again:

"There is only one chance of doing it known to me. It has never failed in kindred afflictions — that I can declare. But it is hard to carry out, and especially for a woman."

"Tell me!" said she.

"You must touch with the limb the neck of a man who's been hanged."

She started a little at the image he had raised.

"Before he's cold — just after he's cut down," continued the conjuror impassively.

"How can that do good?"

"It will turn the blood and change the constitution. But, as I say, to do it is hard. You must go to the jail when there's a hanging, and wait for him when he's brought off the gallows. Lots have done it, though perhaps not such pretty women as you. I used to send dozens of skin complaints. But that was in former times. The last I sent was in '13 — near twelve years ago."

The Withered Arm

More Wizards and Wise Men . . .

There used to come to a little bridge, close to [William Barnes's] father's door, till quite recently, a conjuror or "white wizard", who cured afflicted persons by means of the toad-bag — a small piece of linen having a limb from a living toad sewn up inside, to be worn round the sufferer's neck and next his skin, the twitching movement of which limb gave, so it was said, "a turn" to the blood of the wearer, and effected a radical change in his constitution.[73]

Obituary notice by Hardy of the Rev. William Barnes, *The Athenaeum*

There was a great stir in the milk-house just after breakfast. The churn revolved as usual, but the butter would not come. . . .

" 'Tis years since I went to Conjuror Trendle's son in Egdon — years!" said the dairyman bitterly. "And he was nothing to what his father had been. I have said fifty times, if I have said once, that I don't believe in 'en; 'though he do cast folks' waters very true. But I shall have to go to 'n if he's alive. O yes, I shall have to go to 'n if this sort of thing continnys! . . . My grandfather used to go to Conjuror Mynterne, out at Owlscombe, and a clever man a' were, so I've heard grandf'er say," continued Mr Crick. "But there's no such genuine folk about nowadays!"

Mrs Crick's mind kept nearer to the matter in hand.

"Perhaps somebody in the house is in love," she said tentatively. "I've heard tell in my younger days that that will cause it."

Tess of the d'Urbervilles

Hardy's notes show that Conjuror Mynterne actually existed.

The corn-merchant visits Conjuror Fall for a weather forecast:

He existed on unseen supplies; for it was an anomalous thing that while there was hardly a soul in the neighbourhood but affected to laugh at this man's assertions, uttering the formula, "There's nothing in 'em," with full assurance on the surface of their faces, very few of them were unbelievers in their secret hearts. Whenever they consulted him they did it "for a fancy". When they paid him they said, "Just a trifle for Christmas," or "Candlemas," as the case might be.

He would have preferred more honesty in his clients, and less sham ridicule; but fundamental belief consoled him for superficial irony. As stated, he was enabled to live; people supported him with their backs turned. He was sometimes astonished that men could profess so little and believe so much at his house, when at church they professed so much and believed so little.

Behind his back he was called "Wide-oh," on account of his reputation; to his face "Mr" Fall.

The hedge of his garden formed an arch over the entrance, and a door was inserted as in a wall. Outside the door the tall traveller stopped, bandaged his face with a handkerchief as if he were suffering from toothache, and went up the path. The window shutters were not closed, and he could see the prophet within, preparing his supper.

In answer to the knock, Fall came to the door, candle in hand. The visitor stepped back a little from the light, and said, "Can I speak to 'ee?" in significant tones. The other's invitation to come in was responded to by the country formula, "This will do, thank 'ee," after which the householder has no alternative but to come out. He placed the candle on the corner of the dresser, took his hat from a nail, and joined the stranger in the porch, shutting the door behind him.

"I've long heard that you can — do things of a sort?" began the other, repressing his individuality as much as he could.

"Maybe so, Mr Henchard," said the weather-caster.

"Ah — why do you call me that?" asked the visitor with a start.

"Because it's your name. Feeling you'd come I've waited for 'ee; and thinking you might be leery from your walk I laid two supper plates — look ye here." He threw open the door and disclosed the supper-table, at which appeared a second chair, knife and fork, plate and mug, as he had declared.

Henchard felt like Saul at his reception by Samuel;[74] he remained in silence for a few moments, then throwing off the disguise of frigidity which he had hitherto preserved he said, "Then I have not come in vain.... Now, for instance, can ye charm away warts?"

"Without trouble."

"Cure the evil?"[75]

"That I've done — with consideration — if they will wear the toad-bag by night as well as by day."

"Forecast the weather?"

"With labour and time."

"Then take this," said Henchard. "'Tis a crown-piece. Now, what is the harvest fortnight to be? When can I know?"

"I've worked it out already, and you can know at once." (The fact was that five farmers had already been there on the same errand from different parts of the country.) "By the sun, moon, and stars, by the clouds, the winds, the trees, and grass, the candle-flame and swallows, the smell of the herbs; likewise by the cats' eyes, the ravens, the leeches, the spiders, and the dungmixen, the last fortnight in August will be — rain and tempest."

"You are not certain, of course?"

"As one can be in a world where all's unsure. 'Twill be more like living in Revelations this autumn than in England. Shall I sketch it out for 'ee in a scheme?"

"O no, no," said Henchard. "I don't altogether believe in forecasts, come to second thoughts on such. But I —"

"You don't — you don't — 'tis quite understood," said Wide-oh, without a sound of scorn. "You have given me a crown because you've one too many. But won't you join me at supper, now 'tis waiting and all?"

Henchard would gladly have joined; for the savour of the stew had floated from the cottage into the porch with such appetizing distinctness that the meat, the onions, the pepper, and the herbs could be severally recognized by his nose. But as sitting down to hob-and-nob there would have seemed to mark him too implicitly as the weather-caster's apostle, he declined, and went his way.

The Mayor of Casterbridge

Witches and a wise woman....

"Who's Miss Vye?" said Clym....

"A proud girl from Budmouth," said Mrs Yeobright. "One not much to my liking. People say she's a witch, but of course that's absurd."

The Return of the Native

"'Tis news you have brought us, then, Christian?" said Mrs Yeobright.

"Ay, sure, about a witch.... I assure you it made me shake like a driven leaf.... This morning at church we was all standing up, and the pa'son said, 'Let us pray'. 'Well,' thinks I, 'one may as well kneel as stand; so down I went; and, more than that, all the rest were as willing to oblige the man as I. We hadn't been hard at it for more than a minute when a most terrible screech sounded through church, as if somebody had just gied up their heart's blood. All the folk jumped up, and then we found that Susan Nunsuch had pricked Miss Vye with a long stocking-needle, as she had threatened to do as soon as ever she could get the young lady to church, where she don't come very often. She've waited for this chance for weeks, so as to draw her blood and put an end to the bewitching of Susan's children that has been carried on so long."

The Return of the Native

In the yard there was a conversation going on about the mare; the man who attended to the horses, Darling included, insisted that the latter was "hag-rid"; for when he had arrived at the stable that morning she was in such a state as no horse could be in by honest riding.... The unprecedented exhaustion of Darling, as thus related, was sufficient to develop a whole series of tales about equestrian witches and demons, the narration of which occupied a considerable time.

The Woodlanders

Elizabeth Endorfield had a repute among women which was in its nature something between distinction and notoriety. It was founded on the following items of character. She was shrewd and penetrating; her house stood in a lonely place; she never went to church; she wore a red cloak; she always retained her bonnet indoors; and she had a pointed chin. Thus far her attributes were distinctly Satanic; and those who looked no further called her, in plain terms, a witch. But she was not gaunt, nor ugly in the upper part of her face, nor particularly strange in manner; so that, when her more intimate acquaintances spoke of her the term was softened, and she became simply a Deep Body, who was as long-headed as she was high. It may be stated that Elizabeth belonged to a class of suspects who were gradually losing their mysterious characteristics under the administration of the young vicar; though during the long reign of Mr Grinham the parish of Mellstock had proved extremely favourable to the growth of witches.

Under the Greenwood Tree

SUPERSTITIOUS PRACTICES

On Thomasin's wedding-day:

"Well, God bless you! There, I don't believe in old superstitions, but I'll do it." [Mrs Yeobright] threw a slipper at the retreating figure of the girl, who turned, smiled, and went on again.

The Return of the Native

A widow attempts to check new love:

"I've pulled grass from my husband's grave to cure it — wove the blades into true lover's knots; took off my shoes upon the sod; but, avast, my shipmate! —"

"Upon the sod — why?"

"To feel the damp earth he's in, and make the sense of it enter my soul. But no. It has swelled to a head; he is going to meet me at the Yeomanry Review."

The Romantic Adventures of a Milkmaid

Divination by Bible and key:

On the table lay an old quarto Bible, bound in leather. Liddy looking at it said, —

"Did you ever find out, miss, who you are going to marry by means of the Bible and key?"

"Don't be so foolish, Liddy. As if such things could be."

"Well, there's a good deal in it, all the same."

"Nonsense, child."

"And it makes your heart beat fearful. Some believe in it; some don't; I do."

"Very well, let's try it," said Bathsheba, bounding from her seat with that total disregard of consistency which can be indulged in towards a dependant, and entering into the spirit of divination at once. "Go and get the front door key."

Liddy fetched it. "I wish it wasn't Sunday," she said, on returning. "Perhaps 'tis wrong."

"What's right week days is right Sundays," replied her mistress in a tone which was a proof in itself.

The book was opened — the leaves, drab with age, being quite worn away at much-read verses by the forefingers of unpractised readers in former days, where they were moved along under the line as an aid to the vision. The special verse in the Book of Ruth* was sought out by Bathsheba, and the sublime words met her eye. They slightly thrilled and abashed her. It was Wisdom in the abstract facing Folly in the concrete. Folly in the concrete blushed, persisted in her attention, and placed the key on the book. A rusty patch immediately upon the verse, caused by previous pressure of an iron substance thereon, told that this was not the first time the old volume had been used for the purpose.

"Now keep steady, and be silent," said Bathsheba.

The verse was repeated; the book turned round; Bathsheba blushed guiltily.

"Who did you try?" said Liddy curiously.

"I shall not tell you."

*(Ruth I, verse 16) *Far from the Madding Crowd*

Roasting a waxen image:

The distant light which Eustacia had cursorily observed in leaving the house came, as she had divined, from the cottage-window of Susan Nunsuch. What Eustacia did not divine was the occupation of the woman within at that moment. Susan's sight of her passing figure earlier in the evening, not five minutes after the sick boy's exclamation, "Mother, I do feel so bad!" persuaded the matron that an evil influence was certainly exercised by Eustacia's propinquity.

On this account Susan did not got to bed as soon as the evening's work was over, as she would have done at ordinary times. To counteract the malign spell which she imagined poor Eustacia to be working, the boy's mother busied herself with a ghastly invention of superstition, calculated to bring powerlessness, atrophy, and annihilation on any human being against whom it was directed. It was a practice well known on Egdon at that date, and one that is not quite extinct at the present day.

Susan moulds a figure from beeswax, and asks Johnny what Mrs Eustacia was wearing:

Susan held the object at arm's length and contemplated it with a satisfaction in which there was no smile. To anybody acquainted with the inhabitants of Egdon Heath the image would have suggested Eustacia Yeobright.

From her work-basket in the window-seat the woman took a paper of pins, of the old long and yellow sort, whose heads were disposed to come off at their first usage. These she began to thrust into the image in all directions, with apparently excruciating energy. Probably as many as fifty were thus inserted, some into the head of the wax model, some into the shoulders, some into the trunk, some upwards through the soles of the feet, till the figure was completely permeated with pins.

She turned to the fire. It had been of turf; and though the high heap of ashes which turf fires produce was somewhat dark and dead on the outside, upon raking it abroad with the shovel the inside of the mass showed a glow of red heat. She took a few pieces of fresh turf from the chimney-corner and built them together over the glow, upon which the fire brightened. Seizing with the tongs the image that she had made of Eustacia, she held it in the heat, and watched it as it began to waste slowly away. And while she stood thus engaged there came from between her lips a murmur of words.

It was a strange jargon — the Lord's Prayer repeated backwards — the incantation usual in proceedings for obtaining unhallowed assistance against an enemy. Susan uttered the lugubrious discourse three times slowly, and when it was completed the image had considerably diminished. As the wax dropped into the fire a long flame arose from the spot, and curling its tongue round the figure ate still further into its substance. A pin occasionally dropped with the wax, and the embers heated it red as it lay.

The Return of the Native

[1871] *June.* . . . Another old custom: All hallow's eve. Kill a pigeon: stick its heart full of pins. Roast the heart in the candle flame. Faithless lover will twist and toss with nightmare in his sleep.

Memoranda I

Old Midsummer's Eve — which until the calendar change of 1752 was 5 July, the old dates being kept for many generations in country districts — was the occasion for many superstitious beliefs and pagan rites. (See Sir James Frazer's The Golden Bough, *abridged edition, 1922, chapters 29–33.)*

[1871] *June.* Old Midsummer custom: on old Midsummer eve, at going to bed:

> "I put my shoes in the form of a T,
> And trust my true-love for to see."

Another: On old Midsummer noon dig a hole in the grass plot, and place your ear thereon precisely at 12. The occupation of your future husband will be revealed by the noises heard.

Memoranda I

"Well!" said Mrs Penny, flopping into a chair, "my heart haven't been in such a thumping state of uproar since I used to sit up on old Midsummer-eves to see who my husband was going to be. . . . Yes," said Mrs Penny, throwing her glance into past times . . . "yes; never was I in such a taking as on that Midsummer-eve! I sat up, quite determined to see if John Wildway was going to marry me or no. I put the bread-and-cheese and beer quite ready, as the witch's book ordered, and I opened the door, and I waited till the clock struck twelve, my nerves all alive and so strained that I could feel everyone of 'em twitching like bell-wires. Yes, sure! and when the clock had struck, lo and behold I could see through the door a *little small* man in the lane wi' a shoemaker's apron on."

Here Mr Penny stealthily enlarged himself an inch. . . .

Under the Greenwood Tree

It was not Grace who had passed, however, but several of the ordinary village girls in a group; some steadily walking, some in a mood of wild gaiety. [Fitzpiers] quietly asked his landlady . . . what these girls were intending, and she informed him that it being old Midsummer Eve they were about to attempt some spell or enchantment which would afford them a glimpse of their future partners for life. . . .

At that minute the girls, some of whom were from Great Hintock, were seen advancing to work the incantation, it being now about midnight . . .

"I wish we had not thought of trying this," said [one], "but had contented ourselves with the hole-digging to-morrow at twelve, and hearing our husbands' trades. It is too much like having dealings with the evil one to try to raise their forms."

However, they had gone too far to recede, and slowly began to march forward in a skirmishing line through the trees, each intending to plunge alone into a deep recess of the wood. As far as the listeners could gather, the particular form of black art to be practised on this occasion was one connected with the sowing of hempseed, a handful of which was carried by each girl.

At the moment of their advance they looked back and discerned the figure of Miss Melbury who, alone of all the observers, stood in the full face of the moonlight, deeply engrossed in the proceedings. By contrast with her life of late years they made her feel as if she had receded a couple of centuries in the world's history.

The Woodlanders

[Jude's] supper still remained spread; and going to the front door, and softly setting it open, he returned to the room and sat as watchers sit on Old-Midsummer eves, expecting the phantom of the Beloved. But she did not come.

Jude the Obscure

Postscript

In a letter written early in 1915 Hardy admitted that in one sense he "believed" (especially when he was writing poetry) in "spectres, mysterious voices, intuitions, omens, dreams, haunted places etc".[76] *In 1901 he had told William Archer in a discussion on the spirit world:*

. . . For my part I say in all sincerity, "Better be inconvenienced by visitants from beyond the grave than see none at all." The material world is so uninteresting, human life is so miserably bounded, circumscribed, cabin'd, cribb'd, confined. I want another domain for the imagination to expatiate in.

W. Archer, *Real Conversations*

I am most anxious to believe in what, roughly speaking, we may call the supernatural — but I find no evidence for it! People accuse me of scepticism, materialism, and so forth; but, if the accusation is just at all, it is quite against my will. For instance, I seriously assure you that I would give ten years of my life — well, perhaps that offer is rather beyond my means — but when I was a younger man, I would cheerfully have given ten years of my life to see a ghost — an authentic, indubitable spectre.

W.A. And you have never seen one?

Mr Hardy. Never the ghost of a ghost. Yet I should think I am cut out by nature for a ghost-seer. My nerves vibrate very readily; people say I am almost morbidly imaginative; my will to believe is perfect. If ever ghost wanted to manifest himself, I am the very man he should apply to. But no — the spirits don't seem to see it!

W. Archer, *Real Conversations*

Hardy had to wait seventeen years for this, as a letter from Florence Hardy shows:

Dec. 27th, 1919

Dear Mr Cockerell,

We had a very quiet Christmas, we too, alone, with Wessie [her dog] — our only diversion being that T.H. *would* give Wessie goose and plum-pudding, and the result was what might have been expected.... He saw a ghost in Stinsford Churchyard on Christmas Eve, and his sister Kate says it must have been their grandfather upon whose grave T.H. had just placed a sprig of holly — the first time he had ever done so. The ghost said: "A green Christmas" — T.H. replied "I like a green Christmas." Then the ghost went into the church, and, being full of curiosity, T. followed, to see who this strange man in 18th century dress might be — and found no-one. That is quite true — a real Christmas ghost story....

Viola Meynell, *Friends of a Lifetime*

Yuletide in a Younger World

We believed in highdays then,
And could glimpse at night
On Christmas Eve
Imminent oncomings of radiant revel —
Doings of delight: —
Now we have no such sight.

We had eyes for phantoms then,
And at bridge or stile
On Christmas Eve
Clear beheld those countless ones who had crossed it
Cross again in file: —
Such has ceased longwhile!

We liked divination then,
And, as they homeward wound
On Christmas Eve,
We could read men's dreams within them spinning
Even as wheels spin round: —
Now we are blinker-bound.

We heard still small voices then,
And, in the dim serene
Of Christmas Eve,
Caught the far-time tones of fire-filled prophets
Long on earth unseen...
— Can such ever have been?

Winter Words

Paganism

Until the railway first came to Dorchester in 1847 and began to open up the county, Dorset was isolated and backward, its people feeding on their ancient traditions and beliefs, their backs turned to more sophisticated cultures. Hardy's mother in particular had an apparently inexhaustible fund of folklore. His knowledge of this, his unfailing consciousness of the omnipresent past, and of the bond with nature of the country people around him, led him to see how much of their life — particularly their entertainment — was based on pagan attitudes and customs.

As Tess approaches her new life in the Froom valley, she sings for gladness:

And probably the half-unconscious rhapsody was a Fetichistic utterance in a Monotheistic setting; women whose chief companions are the forms and forces of outdoor Nature retain in their souls far more of the Pagan fantasy of their remote forefathers than of the systematized religion taught their race at a later date. However, Tess found at least approximate expression for her feelings in the old *Benedicite* that she had lisped from infancy; and it was enough.

Tess of the d'Urbervilles

Maypole Day on Egdon:

The impulses of all such outlandish hamlets are pagan still: in these spots homage to nature, self-adoration, frantic gaieties, fragments of Teutonic rites to divinities whose names are forgotten, seem in some way or other to have survived mediaeval doctrine.[77]

The Return of the Native

On the Isle of Slingers:

They climbed homeward slowly by the Old Road.... At the top they turned and stood still.... Under their front, at periods of a quarter of a minute, there arose a deep, hollow stroke like the single beat of a drum, the intervals being filled with a long-drawn rattling, as of bones between huge canine jaws. It came from the vast concave of Deadman's Bay, rising and falling against the pebble dyke.

The evening and night winds here were, to Pierston's mind, charged with a something that did not burden them elsewhere. They brought it up from that sinister Bay to the west, whose movement she and he were hearing now. It was a presence — an imaginary shape or essence from the human multitude lying below: those who had gone down in vessels of war, East Indiamen, barges, brigs, and ships of the Armada — select people, common, and debased, whose interests and hopes had been as wide asunder as the poles, but who had rolled each other to oneness on that restless sea-bed. There could almost be felt the brush of their huge composite ghost as it ran a shapeless figure over the isle, shrieking for some good god who would disunite it again.

The twain wandered a long way that night amid these influences — so far as to the old Hope churchyard, which lay in a ravine formed by a landslip ages ago. The church had slipped down with the rest of the cliff, and had long been a ruin. It seemed to say that in this last local stronghold of the Pagan divinities, where Pagan customs lingered yet, Christianity had established itself precariously at best. In that solemn spot Pierston kissed her.

The Well-Beloved

The Vale of Blackmoor — "an engirdled and secluded region":

The Vale was known in former times as the Forest of White Hart, from a curious legend of King Henry III's reign, in which the killing by a certain Thomas de la Lynd of a beautiful white hart which the king had run down and spared, was made the occasion of a heavy fine. In those days, and till comparatively recent times, the country was densely wooded. Even now, traces of its earlier condition are to be found in the old oak copses and irregular belts of timber that yet survive upon its slopes, and the hollow-trunked trees that shade so many of its pastures.

The forests have departed, but some old customs of their shades remain. Many, however, linger only in a metamorphosed or disguised form. The May-Day dance, for instance, was to be discerned on the afternoon under notice, in the guise of the club revel, or "club-walking", as it was called.

... The Club of Marlott alone lived to uphold the local Cerealia.[78] It had walked for hundreds of years, if not as benefit-club, as votive sisterhood of some sort; and it walked still.

Tess of the d'Urbervilles

The Chase:

— a truly venerable tract of forest land, one of the few remaining woodlands in England of undoubted primaeval date, wherein Druidical mistletoe was still found on aged oaks, and where enormous yew-trees, not planted by the hand of man, grew as they had grown when they were pollarded for bows.

Tess of the d'Urbervilles

Everywhere Nature proclaims the old worship:

It was a hazy sunshine in August.... The sun, on account of the mist, had a curious sentient, personal look, demanding the masculine pronoun for its adequate expression. His present aspect, coupled with the lack of all human forms in the scene, explained the old-time heliolatries in a moment. One could feel that a saner religion had never prevailed under the sky. The luminary was a golden-haired, beaming, mild-eyed, God-like creature, gazing down in the vigour and intentness of youth upon an earth that was brimming with interest for him.

Tess of the d'Urbervilles

To the aesthetic, sensuous, pagan pleasure in natural life and lush womanhood which his son Angel had lately been experiencing in Var Vale, [old Mr Clare's] temper would have been antipathetic in a high degree.... Latterly [Angel] had seen only Life, felt only the great passionate pulse of existence, unwarped, uncontorted, untrammelled by those creeds which futilely attempt to check what wisdom would be content to regulate.

Tess of the d'Urbervilles

[Grace] saw nothing of Winterborne during the days of her recovery; and perhaps on that account her fancy wove about him a more romantic tissue than it could have done if he had stood before her with all the specks and flaws inseparable from concrete humanity. He rose upon her memory as the fruit-god and the wood-god in alternation: sometimes leafy and smeared with green lichen, as she had seen him amongst the sappy boughs of the plantations: sometimes cider-stained and starred with apple-pips, as she had met him on his return from cider-making in Blackmoor Vale, with his vats and presses beside him.

The Woodlanders

"The lonely country nooks where fatalism is a strong sentiment"[79]

Tess was now carried along upon the wings of the hours, without the sense of a will. The word had been given; the number of the day had been written down. Her naturally bright intelligence had begun to admit the fatalistic convictions common to field-folk and those who associate more extensively with natural phenomena than with their fellow-creatures; and she accordingly drifted into that passive responsiveness to all things her lover suggested, characteristic of the frame of mind.

Tess of the d'Urbervilles

Matrimony is fate:

"You think to yourself, 'twas to be," cried Enoch from his distant corner, by way of filling up the vacancy caused by Geoffrey's momentary absence. "And so you marry her, Master Dewy, and there's an end on't."

"Pray don't say such things, Enoch," came from Fancy severely, upon which Enoch relapsed into servitude.

"If we be doomed to marry, we marry; if we be doomed to remain single, we do," replied Dick.

Under the Greenwood Tree

Jim woos the wayward Margery:

Instead of saying yes, the fair maid repressed another sigh.

"What, won't it then?" he said.

"I suppose so," she answered. "If it is to be, it is."

"Well said — very well said, my dear."

"And if it isn't to be, it isn't."

"What? Who's been putting that into your head?"

The Romantic Adventures of a Milkmaid

And after...

"Here, Mr Penny," resumed Mrs Dewy, "you sit in this chair. And how's your daughter, Mrs Brownjohn?"

"Well, I suppose I must say pretty fair." He adjusted his spectacles a quarter of an inch to the right. "But she'll be worse before she's better, 'a believe."

"Indeed — poor soul! And how many will that make in all, four or five?"

"Five; they've buried three. Yes, five; and she not much more than a maid yet. She do know the multiplication table onmistakable well. However, 'twas to be, and none can gainsay it."[80]

Under the Greenwood Tree

Fate and faith:

"No baily — I deserved that place," wailed Henery.... "There, 'twas to be, I suppose. Your lot is your lot, and Scripture is nothing; for if you do good you don't get rewarded according to your works, but be cheated in some mean way out of your recompense."

"No, no; I don't agree with 'ee there," said Mark Clark. "God's a perfect gentleman in that respect."

"Good works good pay, so to speak it," attested Joseph Poorgrass.

A short pause ensued....

Far from the Madding Crowd

Legends and Traditions

Legends and old stories appear frequently in Hardy's writings, many in the form of poems, some mulled over in countrymen's conversations as they work. Most of these poems — such as "The Lost Pyx", "At Shag's Heath", "The Trampwoman's Tragedy", "The Colour" — are too long to quote here but "A Sound in the Night" (page 68) is one example. Other traditions (apart from those connected with the supernatural — see above) are often family ones, as in the short stories collected as A Group of Noble Dames, *eyewitness accounts (the stories of Napoleonic times), or scraps of accumulated natural lore and folk rhymes.*

Traditions of Napoleonic times:

The present tale is founded more largely on testimony — oral and written — than any other in this series. The external incidents which direct its course are mostly an unexaggerated reproduction of the recollections of old persons as well known to the author in childhood, but now long dead, who were eye-witnesses to those scenes. If wholly transcribed their recollections would have filled a volume thrice the length of *The Trumpet-Major.*

Preface to *The Trumpet-Major*

An experience of the writer in respect of the tale called *A Tradition of Eighteen Hundred and Four* is curious enough to be mentioned here. The incident of Napoleon's visit to the English coast by night, with a view to discovering a convenient spot for landing his army of invasion, was an invention of the author's on which he had some doubts because of its improbability. This was in 1882, when it was first published. Great was his surprise several years later to be told that it was a real tradition. How far this is true he is unaware.

Preface to *Wessex Tales*

[The deserters'] graves were dug at the back of the little church, near the wall. There is no memorial to mark the spot, but Phyllis pointed it out to me. While she lived she used to keep their mounds neat; but now they are overgrown with nettles and sunk nearly flat. The older villagers, however, who know of the episode from their parents, still recollect the place where the soldiers lie. Phyllis lies near.

The Melancholy Hussar of the German Legion

Family traditions:

The pedigrees of our county families, arranged in diagrams on the pages of county histories, mostly appear at first sight to be as barren of any touch of nature as a table of logarithms. But given a clue — the faintest tradition of what went on behind the scenes, and this dryness as of dust may be transformed into a palpitating drama....

Out of such pedigrees and supplementary material most of the following stories have arisen and taken shape.

Preface to *A Group of Noble Dames*

Country lore:

Marty prepared her a comfortable place and she sat down in the circle, and listened to Fitzpiers while he drew from her father and the bark-rippers sundry narratives of their fathers', their grandfathers', and their own adventures in these woods; of the mysterious sights they had seen — only to be accounted for by supernatural agency; of white witches and black witches: and the standard story of the spirits of the Two Brothers who had fought and fallen, and had haunted King's Hintock Court a few miles off till they were exorcised by the priest, and compelled to retreat to a swamp, whence they were returning to their old quarters at the Court at the rate of a cock's stride every New Year's Day, Old Style;[81] hence the local saying, "On new-year's tide, a cock's stride."

It was a pleasant time. The smoke from the little fire of peeled sticks rose between the sitters and the sunlight, and behind its blue films stretched the naked arms of the prostrate trees. The smell of the uncovered sap mingled with the smell of the burning wood, and the sticky inner surface of the scattered bark glistened as it revealed its pale madder hues to the eye.

The Woodlanders

Margery the milkmaid worries about her brown hands before she visits the Baron:

She held them up and looked at them with some misgiving, the fourth finger on her left hand more especially. Hot washings and cold washings, certain products from bee and flower known only to country girls, everything she could think of, were used upon those sunburnt little hands....

The Romantic Adventures of a Milkmaid

A Saint's Day tradition:

"And when is the wedding to be, Hayward?" the Baron asked.... "It is not quite certain yet, my noble lord," said Jim cheerfully. "But I hope 'twill not be long after the time when God A'mighty christens the little apples."

"And when is that?"

"St Swithin's — the middle of July."

The Romantic Adventures of a Milkmaid

The children's bogey:

A child's first sight of a reddleman was an epoch of his life. That blood-coloured figure was a sublimation of all the horrid dreams which had afflicted the juvenile spirit since imagination began. "The reddleman is coming for you!" had been the formulated threat of Wessex mothers for many generations. He was successfully supplanted for a while, at the beginning of the present century, by Buonaparte; but as process of time rendered the latter personage stale and ineffective the older phrase resumed its early prominence. And now the reddleman has in his turn followed Buonaparte to the land of worn-out bogeys, and his place is filled by modern inventions.

The Return of the Native

The Oxen

Christmas Eve, and twelve of the clock.
"Now they are all on their knees,"
An elder said as we sat in a flock
By the embers in hearthside ease.

We pictured the meek mild creatures where
They dwelt in their strawy pen,
Nor did it occur to one of us there
To doubt they were kneeling then.

So fair a fancy few would weave
In these years! Yet, I feel,
If someone said on Christmas Eve,
"Come; see the oxen kneel

"In the lonely barton by yonder coomb
Our childhood used to know,"
I should go with him in the gloom,
Hoping it might be so.

1915

Moments of Vision

A Sound in the Night
(Woodsford Castle: 17—)

"What do I catch upon the night-wind, husband? —
What is it sounds in this house so eerily?
It seems to be a woman's voice: each little while I hear it,
And it much troubles me!"

"'Tis but the eaves dripping down upon the plinth-slopes:
Letting fancies worry thee! — sure 'tis a foolish thing,
When we were on 'y coupled half an hour before the noontide,
And now it's but evening."

"Yet seems it still a woman's voice outside the castle, husband,
And 'tis cold to-night, and rain beats, and this is a lonely place.
Didst thou fathom much of womankind in travel or adventure
Ere ever thou sawest my face?"

"It may be a tree, bride, that rubs his arms acrosswise,
If it is not the eaves-drip upon the lower slopes,
Or the river at the bend, where it whirls about the hatches
Like a creature that sighs and mopes."

"Yet it still seems to me like the crying of a woman,
And it saddens me much that so piteous a sound
On this my bridal night when I would get agone from sorrow
Should so ghost-like wander round!"

"To satisfy thee, Love, I will strike the flint-and-steel, then,
And set the rush-candle up, and undo the door,
And take the new horn-lantern that we bought upon our journey,
And throw the light over the moor."

He struck a light, and breeched and booted in the further chamber,
And lit the new horn-lantern and went from her sight,
And vanished down the turret; and she heard him pass the postern,
And go out into the night.

She listened as she lay, till she heard his step returning,
And his voice as he unclothed him: "'Twas nothing, as I said,
But the nor'-west wind a-blowing from the moor ath'art the river,
And the tree that taps the gurgoyle-head."

"Nay, husband, you perplex me; for if the noise I heard here,
Awaking me from sleep so, were but as you avow,
The rain-fall, and the wind, and the tree-bough, and the river,
Why is it silent now?

"And why is thy hand and thy clasping arm so shaking,
And thy sleeve and tags of hair so muddy and so wet,
And why feel I thy heart a-thumping every time thou kissest me,
And thy breath as if hard to get?"

He lay there in silence for a while, still quickly breathing,
Then started up and walked about the room resentfully:
"O woman, witch, whom I, in sooth, against my will have wedded,
Why castedst thou thy spells on me?

"There was one I loved once: the cry you heard was her cry:
She came to me to-night, and her plight was passing sore,
As no woman.... Yea, and it was e'en the cry you heard, wife,
But she will cry no more!

"And now I can't abide thee: this place, it hath a curse on't,
This farmstead once a castle: I'll get me straight away!"
He dressed this time in darkness, unspeaking, as she listened,
And went ere the dawn turned day.

They found a woman's body at a spot called Rocky Shallow,
Where the Froom stream curves amid the moorland, washed aground,
And they searched about for him, the yeoman, who had darkly known her,
But he could not be found.

And the bride left for good-and-all the farmstead once a castle,
And in a county far away lives, mourns, and sleeps alone,
And thinks in windy weather that she hears a woman crying,
And sometimes an infant's moan.

Late Lyrics and Earlier

Customs

At the dates represented in the various narrations things were like that in Wessex: the inhabitants lived in certain ways, engaged in certain occupations; kept alive certain customs, just as they are shown doing in these pages.... If these country customs and vocations, obsolete and obsolescent, had been detailed wrongly, nobody would have discovered such errors to the end of Time. Yet I have instituted inquiries to correct tricks of memory, and striven against temptations to exaggerate, in order to preserve for my own satisfaction a fairly true record of a vanishing life.

General Preface to the *Novels and Poems, 1912*

In "the village called Weatherbury" (in real life Puddletown, home of many of Hardy's relations):

The game of prisoner's-base, which not so long ago seemed to enjoy a perennial vitality in front of the worn-out stocks, may, so far as I can say, be entirely unknown to the rising generation of schoolboys there. The practice of divination by Bible and key, the regarding of valentines as things of serious import, the shearing-supper, the long smock-frocks, and the harvest-home, have, too, nearly disappeared in the wake of the old houses; and with them has gone, it is said, much of that love of fuddling to which the village at one time was notoriously prone. The change at the root of this has been the recent supplanting of the class of stationary cottagers, who carried on the local traditions and humours, by a population of more or less migratory labourers, which has led to a break of continuity in local history, more fatal than any other thing to the preservation of legend, folk-lore, close inter-social relations, and eccentric individualities. For these the indispensable conditions of existence are attachment to the soil of one particular spot by generation after generation.

Preface to *Far from the Madding Crowd, 1895 and 1902*

[1888] *October.* A game that used to be played at Bockhampton. All kinds of materials are put down in a circle (wood, iron, brick etc.): girls blindfolded, turned round, and made to crawl from centre, whichever material they crawl to will bear upon their future husband's vocation.

Memoranda I

Seasonal customs:

"I can just remember the time when written Valentines were customary . . ." wrote Hardy to a young woman who had sent him one when he was a writer of established reputation;[82] *the sending of a particular Valentine crucially affects the fates of several characters in* Far from the Madding Crowd.

In his notebooks Hardy records other seasonal customs in the country:

[1873] *February.* Shroving in Dorset. When going Shroving they used to carry a bag for flour, and a basin for fat. Their words were:

Ma'am, Ma'am, Ma'am,
I be come a-shroving
For a piece of pancake,
Or a piece of bacon,
Or a round ruggle cheese
Of your own making,

	Ma'am, Ma'am, Ma'am.
subjoined at Puddlehinton and other villages	Hot, hot, the pan's hot, Buttery doors open. Pray mis'ess, good mis'ess Is your heart open? I be come 'ithout my bag, Afeard I shall have nothing.

Memoranda I

[1873] *February.* At Melbury, on a certain day of the year, a family used to go round to the houses saying:—

Wassail, wassail
All round the town
The cup is white
And the ale is brown:
The cup is made of an ashen tree
And the ale is made of good bar-ley.
We'll set the cup upon the bran' [brand]
And hope we shall have good luck anon.
Hope all the apple trees 'ill bud, bear, and bloo',
This year, next year, the year after too
For this our 'sail, our jolly wassail,
O joy go with our jolly wassail!

Memoranda I

Habits and customs on Egdon Heath:

On the Sunday morning following the week of Thomasin's marriage a discussion on this subject was in progress at a hair-cutting before Fairway's house. Here the local barbering was always done at this hour on this day; to be followed by the great Sunday wash of the inhabitants at noon, which in its turn was followed by the great Sunday dressing an hour later. On Egdon Heath Sunday proper did not begin till dinner-time, and even then it was a somewhat battered specimen of the day.

These Sunday-morning hair-cuttings were performed by Fairway; the victim sitting on a chopping-block in front of the house, without a coat, and the neighbours gossiping around, idly observing the locks of hair as they rose upon the wind after the snip, and flew away out of sight to the four quarters of the heavens. Summer and winter the scene was the same, unless the wind were more than usually blusterous, when the stool was shifted a few feet round the corner. To complain of cold in sitting out of doors, hatless and coatless, while Fairway told true stories between the cuts of the scissors, would have been to pronounce yourself no man at once. To flinch, exclaim, or move a muscle of the face at the small stabs under the ear received from those instruments, or at scarifications of the neck by the comb, would have been thought a gross breach of good manners, considering that Fairway did it all for nothing. A bleeding about the poll on Sunday afternoons was amply accounted for by the explanation, "I have had my hair cut, you know."

The Return of the Native

To see the heathmen in their Sunday condition, that is, with their hands in their pockets, their boots newly oiled, and not laced up (a particularly Sunday sign), walking leisurely among the turves and furze-faggots they had cut during the week, and kicking them critically as if their use were unknown, was a fearful heaviness to [Eustacia]. To relieve the tedium of this untimely day she would overhaul the cupboards containing her grandfather's old charts and other rubbish, humming Saturday-night ballads of the country people the while. . . .

The Return of the Native

Time:

On Egdon there was no absolute hour of the day. The time at any moment was a number of varying doctrines professed by the different hamlets, some of them having originally grown up from a common root, and then become divided by secession, some having been alien from the beginning. West Egdon believed in Blooms-End time, East Egdon in the time of the Quiet Woman Inn. Grandfer Cantle's watch had numbered many followers in years gone by, but since he had grown older faiths were shaken. Thus, the mummers having gathered hither from scattered points, each came with his own tenets on early and late.

The Return of the Native

The simple life-style:

[Not long after daybreak] When Yeobright reached the cottage of Susan Nunsuch, the mother of the boy he sought, he found that the inmates were not yet astir. But in upland hamlets the transition from a-bed to abroad is surprisingly swift and easy. There no dense partition of yawns and toilets divides humanity by night from humanity by day. Yeobright tapped at the upper window-sill, which he could reach with his walking-stick; and in three or four minutes the woman came down.

The Return of the Native

The custom of the country: the November 5th bonfires:

While the men and lads were building the pile, a change took place in the mass of shade which denoted the distant landscape. Red suns and tufts of fire one by one began to arise, flecking the whole country round. They were the bonfires of other parishes and hamlets that were engaged in the same sort of commemoration.

Some were distant, and stood in a dense atmosphere, so that bundles of pale strawlike beams radiated around them in the shape of a fan. Some were large and near, glowing scarlet-red from the shade, like wounds in a black hide. Some were Mænades,[83] with winy faces and blown hair. These tinctured the silent bosom of the clouds above them and lit up their ephemeral caves, which seemed thenceforth to become scalding caldrons. Perhaps as many as thirty bonfires could be counted within the whole bounds of the district; and as the hour may be told on a clock-face when the figures themselves are invisible, so did the men recognize the locality of each fire by its angle and direction, though nothing of the scenery could be viewed.

The first tall flame from Rainbarrow sprang into the sky, attracting all eyes that had been fixed on the distant conflagrations back to their own attempt in the same kind. The cheerful blaze streaked the inner surface of the human circle — now increased by other stragglers, male and female — with its own gold livery, and even overlaid the dark turf around with a lively luminousness, which softened off into obscurity where the barrow rounded downwards out of sight. It showed the barrow to be the segment of a globe, as perfect as on the day when it was thrown up, even the little ditch remaining from which the earth was dug. Not a plough had ever disturbed a grain of that stubborn soil. In the heath's barrenness to the farmer lay its fertility to the historian. There had been no obliteration, because there had been no tending....

It was as if these men and boys had suddenly dived into past ages, and fetched therefrom an hour and deed which had before been familiar with this spot. The ashes of the original British pyre which blazed from that summit lay fresh and undisturbed in the barrow beneath their tread. The flames from funeral piles long ago kindled there had shone down upon the lowlands as these were shining now. Festival fires to Thor and Woden[84] had followed on the same ground and duly had their day. Indeed, it is pretty well known that such blazes as this the heathmen were now enjoying are rather the lineal descendants from jumbled Druidical rites and Saxon ceremonies than the invention of popular feeling about Gunpowder Plot.

The Return of the Native

Marriage and betrothal customs:

The country custom of unreserved comradeship out of doors during betrothal was the only custom she knew, and to her it had no strangeness; though it seemed oddly anticipative to Clare till he saw how normal a thing she, in common with all the other dairy-folk, regarded it. Thus, during this October month of wonderful afternoons they roved along the meads by creeping paths which followed the brinks of trickling tributary brooks, hopping across by little wooden bridges to the other side, and back again. They were never out of the sound of some purling weir, whose buzz accompanied their own murmuring, while the beams of the sun, almost as horizontal as the mead itself, formed a pollen of radiance over the landscape. They saw tiny blue fogs in the shadows of trees and hedges, all the time that there was bright sunshine elsewhere. The sun was so near the ground, and the sward so flat, that the shadows of Clare and Tess would stretch a quarter of a mile ahead of them, like two long fingers pointing afar to where the green alluvial reaches abutted against the sloping sides of the vale.

Tess of the d'Urbervilles

Bride and bridegroom walk together to their own wedding:

An observer must have been very close indeed to discover that the forms under the umbrellas were those of Oak and Bathsheba, arm-in-arm for the first time in their lives. . . .

Far from the Madding Crowd

The appointed morning came. The arrangement with Wildeve was that he should meet her at the church to guard against any unpleasant curiosity which might have affected them had they been seen walking off together in the usual country way.

The Return of the Native

On the Isle of Slingers (Portland) in the very early part of the century the old custom of sexual relations as a ratification of a betrothal, only to be made official if the union proved to be fertile, was only just dying out.

Avice fails to keep her appointment with Jocelyn:

When the boy had gone Jocelyn retraced his steps to the last lamp and read, in Avice's hand:

MY DEAREST — I shall be sorry if I grieve you at all in what I am going to say about our arrangement to meet to-night in the Sandsfoot ruin. But I have fancied that my seeing you again and again lately is inclining your father to insist, and you as his heir to feel, that we ought to carry out Island Custom in our courting — your people being such old inhabitants in an unbroken line. Truth to say, mother supposes that your father, for natural reasons, may have hinted to you that we ought. Now, the thing is contrary to my feelings: it is nearly left off; and I do not think it good, even when there is property, as in your case, to justify it, in a measure. I would rather trust in Providence.

On the whole, therefore, it is best that I should not come — if only for appearances — and meet you at a time and place suggesting the custom, to others than ourselves, at least, if known.

I am sure that this decision will not disturb you much; that you will understand my modern feelings, and think no worse of me for them. And dear, if it were to be done, and we were unfortunate in it, we might both have enough old family feeling to think, like our forefathers, and possibly your father, that we could not marry honourably; and hence we might be made unhappy.

However, you will come again shortly, will you not, dear Jocelyn? — and then the time will soon draw on when no more good-byes will be required. Always and ever yours,

AVICE

Jocelyn, having read the letter, was surprised at the naïveté it showed, and at Avice and her mother's antiquated simplicity in supposing that to be still a grave and operating principle which was a bygone barbarism to himself and other absentees from the island.

The reader is asked to remember that the date, though recent in the history of the Isle of Slingers, was more than forty years ago.*

* *i.e. about 1850*

The Well-Beloved

Funeral customs

The earliest surviving MS of a Hardy poem is the original draft of parts of what he later published as "Retty's Phases". At the end he gives the following explanatory note:

In many villages it was customary after the funeral of an unmarried young woman to ring a peal as for her wedding while the grave was being filled in, as if Death were not to be allowed to balk her of her bridal honours. Young unmarried men were always her bearers.

After "The Hatband" (page 129) he makes another note about current mourning customs; and after the following:

Julie-Jane

Sing; how 'a would sing!
How 'a would raise the tune
When we rode in the waggon from harvesting
By the light o' the moon!

Dance; how 'a would dance!
If a fiddlestring did but sound
She would hold out her coats, give a slanting glance,
And go round and round.

Laugh; how 'a would laugh!
Her peony lips would part
As if none such a place for a lover to quaff
At the deeps of a heart.

Julie, O girl of joy,
Soon, soon that lover he came.
Ah, yes; and gave thee a baby-boy,
But never his name....

Tolling for her, as you guess;
And the baby too.... 'Tis well.
You knew her in maidhood likewise? — Yes,
That's her burial bell.

"I suppose," with a laugh, she said,
"I should blush that I'm not a wife;
But how can it matter, so soon to be dead,
What one does in life!"

When we sat making the mourning
By her death-bed side, said she,
"Dears, how can you keep from your lovers, adorning
In honour of me!"

Bubbling and brightsome eyed!
But now — O never again.
She chose her bearers before she died
From her fancy-men.

NOTE. — It is, or was, a common custom in Wessex, and probably other country places, to prepare the mourning beside the death-bed, the dying person sometimes assisting, who also selects his or her bearers on such occasions.[85]

Time's Laughingstocks

2 The Law

In the neighbourhood of county-towns hanging matters used to form a large proportion of the local tradition....

Preface to *Wessex Tales*

Thomas Hardy was born in brutal times. Only six years previously the Tolpuddle Martyrs had been sentenced to transportation for daring to form a workers' union; the Dorset County Record Office holds a terrifying account of his transportation experiences by a (probably unrelated) John Hardy of Wareham. Handed-down memories of Judge Jeffreys' notoriously savage death-sentences after the Monmouth rebellion, although more than 150 years before, were still common folklore in Dorchester, as were stories of the cruel Jack Ketch, Monmouth's executioner, who according to a note made by Hardy as late as 1879, after flogging prisoners by the Dorchester Town Pump would walk back with his "cats" held erect – one to each prisoner, and made of knotted whipcord. In the poem "One We Knew" (page 24), Hardy refers to one of his grandmother's memories of a late eighteenth-century punishment, when young offenders were tied to a moving cart and whipped as it went through the streets. Women could still be judicially whipped in private until 1820.

Whippings continued to be imposed as punishments during Hardy's lifetime; other sentences at the dates he often wrote about, shortly before his birth, seem surprisingly harsh. A note made in 1892 tells how two girls worked a spell by sticking a pigeon's heart full of pins and, with a tripod of knitting-needles, roasting it over a lamp, using a young man's name in an incantation the while. The young man, feeling heart-pains, went to the constables, and the girls were sent to prison. The date was about 1830.

Suicides were (until 1830, according to a note of Hardy's) often buried at cross-roads, coffinless, and with stakes driven through their bodies. Hardy's mother, that fount of folklore, told him of one such burial, that of a young girl, that she remembered happening in her childhood; he later wrote "The Grave by the Handpost" on this very theme.[86]

Transportation continued to loom in the country people's consciousness even after it was finally ended in 1852. Hardy's notebooks contain several accounts of transportation details taken from Dorset newspapers of 1826.

Hardy's father, source of so many of these stories, told him a typically sad tale about the local smith's journeyman, Dick Facey, who was sometimes called secretly by night to rivet the fetters of criminals – for they were taken by night in a specially-ordered stage-coach, for transportation. One poacher, who had been involved in a "great fray" about 1825, was brought past his own door like this. He shouted to his wife and family, who ran out to say goodbye. This, in chains, was the last they ever saw or heard of him.[87]

Eustacia tries to shoot herself, but is prevented by the faithful Charley, who secretly worships her:

"O, why did you, Charley! What makes death painful except the thought of others' grief? — and that is absent in my case, for not a sigh would follow me!"

"Ah, it is trouble that has done this! I wish in my very soul that he who brought it about might die and rot, even if 'tis transportation to say it!"

The Return of the Native

But the shadow of the gallows fell even more darkly, at a time when sheep-and-horse stealing and night-burglary were punishable by death. Hardy's father's story of the four men he had seen hanged, for their mere presence when a rick was burnt down, reappeared in his son's writings; not forgetting the eighteen-year-old lad among them who was so gaunt from near-starvation that the hangman had to attach weights to his feet to ensure the breaking of his neck. Hardy himself as a youth watched two hangings – it must be admitted with some relish – one from close under the gallows, one by telescope from the heath behind his home; they were to have lifelong significance for him.

Above the cliff, and behind the river, rose a pile of buildings, and in the front of the pile a square mass cut into the sky. It was like a pedestal lacking its statue. This missing feature, without which the design remained incomplete, was, in truth, the corpse of a man; for the square mass formed the base of the gallows, the extensive buildings at the back being the county gaol. In the meadow where Henchard now walked the mob were wont to gather whenever an execution took place, and there to the tune of the roaring weir they stood and watched the spectacle.

The Mayor of Casterbridge

Jack Winter, goaded by his supercilious past love Harriet's hint that she might make fun of his love-letters with her new lover, breaks in by night to recover them – unaware that at the bottom of the box there are also her aunt's sovereigns:

"Jack's act amounted to night burglary — though he had never thought of it — and burglary was felony, and a capital offence in those days....

"Whether his protestation that he went only for his letters, which he believed to be wrongfully kept from him, would have availed him anything if supported by other evidence I do not know; but the one person who could have borne it out was Harriet, and she acted entirely under the sway of her aunt.... The trial was a short one, and the death sentence was passed.

"The day o' young Jack's execution was a cold dusty Saturday in March. He was so boyish and slim that they were obliged in mercy to hang him in the heaviest fetters kept in the jail, lest his heft should not break his neck, and they weighed so upon him that he could hardly drag himself up to the drop. At that time the gover'ment was not strict about burying the body of an executed person within the precincts of the prison, and at the earnest prayer of his poor mother his body was allowed to be brought home. All the parish waited at their cottage doors in the evening for its arrival: I remember how, as a very little girl, I stood by my mother's side. About eight o'clock, as we hearkened on our doorstones in the cold bright starlight, we could hear the faint crackle of a waggon from the direction of the turnpike-road. The noise was lost as the waggon dropped into a hollow, then it was plain again as it lumbered down the next long incline, and presently it entered Longpuddle. The coffin was laid in the belfry for the night, and the next day, Sunday, between the services, we buried him. A funeral sermon was preached the same afternoon, the text chosen being, 'He was the only son of his mother, and she was a widow.' . . . Yes, they were cruel times!"

The Winters and the Palmleys

"Hanging matters" recur in Hardy's notebooks, many of them taken from old Dorset County Chronicles of the 1820s and 30s. Not only his father, but visitors to tea discussed them. He learnt from one that as late as 1835 part of a gibbet was still standing near Wincanton, including "part of the cage in which the body had formerly hung".[88] *Noting this in 1882 Hardy somewhat regretfully comments that it would still be there but for some young men and their Fifth of November activities. . . . And in his stories:*

Gertrude Lodge seeks out the Casterbridge hangman, in the hope that by applying her withered arm to the neck of his newly-hanged victim the blight may be removed:

The candle-light, such as it was, fell upon her imploring, pale, upturned face, and Davies (as the hangman was called) backed down the ladder. "I was just going to bed," he said. "'Early to bed and early to rise', but I don't mind stopping a minute for such a one as you. Come into house." He re-opened the door, and preceded her to the room within.

The implements of his daily work, which was that of a jobbing gardener, stood in a corner, and seeing probably that she looked rural, he said, "If you want me to undertake country work I can't come, for I never leave Casterbridge for gentle nor simple — not I. My real calling is officer of justice," he added formally.

"Yes, yes! That's it. To-morrow!"

"Ah! I thought so. Well, what's the matter about that? 'Tis no use to come here about the knot — folks do come continually, but I tell 'em one knot is as merciful as another if ye keep it under the ear. Is the unfortunate man a relation: or, I should say, perhaps" (looking at her dress) "a person who's been in your employ?"

"No. What time is the execution?"

"The same as usual — twelve o'clock, or as soon after as the London mail-coach gets in. We always wait for that, in case of a reprieve."

"O — a reprieve — I hope not!" she said involuntarily.

"Well, — hee, hee! — as a matter of business, so do I! But still, if ever a young fellow deserved to be let off, this one does; only just turned eighteen, and only present by chance when the rick was fired. Howsomever, there's not much risk of it, as they are obliged to make an example of him, there having been so much destruction of property that way lately."[89]

The Withered Arm

Another hangman – and reaction to him:

Two strangers have joined the christening party in the lonely shepherd's cottage on the down at Higher Crowstairs. As the rain that night "smote walls, slopes, and hedges like the clothyard shafts of Senlac and Crecy", the talk among the guests turned to trades and occupations.

"You may generally tell what a man is by his claws," observed the hedge-carpenter, looking at his own hands. "My fingers be as full of thorns as an old pin-cushion is of pins."

The hands of the man in the chimney-corner instinctively sought the shade, and he gazed into the fire as he resumed his pipe. The man at the table took up the hedge-carpenter's remark, and added smartly, "True; but the oddity of my trade is that, instead of setting a mark upon me, it sets a mark upon my customers."

No observation being offered by anybody in elucidation of this enigma the shepherd's wife once more called for a song.

Thrusting one thumb into the arm-hole of his waistcoat, he waved the other hand in the air, and, with an extemporizing gaze at the shining sheep-crooks above the mantelpiece, began:

"O my trade it is the rarest one,
Simple shepherds all —
My trade is a sight to see;
For my customers I tie, and take them up on high,
And waft 'em to a far countree!"

The room was silent when he had finished the verse — with one exception, that of the man in the chimney-corner, who, at the singer's word, "Chorus!" joined him in a deep bass voice of musical relish —

"And waft 'em to a far countree!"

Oliver Giles, John Pitcher the dairyman, the parish-clerk, the engaged man of fifty, the row of young women against the wall, seemed lost in thought not of the gayest kind. The shepherd looked meditatively on the ground, the shepherdess gazed keenly at the singer, and with some suspicion; she was doubting whether this stranger were merely singing an old song from recollection, or was composing one there and then for the occasion. All were as perplexed at the obscure revelation as the guests at Belshazzar's Feast, except the man in the chimney-corner, who quietly said, "Second verse, stranger," and smoked on.

The singer thoroughly moistened himself from his lips inwards, and went on with the next stanza as requested:—

"My tools are but common ones,
Simple shepherds all —
My tools are no sight to see:
A little hempen string, and a post whereon to swing,
Are implements enough for me!"

Shepherd Fennel glanced round. There was no longer any doubt that the stranger was answering his question rhythmically. The guests one and all started back with suppressed exclamations. The young woman engaged to the man of fifty fainted half-way, and would have proceeded, but finding him wanting in alacrity for catching her she sat down trembling.

"O, he's the —!" whispered the people in the background, mentioning the name of an ominous public officer. "He's come to do it! 'Tis to be at Casterbridge jail to-morrow — the man for sheep-stealing — the poor clockmaker we heard of, who used to live away at Shottsford and had no work to do — Timothy Summers, whose family were a-starving, and so he went out of Shottsford by the high-road, and took a sheep in open daylight, defying the farmer and the farmer's wife and the farmer's lad, and every man jack among 'em. He" (and they nodded towards the stranger of the deadly trade) "is come from up the country to do it because there's not enough to do in his own county-town, and he's got the place here now our own county man's dead; he's going to live in the same cottage under the prison wall."

The Three Strangers

Next day, accordingly, the quest for the clever sheep-stealer became general and keen, to all appearance at least. But the intended punishment was cruelly disproportioned to the transgression, and the sympathy of a great many country-folk in that district was strongly on the side of the fugitive.

The Three Strangers

When the crazed Boldwood has shot Sergeant Troy, he gives himself up:

A petition was addressed to the Home Secretary, advancing the circumstances which appeared to justify a request for a reconsideration of the sentence....

The upshot of the petition was waited for in Weatherbury with solicitous interest. The execution had been fixed for eight o'clock on a Saturday morning about a fortnight after the sentence was passed, and up to Friday afternoon no answer had been received. At that time Gabriel came from Casterbridge Gaol, whither he had been to wish Boldwood good-bye, and turned down a by-street to avoid the town. When past the last house he heard a hammering, and lifting his bowed head he looked back for a moment. Over the chimneys he could see the upper part of the gaol entrance, rich and glowing in the afternoon sun, and some figures were there. They were carpenters lifting a post into a vertical position within the parapet. He withdrew his eyes quickly and hastened on.

It was dark when he reached home, and half the village was out to meet him.

"No tidings," Gabriel said, wearily. "And I'm afraid there's no hope. I've been with him more than two hours. . . .

"So Laban . . . What I've arranged is, that you shall ride to town the last thing to-night; leave here about nine, and wait a while there, getting home about twelve. If nothing has been received by eleven to-night, they say there's no chance at all." . . .

* * *

"We shall soon know now, one way or other," said Coggan, and they all stepped down from the bank on which they had been standing into the road, and the rider pranced into the midst of them.

"Is that you, Laban?" said Gabriel.

"Yes — 'tis come. He's not to die. 'Tis confinement during Her Majesty's pleasure."

"Hurrah!" said Coggan, with a swelling heart. "God's above the devil yet!"

Far from the Madding Crowd

From "The Trampwoman's Tragedy"

The taverns tell the gloomy tale,
    The gloomy tale,
How that at Ivel-chester jail
    My Love, my sweetheart swung;
Though stained till now by no misdeed
Save one horse ta'en in time of need;
(Blue Jimmy stole right many a steed
    Ere his last fling he flung.)

At the end of this poem – one of his favourites – Hardy added a long note. It included this:

"Blue Jimmy" (stanza X) was a notorious horse-stealer of Wessex in those days, who appropriated more than a hundred horses before he was caught, among others one belonging to the writer's grandfather. He was hanged at the now-demolished Ivelchester or Ilchester jail above mentioned — that building formerly of so many sinister associations in the minds of the local peasantry, and the continual haunt of fever, which at last led to its condemnation. Its site is now an innocent-looking green meadow.

April 1902 *Time's Laughingstocks*

In contrast with the savagery of the death-sentence, Hardy often makes those who must enforce the law appear ludicrous or incompetent. His constables are worthy successors to Shakespeare's.

The old furmity-woman makes rings round the magistrates:

"She is charged, sir, with the offence of disorderly female and nuisance," whispered Stubberd.

"Where did she do that?" said the other magistrate.

"By the church, sir, of all the horrible places in the world! — I caught her in the act, your worship."

"Stand back then," said Henchard, "and let's hear what you've got to say.'

Stubberd was sworn, the magistrate's clerk dipped his pen, Henchard being no note-taker himself, and the constable began —

"Hearing a' illegal noise I went down the street at twenty-five minutes past eleven P.M. on the night of the fifth instinct, Hannah Dominy. When I had —"

"Don't go on so fast, Stubberd," said the clerk.

The constable waited, with his eyes on the clerk's pen, till the latter stopped scratching and said, "yes." Stubberd continued: "When I had proceeded to the spot I saw defendant at another spot, namely, the gutter." He paused, watching the point of the clerk's pen again.

"Gutter, yes, Stubberd."

"Spot measuring twelve feet nine inches or thereabouts, from where I —" Still careful not to outrun the clerk's penmanship Stubberd pulled up again; for having got his evidence by heart it was immaterial to him whereabouts he broke off.

"I object to that," spoke up the old woman, "'spot measuring twelve feet nine or thereabouts from where I,' is not sound testimony!"

The magistrate consulted, and the second one said that the bench was of opinion that twelve feet nine inches from a man on his oath was admissible.

Stubberd, with a suppressed gaze of victorious rectitude at the old woman, continued: "Was standing myself. She was wambling about quite dangerous to the thoroughfare, and when I approached to draw near she committed the nuisance, and insulted me."

"Insulted me." ... Yes, what did she say?"

"She said, 'Put away that dee lantern,' she says."

"Yes."

"Says she, 'Dost hear, old turmit-head? Put away that dee lantern. I have floored fellows a dee sight finer-looking than a dee fool like thee, you son of a bee, dee me if I haint,' she says."

"I object to that conversation!" interposed the old woman. "I was not capable enough to hear what I said, and what is said out of my hearing is not evidence."

There was another stoppage for consultation, a book was referred to, and finally Stubberd was allowed to go on again. The truth was that the old woman had appeared in court so many more times than the magistrates themselves, that they were obliged to keep a sharp look-out upon their procedure. However, when Stubberd had rambled on a little further Henchard broke out impatiently, "Come — we don't want to hear any more of them cust dees and bees! Say the words out like a man, and don't be modest, Stubberd; or else leave it alone!" Turning to the woman, "Now then, have you any questions to ask him, or anything to say?"

"Yes," she replied with a twinkle in her eye; and the clerk dipped his pen.

The Mayor of Casterbridge

More comic constables: "the rusty-jointed executors of the law"[90]

A prisoner awaiting execution has escaped:

The firing of the alarm gun went on at intervals, low and sullenly, and their suspicions became a certainty. The sinister gentleman in cinder-gray roused himself. "Is there a constable here?" he asked, in thick tones. "If so, let him step forward."

The engaged man of fifty stepped quavering out from the wall, his betrothed beginning to sob on the back of the chair.

"You are a sworn constable?"

"I be, sir."

"Then pursue the criminal at once, with assistance, and bring him back here. He can't have gone far."

"I will, sir, I will – when I've got my staff. I'll go home and get it, and come sharp here, and start in a body."

"Staff! — never mind your staff; the man'll be gone!"

"But I can't do nothing without my staff — can I, William, and John, and Charles Jake? No; for there's the king's royal crown a painted on en in yaller and gold, and the lion and the unicorn, so as when I raise en up and hit my prisoner, 'tis made a lawful blow thereby. I wouldn't 'tempt to take up a man without my staff — no, not I. If I hadn't the law to gie me courage, why, instead o' my taking him up he might take up me!"

The Three Strangers

Not all punishments were as grim as hanging and transportation. For a light-hearted reference to the stocks, *see page 257.* *In a conversation with William Archer in 1902 Hardy recalled a boyhood memory of a man in the stocks:*

Mr Hardy. I remember one perfectly — when I was very young. It was in the village I have called Weatherbury. I can see him now, sitting in the scorching sunshine, with the flies crawling over him, and not another human being near except me. I can see his blue worsted stockings projecting through the legholes, and the shining nails in his boots. He was quite a hero in my eyes. I sidled up to him and said goodday to him, and felt mightily honoured when he nodded to me.

W.A. Do you know what his offence was?

Mr Hardy. "Drunk and disorderly," no doubt.

W.A. Then by what authority — by what legal process — was he put in the stocks?

Mr Hardy. I can't say exactly. It used to be understood that the constable could put a man in the stocks, but that only a magistrate could lock them. But perhaps that was only a village superstition.

W. Archer, *Real Conversations*

Stocks were never expressly abolished; they began to die out in England during the early part of the nineteenth century, though their use is recorded exceptionally late in Rugby in 1865. Hardy also used the stocks as a setting for a poem, "In Weatherbury Stocks", which was subtitled "1850".

3 Medicine and Disease

In 1854 the third great cholera epidemic hit Dorchester. 700 prisoners and warders were sent from Millbank Prison, in infected London, to the empty Cavalry Barracks in the West Fordington parish of Dorchester. Here the poor cottagers took in the prisoners' washing, which contaminated the local water-supply. The Vicar of Fordington, the Rev. Henry Moule (father of Hardy's great friend and mentor Horace, and of Henry Moule the watercolourist and first Curator of the Dorset County Museum) became a byword as, single-handed, he worked among his sick parishioners, burning and disinfecting, and substituting open-air prayers for the more risky gatherings inside the church. In addition he wrote and published no fewer than eight letters about the outbreak's scandalous cause and the chronically wretched local conditions to the Prince Consort, in whose Duchy of Cornwall the parish was.

Hardy's childhood memory of the cholera outbreak is used in the story of "A Changed Man".

Captain Maumbry, of the –th Hussars, is converted by a local clergyman, and to his lively wife Laura's dismay, is ordained, subsequently becoming curate of "a low-lying district of [Casterbridge] which at that date was crowded with impoverished cottagers". When cholera strikes, he sends Laura away for safety; idling by the sea, a friendship with a certain Lieut. Vannicock ripens into an agreement to run away with him:

"I have noticed for some time," she said, "a lurid glare over the Durnover end of the town. It seems to come from somewhere about Mixen Lane."

"The lamps," he suggested.

"There's not a lamp as big as a rushlight in the whole lane. It is where the cholera is worst."

By Standfast Corner, a little beyond the Cross, they suddenly obtained an end view of the lane. Large bonfires were burning in the middle of the way, with a view to purifying the air; and from the wretched tenements with which the lane was lined in those days persons were bringing out bedding and clothing. Some was thrown into the fires, the rest placed in wheel-barrows and wheeled into the moor directly in the track of the fugitives.

They followed on, and came up to where a vast copper was set in the open air. Here the linen was boiled and disinfected. By the light of the lanterns Laura discovered that her husband was standing by the copper, and that it was he who unloaded the barrow and immersed its contents. The night was so calm and muggy that the conversation by the copper reached her ears.

"Are there many more loads to-night?"

"There's the clothes o' they that died this afternoon, sir. But that might bide till to-morrow, for you must be tired out."

"We'll do it at once, for I can't ask anybody else to undertake it. Overturn that load on the grass and fetch the rest."

The man did so and went off with the barrow. Maumbry paused for a moment to wipe his face, and resumed his homely drudgery amid this squalid and reeking scene, pressing down and stirring the contents of the copper, with what looked like an old rolling-pin. The steam therefrom, laden with death, travelled in a low trail across the meadow.

Laura spoke suddenly: "I won't go to-night after all. He is so tired, and I must help him. I didn't know things were so bad as this!"

A Changed Man

Medicine was in many ways rudimentary in the nineteenth century especially in the country. Hygiene remained primitive. At Buckingham Palace in the 1840s a new lavatory still discharged its waste through the rainwater pipe onto leads outside the Queen's window; at Max Gate Hardy's second wife Florence had to work hard on her husband to get a bath installed by August 1920.

Hardy's notebooks contain several references to disease, many taken from old newspapers:

Deaf & Dumb — the whole family, 5, of a labouring man. Dec. 13, 1827.
Smallpox very prevalent in Sherborne, and in Bodmin jail. — *Dorset County Chronicle,* 27 December 1827.

Procession of conveyances laden with persons afflicted with the King's evil[91] passed through Sturminster Newton on way to Hazelbury, near where resides a man named Buckland, who has attained a reputation for curing, in a miraculous manner, the King's evil, at his yearly fair or feast. Exactly 24 hours before the new moon in month of May every year, whether it happens by night or day, the afflicted assemble at the doctor's residence, where they are supplied by him with the hind legs of a toad enclosed in a small bag (accompanied with some verbal charm or incantation) and also a lotion and salve of the doctor's preparation. The bag is worn suspended from the neck, and the lotion and salve applied in the usual manner until the cure is completed, or until the next year's fair . . . The appearances of many showed that they moved in respectable spheres of life. — *Dorset County Chronicle,* 28 May 1829

Notebook III

[1869] *March 8th.* At Moreton some years ago a man called at a house and said that he would put in the bailiffs if he were not paid immediately what had been long owing him. The people in the house were suffering from itch. The money was handed out to him, with warning of the fact. After looking at it longingly he shook his head, and went on without taking it.

Memoranda I

Hardy's attitude to doctors was never very favourable (as for example in The Dynasts *when the King is bled). On a visit to Lyme Regis in 1882 Hardy and his wife met an old man whose commendably tolerant account of a cataract operation, "like a red-hot needle in yer eye",*[92] *with no anaesthetic for three-quarters of an hour, Hardy records.*

Asked about doctoring the Hintocks:

Fitzpiers answered readily:

"O no. The real truth is, Winterborne, that medical practice in places like this is a very rule of thumb matter; a bottle of bitter stuff for this and that old woman — the bitterer the better — compounded from a few simple stereotyped prescriptions; occasional attendance at births, where mere presence is almost sufficient, so healthy and strong are the people; and a lance for an abscess now and then. Investigation and experiment cannot be carried on without more appliances than one has here — though I have attempted a little."

The Woodlanders

Fitzpiers's private life was not blameless; Hardy also tells the amusing story (in a note of Christmas Day, 1890) of the girl who, having had an illegitimate son by the local doctor, christened him, and always called him by, all the doctor's names complete – Frederick Washington Ingen. And because the doctor squinted she hung a bobbin between the baby's eyes so that he too might squint. . . .[93]

He also portrays the unscrupulous country quack:

Vilbert was an itinerant quack-doctor, well known to the rustic population, and absolutely unknown to anybody else, as he, indeed, took care to be, to avoid inconvenient investigations. Cottagers formed his only patients, and his Wessex-wide repute was among them alone. His position was humbler and his field more obscure than those of the quacks with capital and an organized system of advertising. He was, in fact, a survival. The distances he traversed on foot were enormous, and extended nearly the whole length and breadth of Wessex. Jude had one day seen him selling a pot of coloured lard to an old woman as a certain cure for a bad leg, the woman arranging to pay a guinea, in instalments of a shilling a fortnight, for the precious salve, which, according to the physician, could only be obtained from a particular animal which grazed on Mount Sinai, and was to be captured only at great risk to life and limb. Jude, though he already had his doubts about this gentleman's medicines, felt him to be unquestionably a travelled personage, and one who might be a trustworthy source of information on matters not strictly professional.[94]

Jude the Obscure

CHILD MORTALITY[95] — AND "THE VILLAGE IDIOT"

There was an interval of four years and more between Tess and the next of the family, the two who had filled the gap having died in their infancy. Next in juvenility to Abraham [after Liza-Lu] came two more girls, Hope and Modesty; then a boy of three, and then the baby, who had just completed his first year.

Tess of the d'Urbervilles

"He don't want to go much; do ye, Thomas Leaf?" said William.

"Hee-hee! no; I don't want to. Only a teeny bit!"

"I be mortal afeard, Leaf, that you'll never be able to tell how many cuts d'take to sharpen a spar," said Mail.

"I never had no head, never! that's how it happened to happen, hee-hee!"

They all assented to this, not with any sense of humiliating Leaf by disparaging him after an open confession, but because it was an accepted thing that Leaf didn't in the least mind having no head, that deficiency of his being an unimpassioned matter of parish history.

"But I can sing my treble!" continued Thomas Leaf, quite delighted at being called a fool in such a friendly way; "I can sing my treble as well as any maid, or married woman either, and better! And if Jim had lived, I should have had a clever brother! Tomorrow is poor Jim's birthday. He'd ha' been twenty-six if he'd lived till to-morrow."

"You always seem very sorry for Jim," said old William musingly.

"Ah! I do. Such a stay to mother as he'd always have been! She'd never have had to work in her old age if he had continued strong, poor Jim!"

"What was his age when 'a died?"

"Four hours and twenty minutes, poor Jim. 'A was born as might be at night; and 'a didn't last as might be till the morning. No, 'a didn't last. Mother called en Jim on the day that would ha' been his christening-day if he had lived; and she's always thinking about en. You see, he died so very young."

"Well, 'twas rather youthful," said Michael.

"Now to my mind that woman is very romantical on the matter o' children?" said the tranter, his eye sweeping his audience.

"Ah, well she mid be," said Leaf. "She had twelve regular one after another, and they all, except myself, died very young; either before they was born or just afterwards."

"Pore feller, too. I suppose th'st want to come wi' us?" the tranter murmured.

"Well, Leaf, you shall come wi' us as yours is such a melancholy family," said old William rather sadly.

"I never see such a melancholy family as that afore in my life," said Reuben. "There's Leaf's mother, poor woman! Every morning I see her eyes mooning out through the panes of glass like a pot-sick winder-flower; and as Leaf sings a very high treble, and we don't know what we should do without en for upper G, we'll let en come as a trate, poor feller."

Under the Greenwood Tree

Inbreeding in isolated country communities may have been the cause of some feeble-mindedness. In more than one story Hardy also puts forward extreme fright as another.

You don't mind when the Palmleys were Longpuddle folk, but I do well. She had a son. . . . The child proved to be of rather weak intellect, though his mother loved him as the apple of her eye. . . .

Well, in some way or other . . . Mrs Winter sent the little boy with a message to the next village one December day, much against his will. It was getting dark, and the child prayed to be allowed not to go, because he would be afraid coming home. But the mistress insisted. . . . On his way back he had to pass through Yalbury Wood, and something came out from behind a tree and frightened him into fits. The child was quite ruined by it; he became quite a drivelling idiot, and soon afterward died.[96]

The Winters and the Palmleys

Hardy paints the so-called "village idiot" with some compassion and perception. It is one of the strengths of his country community that it can contain and care for its more simple-minded members without illusion or hypocrisy, while yet enabling them to use the talents they have. Christian Cantle in The Return of the Native *can carry messages with reasonable accuracy and manage as general servant to the Yeobrights; Thomas Leaf is indispensable in the church choir.*

"Whatever is Christian Cantle's teeth a-chattering for?" said a boy from amid the smoke and shades on the other side of the blaze. "Be ye a-cold Christian?"

A thin jibbering voice was heard to reply, "No, not at all."

"Come forward, Christian, and show yourself. I didn't know you were here," said Fairway, with a humane look across towards that quarter.

Thus requested, a faltering man, with reedy hair, no shoulders, and a great quantity of wrist and ankle beyond his clothes, advanced a step or two by his own will, and was pushed by the will of others half a dozen steps more. He was Grandfer Cantle's youngest son.

"What be ye quaking for, Christian?" said the turf-cutter kindly.

"I'm the man."

"What man?"

"The man no woman will marry."

"The deuce you be!" said Timothy Fairway, enlarging his gaze to cover Christian's whole surface and a great deal more; Grandfer Cantle meanwhile staring as a hen stares at the duck she has hatched.

"Yes, I be he; and it makes me afeard," said Christian. "D'ye think 'twill hurt me? I shall always say I don't care, and swear to it, though I do care all the while. . . . 'Twas to be if 'twas, I suppose. I can't help it, can I?" He turned upon them his painfully circular eyes, surrounded by concentric lines like targets.

. . . " 'Tis a sad thing for ye, Christian. How'st know the women won't hae thee?"

"I've asked 'em."

"Sure I should never have thought you had the face. Well, and what did the last one say to ye? Nothing that can't be got over, perhaps, after all?"

"'Get out of my sight, you slack-twisted, slim-looking maphrotight[97] fool,' was the woman's words to me."

"Not encouraging, I own," said Fairway. "'Get out of my sight, you slack-twisted, slim-looking maphrotight fool' is rather a hard way of saying No. But even that might be overcome by time and patience, so as to let a few grey hairs show themselves in the hussy's head. How old be you, Christian?"

"Thirty-one last tatie-digging, Mister Fairway."

"Not a boy — not a boy. Still there's hope yet."

"That's my age by baptism, because that's put down in the great book of the Judgment[98] that they keep in church vestry; but mother told me I was born some time afore I was christened."

"Ah!"

"But she couldn't tell when, to save her life, except that there was no moon."

"No moon: that's bad. Hey, neighbours, that's bad for him!"

"Yes, 'tis bad," said Grandfer Cantle, shaking his head.

"Mother know'd 'twas no moon, for she asked another woman that had an almanac, as she did whenever a boy was born to her, because of the saying, 'No moon, no man,' which made her afeard every man-child she had. Do ye really think it serious, Mister Fairway, that there was no moon?"

"Yes; 'No moon, no man.' 'Tis one of the truest sayings ever spit out. The boy never comes to anything that's born at new moon. A bad job for thee, Christian, that you should have showed your nose then of all days in the month."

"I suppose the moon was terrible full when you were born?" said Christian, with a look of hopeless admiration at Fairway.

"Well, 'a was not new," Mr Fairway replied, with a disinterested gaze.

"I'd sooner go without drink at Lammas-tide[99] than be a man of no moon," continued Christian, in the same shattered recitative. "'Tis said I be only the rames[100] of a man, and no good for my race at all; and I suppose that's the cause o't."

"Ay," said Grandfer Cantle, somewhat subdued in spirit; "and yet his mother cried for scores of hours when 'a was a boy, for fear he should outgrow hisself and go for a soldier."

"Well, there's many just as bad as he," said Fairway. "Wethers[101] must live their time as well as other sheep, poor soul."

"So perhaps I shall rub on? Ought I to be afeard o' nights, Master Fairway?"

"You'll have to lie alone all your life; and 'tis not to married couples but to single sleepers that a ghost shows himself when 'a do come. One has been seen lately, too. A very strange one."

"No — don't talk about it if 'tis agreeable of ye not to! 'Twill make my skin crawl when I think of it in bed alone. But you will — ah, you will, I know, Timothy; and I shall dream all night o't! A very strange one? What sort of a spirit did ye mean when ye said, a very strange one, Timothy? — no, no — don't tell me."

"I don't half believe in spirits myself. But I think it ghostly enough — what I was told. 'Twas a little boy that zid it."

"What was it like? — no, don't —"

"A red one. Yes, most ghosts be white; but this is as if it had been dipped in blood."

Christian drew a deep breath without letting it expand his body, and Humphrey said, "Where has it been seen?"

"Not exactly here; but in this same heth. But 'tisn't a thing to talk about."[102]

The Return of the Native

Mad Judy

When the hamlet hailed a birth
  Judy used to cry:
When she heard our christening mirth
  She would kneel and sigh.
She was crazed, we knew, and we
Humoured her infirmity.

When the daughters and the sons
  Gathered them to wed,
And we like-intending ones
  Danced till dawn was red,
She would rock and mutter, "More
Comers to this stony shore!"

When old Headsman Death laid hands
  On a babe or twain,
She would feast, and by her brands
  Sing her songs again.
What she liked we let her do,
Judy was insane, we knew.

Poems of the Past and Present

4 Dialect

One grievous failing of Elizabeth's was her occasional pretty and picturesque use of dialect words — those terrible marks of the beast to the truly genteel.

It was dinner-time... and she happened to say when he was rising from table, wishing to show him something, "If you'll bide where you be a minute, father, I'll get it."

"'Bide where you be,'" he echoed sharply. "Good God, are you only fit to carry wash to a pig-trough, that ye use such words as those?"

She reddened with shame and sadness.... The sharp reprimand was not lost upon her, and in time it came to pass that for "fay" she said "succeed"; that she no longer spoke of "dumbledores" but of "humble bees"; no longer said of young men and women that they "walked together", but that they were "engaged"; that she grew to talk of "greggles" as "wild hyacinths"; that when she had not slept she did not quaintly tell the servants next morning that she had been "hag-rid", but that she had "suffered from indigestion".

The Mayor of Casterbridge

Tess Durbeyfield at this time of her life was a mere vessel of emotion untinctured by experience. The dialect was on her tongue to some extent, despite the village school: the characteristic intonation of that dialect for this district being the voicing approximately rendered by the syllable UR, probably as rich an utterance as any to be found in human speech.

Tess of the d'Urbervilles

"Well, I'm glad you've come," her mother said.... "I want to tell 'ee what have happened. Y'll be fess[103] enough, my poppet, when th'st know!" (Mrs Durbeyfield habitually spoke the dialect; her daughter, who had passed the Sixth Standard in the National School under a London-trained mistress, spoke two languages; the dialect at home, more or less; ordinary English abroad and to persons of quality.)...

"Had it anything to do with father's making such a mommet[104] of himself in thik carriage this afternoon? Why did 'er? I felt inclined to sink into the ground with shame!"

"That wer all part of the larry! We've been found to be the greatest gentlefolk in the whole county.... In Saint Charles's days we was made Knights o' the Royal Oak, our real name being d'Urberville!... Don't that make your bosom plim?[105] 'Twas on this account that your father rode home in the vlee;[106] not because he'd been drinking, as people supposed."

"I'm glad of that. Will it do us any good, mother?"

"O yes! 'Tis thoughted that great things may come o't. No doubt a mampus[107] of volk of our own rank will be down here in their carriages as soon as 'tis known. Your father learnt it on his way hwome from Shaston, and he had been telling me the whole pedigree of the matter."

Tess of the d'Urbervilles

"I am that leery[108] that I can feel my stomach rubbing against my backbone!"

Andrey Satchel

"Owing to your coming a day sooner than we first expected," said John, "you'll find us in a turk of a mess, sir — 'sir', says I to my own son! but ye've gone up so, Stephen. We've killed the pig this morning for 'ee, thinking you'd be hungry, and glad of a morsel of fresh meat. And 'a won't be cut up till tonight. However, we can make 'ee a good supper of fry, which will chaw up well wi' a dab o' mustard and a few nice new taters, and a drop of shilling ale to wash it down. Your mother has had the house scrubbed through because you were coming, and dusted all the chimmer furniture, and brought a new basin and jug of a travelling crockery-woman that came to our door, and scoured the candle-sticks, and cleaned the winders! Ay, I don't know what 'a ha'n't a done. Never were such a steer, 'a b'lieve."

A Pair of Blue Eyes

"I have a bit of news.... Why, Miss Hinton took a holiday yesterday."

"Yes?" inquired the cook, looking up with perplexed curiosity.

"D'ye think that's all?"

"Don't be so three-cunning[109] — if it is all, deliver you from the evil of raising a woman's expectations wrongfully; I'll skimmer your pate[110] as sure as you cry Amen!"

"Well, it isn't all. When I got home last night my wife said, 'Miss Adelaide took a holiday this mornen . . . walked over to Nether Mynton, met the chosen man, and got married!' says she."

"Got married! What, Lord-a-mercy, did Springrove come?"

"Springrove, no — no — Springrove's nothen to do wi'it — 'twas Farmer Bollens. They've been playing bo-peep for these two or three months seemingly. Whilst Master Teddy Springrove has been daddlen, and hawken, and spetten[111] about having her, she's quietly left him all forsook."

Desperate Remedies

"If you can't skeer birds, what can ye do? There! Don't ye look so deedy![112] . . . Jude, Jude, why didstn't go off with that schoolmaster of thine to Christminster or somewhere? But, O no — poor or'nary[113] child — there never was any sprawl[114] on thy side of the family, and never will be!"

Jude the Obscure

"Who was that young kimberlin?[115] He don't seem one o' we."

"O, he is, though, every inch o' en. He's Mr Jocelyn Pierston, the stwone-merchant's son up at East Quarriers.... He's worth thousands and thousands, they say, though 'a do live on in the same wold way up in the same wold house. This son is doen great things in London as a' image-carver; and I can mind when, as a boy, 'a first took to carving soldiers out o' bits o' stwone from the soft-bed of his father's quarries; and then 'a made a set o' stwonen chess-men, and so 'a got on."

The Well-Beloved

"Fancy her white hands getting redder every day, and her tongue losing its pretty up-country curl in talking, and her bounding walk becoming the regular Hintock shail-and-wamble!"

"She may shail;[116] but she'll never wamble,"[117] replied his wife decisively.

The Woodlanders

A favourite Dorset phrase appears somewhat incongruously in the third scene of The Dynasts. *In a letter written in 1909 on the death of Swinburne,*[118] *Hardy explained that "running to mixen" meant, in Swinburne's words, being "sick in a corner":*

SPIRIT OF THE YEARS

I'll humour thee,
Though my unpassioned essence could not change
Did I incarn in moulds of all mankind!

SPIRIT IRONIC

'Tis enough to make every little dog in England run to mixen to hear this Pitt sung so strenuously!

The Dynasts

In a letter to Edmund Gosse in 1889, Hardy explained how phrases like "ich woll" and "er woll" were still used by old people in north-west Dorset and Somerset. He said that although the words were fast disappearing, he had heard "ich" only a few days previously (probably from his own parents).

"I am come, Grammer, as you wish. Do let us send for the doctor...?"

"'Ch woll not have him!" said Grammer Oliver decisively.

"Then somebody to sit up with you?"

"Can't abear it! No. I wanted to see you, Miss Grace, because 'ch have something on my mind. Dear Miss Grace, *I took that money of the doctor, after all!*... 'Ch have been going to ask him again to let me off, but I hadn't the face."

The Woodlanders

The Pity of It

I walked in loamy Wessex lanes, afar
From rail-track and from highway, and I heard
In field and farmstead many an ancient word
Of local lineage like "Thu bist", "Er war",

"Ich woll", "Er sholl", and by-talk similar,
Nigh as they speak who in this month's moon gird
At England's very loins, thereunto spurred
By gangs whose glory threats and slaughters are.

Then seemed a Heart crying: "Whosoever they be
At root and bottom of this, who flung this flame
Between kin folk kin tongued even as are we,

"Sinister, ugly, lurid, be their fame;
May their familiars grow to shun their name,
And their brood perish everlastingly."
April 1915 *Moments of Vision*

Local gentry, in real life as in Hardy's stories, sometimes used dialect words or spoke with strong regional accents. When in 1885 he went to stay with Lady Portsmouth he found that Lord Portsmouth had a "broad Devon accent".[119]

"As for drains — how can I put in drains? The pipes don't cost much, that's true; but the labour in sinking the trenches is ruination. And then the gates — they should be hung to stone posts, otherwise there's no keeping them up through harvest." The Squire's voice was strongly toned with the local accent, so that he said "draïns" and "geäts" like the rustics on his estate.

The Waiting Supper

[Squire] Dornell professed to believe not a word of it. "You sha'n't have her till she's dree sixes full — no maid ought to be married till she's dree sixes! — and my daughter sha'n't be treated out of nater!"

The First Countess of Wessex

"I have been waiting till the days are longer before lumpering up again...."

Though well-trained and even proficient masters, they occasionally used a dialect-word of their boyhood to each other in private.

Jude the Obscure

Max Gate, Dorchester *May 15th, 1912*

Dear Mr Cockerell:

... You are quite right in thinking that "form" is, strictly, used only of a hare. I used it somewhere (I fancy) for the nest of a rabbit because I knew no other name that a reader would understand, since a "stop", which is what they call it here, is dialect I suppose, and that is the only specific name I know, as applied to a rabbit. I wish I had sent "stop" to Murray for his dictionary — but perhaps he will have it all the same....

Viola Meynell, *Friends of a Lifetime*

The Spring Call

Down Wessex way, when spring's a-shine,
The blackbird's "pret-ty de-urr!"
In Wessex accents marked as mine
Is heard afar and near.

He flutes it strong, as if in song
No R's of feebler tone
Than his appear in "pretty dear",
Have blackbirds ever known.

Yet they pipe "prattie deerh!" I glean,
Beneath a Scottish sky,
And "pehty de-aw!" amid the treen
Of Middlesex or nigh.

While some folk say – perhaps in play –
Who know the Irish isle,
'Tis "purrity dare!" in treeland there
When songsters would beguile.

Well: I'll say what the listening birds
Say, hearing "pret-ty de-urr!" –
However strangers sound such words,
That's how we sound them here.

Yes, in this clime at pairing time,
As soon as eyes can see her
At dawn of day, the proper way
To call is "pret-ty de-urr!"

Time's Laughingstocks

Hardy, as might be expected, was a lifelong defender of the value and interest of the Dorset dialect. In a conversation with Vere Collins during his last years he told how, although he knew the dialect, it was not spoken at home, except by his mother to "the cottagers" and by his father to his workmen. Whether this is strictly accurate, remembering Hardy's tendency to hide anything which might suggest his humble origins, is not known; as far as accent *is concerned, his father, brother Henry, and sister Kate kept broad Dorset accents all their lives. (One London observer asserted that Thomas as a young man too had a marked one.) Robert Gittings points out that Hardy's annotations to Walker's* Rhyming Dictionary, *which he bought in 1865, show that he himself at that stage certainly pronounced some words with an accent – for example, he adds "groat" to rhyme with "ought" and "brought".*

I chance to be (I believe) one of the few living persons having a practical acquaintance with letters who knew familiarly the Dorset dialect when it was spoken as Barnes writes it, or, perhaps, who know it as it is spoken now. Since his death, education in the west of England as elsewhere has gone on with its silent and inevitable effacements, reducing the speech of this country to uniformity, and obliterating every year many a fine old local word. The process is always the same: the word is ridiculed by the newly taught; it gets into disgrace; it is heard in holes and corners only; it dies and, worst of all, it leaves no synonym.

Preface to *Select Poems of William Barnes*

In the systematic study of his native dialect, [Barnes] has shown the world that far from being, as popularly supposed, a corruption of correct English, it is a distinct branch of Teutonic speech, regular in declension and conjugation, and richer in many classes of words than any other tongue known to him. As an instance of the latter he used to mention the pronouns with particular pride, there being no fewer than four demonstratives to set against the current English two. He would also instance any natural object, such as a tree, and show that there were double the number of names for its different parts in the Dorset dialect to those available in the standard tongue.

Obituary notice on the Rev. William Barnes in *The Athenaeum,* 16 October 1886

For some reason or none, many persons suppose that when anything is penned in the tongue of the countryside, the primary intent is burlesque or ridicule, and this especially if the speech be one in which the sibilant has the rough sound, and is expressed by Z. Indeed, scores of thriving story-tellers and dramatists seem to believe that by transmuting the flattest conversation into a dialect that never existed, and making the talkers say "be" when they would really say "is", a Falstaffian richness is at once imparted to its qualities.

But to a person to whom dialect is native its sounds are as consonant with moods of sorrow as with moods of mirth: there is no grotesqueness in it as such.... And further; gesture and facial expression figure so largely in the speech of the husbandmen as to be speech itself; hence in the mind's eye of those who know it in its original setting each word of theirs is accompanied by the qualifying face-play which no construing can express.

Preface to *Select Poems of William Barnes*

To the Editor of The Spectator, *October 15 1881:*

Sir, In your last week's article on the "Papers of the Manchester Literary Club", there seems a slight error, which, though possibly accidental, calls for a word of correction from myself. In treating of dialect in novels, I am instanced by the writer as one of two popular novelists "whose thorough knowledge of the dialectical peculiarities of certain districts has tempted them to write whole conversations which are, to the ordinary reader, nothing but a series of linguistic puzzles." So much has my practice been the reverse of this (as a glance at my novels will show), that I have been reproved for too freely translating dialect-English into readable English, by those of your contemporaries who attach more importance to the publication of local niceties of speech than I do. The rule of scrupulously preserving the local idiom, together with the words which have no synonym among those in general use, while printing in the ordinary way most of those local expressions which are but a modified articulation of words in use elsewhere, is the rule I usually follow; and it is, I believe, generally recognised as the best, where every such rule must of necessity be a compromise, more or less unsatisfactory to lovers of form. It must, of course, be always a matter for regret that, in order to be understood, writers should be obliged thus slightingly to treat varieties of English which are intrinsically as genuine, grammatical, and worthy of the royal title as is the all-prevailing competitor which bears it; whose only fault was that they happened not to be central, and therefore were worsted in the struggle for existence, when a uniform tongue became a necessity among the advanced classes of the population. — I am, Sir, etc.,

THOMAS HARDY

The Avenue, Wimborne, Dorset. October 11th.

From "The Bride-Night Fire", a poem of nineteen stanzas with the sub-title "A Wessex Tradition":

They had long met o' Zundays — her true love and she —
    And at junketings, maypoles, and flings;
But she bode wi' a thirtover[1] uncle, and he
Swore by noon and by night that her goodman should be
Naibour Sweatley — a wight often weak at the knee —
From taking o' sommat more cheerful than tea —
    Who tranted,[2] and moved people's things.

. . .

The wedding-day dawned and the morning drew on;
The couple stood bridegroom and bride;
The evening was passed, and when midnight had gone
The feasters horned[3] "God save the King", and anon
The pair took their homealong[4] ride.

The lover Tim Tankens mourned heart-sick and leer[5]
To be thus of his darling deprived:
He roamed in the dark ath'art field, mound, and mere,
And, a'most without knowing it, found himself near
The house of the tranter, and now of his Dear,
Where the lantern-light showed 'em arrived.

. . .

The bridegroom yet laitered a beaker to drain,
Then reeled to the linhay[6] for more,
When the candle-snoff kindled some chaff from his grain —
Flames spread, and red vlankers[7] wi' might and wi' main
Around beams, thatch, and chimley-tun[8] roar.

Young Tim away yond, rafted[9] up by the light,
Through brimbles and underwood tears,
Till he comes to the orchet, when crooping[10] from sight
In the lewth[11] of a codlin-tree, bivering[12] wi' fright,
Wi' on'y her night-rail to cover her plight,
His lonesome young Barbree appears.

Her cwold little figure half-naked he views
Played about by the frolicsome breeze,
Her light-tripping totties[13], her ten little tooes,
All bare and besprinkled wi' Fall's[14] chilly dews,
While her great gallied[15] eyes through her hair hanging loose
Shone as stars through a tardle[16] o' trees.

She eyed him; and, as when a weir-hatch is drawn,
Her tears, penned by terror afore,
With a rushing of sobs in a shower were strawn,
Till her power to pour 'em seemed wasted and gone
From the heft[17] o' misfortune she bore.

"I think I mid[18] almost ha' borne it,' she said,
"Had my griefs one by one come to hand;
But O, to be slave to thik husbird,[19] for bread,
"And then, upon top o' that, driven to wed,
  And then, upon top o' that, burnt out o' bed,
Is more than my nater can stand!". . . .

1 *thirtover,* cross
2 *tranted,* traded as carrier
3 *horned,* sang loudly
4 *homealong,* homeward
5 *leer,* empty-stomached
6 *linhay,* lean-to building
7 *vlankers,* fire-flakes
8 *chimley-tun,* chimney-stack
9 *rafted,* roused
10 *crooping,* squatting down
11 *lewth,* shelter
12 *bivering,* with chattering teeth
13 *totties,* feet
14 *Fall,* autumn
15 *gallied,* frightened
16 *tardle,* entanglement
17 *heft,* weight
18 *mid,* might
19 *thik husbird,* that rascal

Wessex Poems

A bowdlerized early version of this poem as "The Fire at Tranter Sweatley's" was published in The Gentleman's Magazine *of November 1875. It was Hardy's first appearance as a poet. Written in 1866 when he was living in London, the dialect was subsequently heightened and the dialect glossary added.*

5 Buildings

The Chimney-Corner

Chimney-corners seem to have special significance as the focus of a home:

"Mr Yeobright, I can't help feeling that your cousin ought to have married you. 'Tis a pity to make two chimley-corners where there need be only one."

The Return of the Native

"O! I must agree to be his wife if he forgives me — of course I must."

. . . He sighed slowly and added, "Well, Selina, 'tis for you to say. I love you, and I love the boy; and there's my chimney-corner and sticks o' furniture ready for 'ee both."

Enter a Dragoon

"Ay, but I don't know about feeling settled, either, Mr Manston. The old window in the chimney-corner of the old house I shall never forget. No window in the chimney-corner where I am now, and I had been used to it for more than fifty years. Ted says 'tis a great loss to me, and he knows exactly what I feel.'

Desperate Remedies

"Everybody sits in the chimney-corner in this parish. You sit on that side. I'll sit here."

Two recesses — one on the right, one on the left hand — were cut in the inside of the fireplace, and here they sat down facing each other, on benches fitted to the recesses, the fire glowing on the hearth between their feet. Its ruddy light shone on the underslopes of their faces, and spread out over the floor of the room with the low horizontality of the setting sun, giving to every grain of sand and tumour in the paving a long shadow towards the door. . . . They were both silent. He listlessly regarded the illuminated blackness overhead, where long flakes of soot floated from the sides and bars of the chimney-throat like tattered banners in ancient aisles; whilst through the square opening in the midst one or two bright stars looked down upon them from the grey March sky.

Desperate Remedies

At Mistover Knap:

Eustacia was indoors in the dining-room, which was really more like a kitchen, having a stone floor and a gaping chimney-corner. The air was still, and while she lingered a moment here alone sounds of voices in conversation came to her ears directly down the chimney. She entered the recess, and, listening, looked up the old irregular shaft, with its cavernous hollows, where the smoke blundered about on its way to the square bit of sky at the top, from which the daylight struck down with a pallid glare upon the tatters of soot draping the flue as sea-weed drapes a rocky fissure.

She remembered: the furze-stack was not far from the chimney, and the voices were those of the workers.

The Return of the Native

At Blooms-End:

The room had been arranged with a view to the dancing, the large oak table having been moved back till it stood as a breast-work to the fireplace. At each end, behind, and in the chimney-corner were grouped the guests, many of them being warm-faced and panting, among whom Eustacia cursorily recognized some well-to-do persons from beyond the heath.... A nose, chin, hands, knees, and toes projected from the seat within the chimney opening, which members she found to unite in the person of Grandfer Cantle, Mrs Yeobright's occasional assistant in the garden, and therefore one of the invited. The smoke went up from an Etna of peat in front of him, played round the notches of the chimney-crook, struck against the salt-box, and got lost among the flitches.

Another part of the room soon riveted her gaze. At the other side of the chimney stood the settle, which is the necessary supplement to a fire so open that nothing less than a strong breeze will carry up the smoke. It is, to the hearths of old-fashioned cavernous fire-places, what the east belt of trees is to the exposed country estate, or the north wall to the garden. Outside the settle candles gutter, locks of hair wave, young women shiver, and old men sneeze. Inside is Paradise. Not a symptom of a draught disturbs the air; the sitters' backs are as warm as their faces, and songs and old tables are drawn from the occupants by the comfortable heat, like fruit from melon-plants in a frame.

The Return of the Native

Cottage Interiors

The shepherd's at Higher Crowstairs:

The guests had arrived before the rain began to fall, and they were all now assembled in the chief or living-room of the dwelling.... It was as cosy and comfortable a nook as could be wished for in boisterous weather. The calling of its inhabitant was proclaimed by a number of highly-polished sheep-crooks without stems that were hung ornamentally over the fireplace, the curl of each shining crook varying from the antiquated type engraved in the patriarchal pictures of old family Bibles to the most approved fashion of the last local sheep fair. The room was lighted by half-a-dozen candles, having wicks only a trifle smaller than the grease which enveloped them, in candlesticks that were never used but at high-days, holy-days, and family feasts. The lights were scattered about the room, two of them standing on the chimney-piece. This position of candles was in itself significant. Candles on the chimney-piece always meant a party.

On the hearth, in front of a back-brand to give substance, blazed a fire of thorns, that crackled "like the laughter of the fool".

The Three Strangers

The house in Yalbury Wood:

It was a satisfaction to walk into the keeper's house, even as a stranger, on a fine spring morning like the present. A curl of wood-smoke came from the chimney and drooped over the roof like a blue feather in a lady's hat; and the sun shone obliquely upon the patch of grass in front, which reflected its brightness through the open doorway and up the staircase opposite, lighting up each riser with a shiny green radiance and leaving the top of each step in shade.

The window-sill of the front room was between four and five feet from the floor, dropping inwardly to a broad low bench, over which, as well as over the whole surface of the wall beneath, there always hung a deep shade, which was considered objectionable on every ground save one, namely, that the perpetual sprinkling of seeds and water by the caged canary above was not noticed as an eyesore by visitors. The window was set with thickly-leaded diamond glazing, formed, especially in the lower panes, of knotty glass of various shades of green. Nothing was better known to Fancy than the extravagant manner in which these circular knots or eyes distorted everything seen through them from the outside — lifting hats from heads, shoulders from bodies; scattering the spokes of cart-wheels, and bending the straight fir-trunks into semicircles. The ceiling was carried by a beam traversing its midst, from the side of which projected a large nail, used solely and constantly as a peg for Geoffrey's hat; the nail was arched by a rainbow-shaped stain, imprinted by the brim of the said hat when it was hung there dripping wet.

The most striking point about the room was the furniture. This was a repetition upon inanimate objects of the old principle introduced by Noah, consisting for the most part of two articles of every sort. The duplicate system of furnishing owed its existence to the forethought of Fancy's mother, exercised from the date of Fancy's birthday onwards. The arrangement spoke for itself: nobody who knew the tone of the household could look at the goods without being aware that the second set was a provision for Fancy when she should marry and have a house of her own. The most noticeable instance was a pair of green-faced eight-day clocks ticking alternately, which were severally two-and-a-half minutes and three minutes striking the hour of twelve, one proclaiming, in Italian flourishes, Thomas Wood as the name of its maker, and the other — arched at the top, and altogether of more cynical appearance — that of Ezekiel Saunders. They were two departed clockmakers of Casterbridge, whose desperate rivalry throughout their lives was nowhere more emphatically perpetuated than here at Geoffrey's. These chief specimens of the marriage provision were supported on the right by a couple of kitchen dressers, each fitted complete with their cups, dishes, and plates, in their turn followed by two dumbwaiters, two family Bibles, two warming-pans, and two intermixed sets of chairs.

But the position last reached — the chimney-corner — was, after all, the most attractive side of the parallelogram. It was large enough to admit, in addition to Geoffrey himself, Geoffrey's wife, her chair, and her work-table, entirely within the line of the mantel, without danger or even inconvenience from the heat of the fire; and was spacious enough overhead to allow of the insertion of wood poles for the hanging of bacon, which were cloaked with long shreds of soot floating on the draught like the tattered banners on the walls of ancient aisles.

These points were common to most chimney-corners of the neighbourhood; but one feature there was which made Geoffrey's fireside not only an object of interest to casual aristocratic visitors — to whom every cottage fireside was more or less a curiosity — but the admiration of friends who were accustomed to fireplaces of the ordinary hamlet models. This peculiarity was a little window in the chimney-back, almost over the fire, around which the smoke crept caressingly when it left the perpendicular course. The windowboard was curiously stamped with black circles, burnt thereon by the heated bottoms of drinking-cups which had rested there after previously standing on the hot ashes of the hearth for the purpose of warming their contents, the result giving to the ledge the look of an envelope which has passed through innumerable post-offices.

Under the Greenwood Tree

A serious use for gardens:

"I've come on purpose to speak to you very particular, Mr Day," [Dick] said. . . . It was the custom in Mellstock and its vicinity to discuss matters of pleasure and ordinary business inside the house, and to reserve the garden for very important affairs: a custom which, as is supposed, originated in the desirability of getting away at such times from the other members of the family when there was only one room for living in, though it was now quite as frequently practised by those who suffered from no such limitation to the size of their domiciles.

Under the Greenwood Tree

Beside her, in case she might require more light, a brass candlestick stood on a little round table curiously formed of an old coffin-stool, with a deal top nailed on, the white surface of the latter contrasting oddly with the black carved oak of the sub-structure. The social position of the household in the past was almost as definitively shown by the presence of this article as that of an esquire or nobleman by his old helmets or shields. It had been customary for every well-to-do villager, whose tenure was by copy of court-roll, or in any way more permanent than that of the mere cotter, to keep a pair of these stools for the use of his own dead; but changes had led to the discontinuance of the custom, and the stools were frequently made use of in the manner described.

The Woodlanders

At Oozewood, in Upper Wessex:

She was sitting in an upper room on one of the lath-backed, willowbottomed "shepherd's" chairs, made on the spot then as to this day, and as they were probably made there in the days of the Heptarchy.

Master John Horseleigh, Knight

At Froom-Everard manor-house (the date is about 1837):

The apartment thus swept by an eye from without was occupied by two persons; they were sitting over dessert, the tablecloth having been removed in the old-fashioned way. The fruits were local, consisting of apples, pears, nuts, and such other products of the summer as might be presumed to grow on the estate. There was strong ale and rum on the table, and but little wine. Moreover, the appointments of the dining-room were simple and homely even for the date, betokening a countrified household of the smaller gentry, without much wealth or ambition — formerly a numerous class, but now in great part ousted by the territorial landlords.

The Waiting Supper

At Bincombe, above Weymouth:

Humphrey was staying at the inn, and had already called to inquire for her. He had brought her a present of a very handsome looking-glass in a frame of *repoussé* silverwork, which her father held in his hand....

Pretty mirrors were rarer in country-houses at that day than they are now, and the one before her won Phyllis's admiration.

The Melancholy Hussar of the German Legion

The cottage looking-glass:

"You must zee yourself!" she cried. "It is much better than you was t' other day."

As the looking-glass was only large enough to reflect a very small portion of Tess's person at one time, Mrs Durbeyfield hung a black cloak outside the casement, and so made a large reflector of the panes, as it is the wont of bedecking cottagers to do. After this she went downstairs to her husband, who was sitting in the lower room.

'I'll tell 'ee what 'tis, Durbeyfield", she said exultingly; "he'll never have the heart not to love her."

Tess of the d'Urbervilles

Unceiled cottages:

Picotee, who had been accustomed to unceiled country cottages all her life, wherein the scamper of a mouse is heard distinctly from floor to floor, exclaimed in a terrified whisper, at viewing all this, "They'll hear you underneath, they'll hear you, and we shall all be ruined!"

The Hand of Ethelberta

"Now, don't you tell him I'm in the house, will you? and then he'll not ask for me." [said Swithin to his grandmother]

"Now, we'll begin," interrupted Mr Torkingham, his mind returning to this world again on concluding his search for a psalm.

Thereupon the racket of chair-legs on the floor signified that they were settling into their seats — a disturbance which Swithin took advantage of by going on tiptoe across the floor above, and putting sheets of paper over knot-holes in the boarding at points where carpet was lacking, that his lamp-light might not shine down. The absence of a ceiling beneath rendered his position virtually that of one suspended in the same apartment.

Two on a Tower

Fancy was stationary upstairs, receiving her layers of clothes and adornments...

The conversation just now going on was concerning the banns, the last publication of which had been on the Sunday previous.

"And how did they sound?" Fancy subtly inquired.

"Very beautiful indeed," said Mrs Penny. "I never heard any sound better."

"But *how*?"

"O, *so* natural and elegant, didn't they, Reuben!" she cried through the chinks of the unceiled floor to the tranter downstairs.

"What's that?" said the tranter, looking up inquiringly at the floor above him for an answer.

"Didn't Dick and Fancy sound well when they were called home in church last

Sunday?" came downstairs again in Mrs Penny's voice.

"Ay, that they did, my sonnies! — especially the first time. There was a terrible whispering piece of work in the congregation, wasn't there, neighbour Penny?" said the tranter, taking up the thread of conversation on his own account and, in order to be heard in the room above, speaking very loud to Mr Penny, who sat at the distance of three feet from him, or rather less.

"I never can mind seeing such a whispering as there was," said Mr Penny, also loudly, to the room above. "And such sorrowful envy on the maidens' faces; really, I never did see such envy as there was!"

Under the Greenwood Tree

Three kitchens — and the great wedding cleaning:

In the kitchen dinner was preparing; for though Melbury dined at one o'clock at other times to-day the meal had been kept back for Grace. A rickety old spit was in motion, its end being fixed in the fire-dog, and the whole kept going by means of a cord conveyed over pulleys along the ceiling to a large stone suspended in a corner of the room. Old Grammer Oliver came and wound it up with a rattle like that of a mill.

The Woodlanders

These two, with a certain dilatoriness which appertained to both, were now in the heat of preparation in the bakehouse, expecting nobody before six o'clock. Winterborne was standing in front of the brick oven in his shirt-sleeves, tossing in thorn-sprays, and stirring about the blazing mass with a long-handled, three-pronged Beelzebub kind of fork,[120] the heat shining out upon his streaming face and making his

eyes like furnaces; the thorns crackling and sputtering; while Creedle, having ranged the pastry dishes in a row on the table till the oven should be ready, was pressing out the crust of a final apple-pie with a rolling-pin. A great pot boiled on the fire; and through the open door of the back-kitchen a boy was seen seated on the fender, emptying the snuffers and scouring the candlesticks, a row of the latter standing upside down on the hob to melt out the grease.

The Woodlanders

The kitchen was by far the pleasantest apartment in Knapwater House on such a morning as this. The vast fire was the centre of the whole system, like a sun, and threw its warm rays upon the figures of the domestics, wheeling about it in true planetary style. A nervously-feeble imitation of its flicker was continually attempted by a family of polished metallic utensils standing in rows and groups against the walls opposite, the whole collection of shines nearly annihilating the weak daylight from outside. A step further in, and the nostrils were greeted by the scent of green herbs just gathered, and the eye by the plump form of the cook, wholesome, white-aproned, and floury — looking as edible as the food she manipulated — her movements being supported and assisted by her satellites, the kitchen and scullery maids. Minute recurrent sounds prevailed — the click of the smoke-jack,[121] the flap of the flames, and the light touches of the women's slippers upon the stone floor.

Desperate Remedies

They make ready for the Illustrious Stranger:

Preparations for Matilda's welcome, and for the event which was to follow, at once occupied the attention of the mill. The miller and his man had but dim notions of housewifery on any large scale; so the great wedding cleaning was kindly supervised by Mrs Garland, Bob being mostly away during the day with his brother, the trumpet-major, on various errands, one of which was to buy paint and varnish for the gig that Matilda was to be fetched in, which he had determined to decorate with his own hands.

By the widow's direction the old familiar incrustation of shining dirt, imprinted along the back of the settle by the heads of countless jolly sitters, was scrubbed and scraped away; the brown circle round the nail whereon the miller hung his hat, stained by the brim in wet weather, was whitened over; the tawny smudges of bygone shoulders in the passage were removed without regard to a certain genial and historical value which they had acquired. The face of the clock, coated with verdigris as thick as a diachylon plaister,[122] was rubbed till the figures emerged into day; while, inside the case of the same chronometer, the cobwebs that formed triangular hammocks, which the pendulum could hardly wade through, were cleared away at one swoop.

Mrs Garland also assisted at the invasion of worm-eaten cupboards, where layers of ancient smells lingered on in the stagnant air, and recalled to the reflective nose the many good things that had been kept there. The upper floors were scrubbed with such abundance of water that the old-established death-watches, wood-lice, and flour-worms were all drowned, the suds trickling down into the room below in so lively and novel a manner as to convey the romantic notion that the miller lived in a cave with dripping stalactites.

They moved what had never been moved before — the oak coffer, containing the miller's wardrobe — a tremendous weight, what with its locks, hinges, nails, dust, framework, and the hard stratification of old jackets, waistcoats, and knee-breeches at the bottom, never disturbed since the miller's wife died, and half pulverized by the moths, whose flattened skeletons lay amid the mass in thousands.

"It fairly makes my back open and shut!" said Loveday, as, in obedience to Mrs Garland's direction, he lifted one corner, the grinder and David assisting at the others. "All together: speak when ye be going to heave. Now!"

The pot covers and skimmers were brought to such a state that, on examining them, the beholder was not conscious of utensils, but of his own face in a condition of hideous elasticity. The broken clock-line[123] was mended, the kettles rocked,[124] the creeper nailed up, and a new handle put to the warming-pan. The large household lantern was cleaned out, after three years of uninterrupted accumulation, the operation yielding a conglomerate of candle-snuffs, candle-ends, remains of matches, lampblack, and eleven ounces and a half of good grease — invaluable as dubbing for skitty boots and ointment for cart-wheels.

Everyone said that the mill residence had not been so thoroughly scoured for twenty years. The miller and David looked on with a sort of awe tempered by gratitude, tacitly admitting by their gaze that this was beyond what they had ever thought of.

The Trumpet-Major

THE ANCIENT COTTAGES OF ENGLAND

Rhoda Brook and Conjuror Fall both lived in mudwalled cottages. Near the end of his life Hardy wrote this article about the cottages of England:

I can with pleasure support the appeal of the Royal Society of Arts for assistance in its plan towards preserving the ancient cottages of England, having been, first and last, familiar with many of these venerable buildings in the West of England, and having also seen many of them vanish under the hands of their owners, through mistaken views not only on their appearance, but on their substantiality and comfort.

They are often as old as the parish church itself, but in consequence of a lack of distinctive architectural features in most, it is difficult to pronounce upon their exact date. In this district they continued to be built in the old style down to about the middle of the last century, when they were ousted by the now ubiquitous brick-and-slate. By the merest chance I was able, when a child, to see the building of what was probably one of the last of these old fashioned cottages of "mudwall" and thatch.

What was called mudwall was really a composition of chalk, clay and straw — essentially, unbaked brick. This was mixed up into a sort of dough pudding, close to where the cottage was to be built. The mixing was performed by treading and shovelling — women sometimes being called in to tread — and the straw was added to bind the mass together, a process that had doubtless gone on since the days of Israel in Egypt and earlier.

It was then thrown up by pitch-forks on to the wall, where it was trodden down, to a thickness of about two feet, till a "rise" of about three feet had been reached all round the building. This was left to settle for a day or two, and then another rise was effected, till the whole height to the wall-plate was reached, and then that of the gables, unless the cottage was hipped, or had a "pinion" end, as it was called. When the wall had dried a little the outer face was cut down to a fairly flat surface with a spade, and the wall then plastered outside and in. The thatch projected sufficiently to prevent much rain running down the outer plaster, and even where it did run down the plaster was so hard as to be unaffected, more lime being used than nowadays. The house I speak of is, I believe, still standing, unless replaced by a colder and damper one of brick-and-slate.

I can recall another cottage of the sort, which had been standing nearly 130 years,[125] where the original external plaster is uninjured by weather, though it has been patched here and there; but the thatch has been renewed half a dozen times in the period. Had the thatch been of straw which had passed through a threshing machine in the modern way it would have required renewal twice as many times during the existence of the walls. But formerly the thatching straw was drawn by hand from the ricks before threshing and, being unbruised, lasted twice as long, especially if not trimmed; thought the thatcher usually liked to trim his work to make it look neater.

I have never heard of any damp coming through these mudwalls, plastered and lime-whitened on the outside. Yet as everybody, at any rate every builder, knows, even when brick walls are built hollow it is difficult to keep damp out entirely in exposed situations.

Landowners who have built some of these latter express their wonder that the villagers prefer their old dingy hovels (as they are regarded) with rooms only six feet high, and small dormer windows with little lead squares, to the new residences with nine-feet rooms and wide windows with large panes. The explanation is the simple one that in the stroke of country winds a high room is not required for fresh air, sufficient ventilation entering through the door and window, and that the draught through the hollow brick wall makes the new cottages cold in winter.

I would therefore urge owners to let as many as are left of their old cottages remain where they are, and to repair them instead of replacing them with bricks, since, apart from their warmth and dryness, they have almost always great beauty and charm. Not only so, but I would suggest that their construction might be imitated when rebuilding is absolutely necessary.

The Preservation of Ancient Cottages

FARMHOUSE, MANOR-HOUSE, BARN, AND INN

A number of factors make Hardy's writing on country buildings unusually interesting. His particular cast of mind, steeped in the past, in folklore, and in human history; his deep visual sensitivity; his training as an architect; his instinct as a poet; and the fact that his manors and farmhouses were in the main drawn from real buildings with real histories — all these enrich his descriptions, each one of which is different, and lend them special significance.

The front of the manor-house, small though it seemed, was solidly built of stone in that never-to-be-surpassed style for the English country residence — the mullioned and transomed Elizabethan.

The Waiting Supper

Using Turnworth House (now pulled down) as a model for Hintock House, Hardy took poetic licence to describe its appearance while ignoring the fact that it was actually a nineteenth-century imitation. His penultimate paragraph is typical of his frequent introduction of historical perspective:

Hintock House appeared immediately beneath her eye. To describe it as standing in a hollow would not express the situation of the manor-house; it stood in a hole. But the hole was full of beauty. From the spot which Grace had reached a stone could easily have been thrown over or into the birds'-nested chimneys of the mansion. Its walls were surmounted by a battlemented parapet; but the grey lead roofs were quite visible behind it, with their gutters, laps, rolls, and skylights, together with letterings and shoe-patterns cut by idlers thereon.

The front of the house was an ordinary manorial presentation of Elizabethan windows, mullioned and hooded, worked in rich snuff-coloured freestone from Ham-hill quarries. The ashlar of the walls, where not overgrown with ivy and other creepers, was coated with lichen of every shade, intensifying its luxuriance with its nearness to the ground till, below the plinth, it merged in moss.

Above the house to the back was a dense plantation, the roots of whose trees were above the level of the chimneys. The corresponding high ground on which Grace stood was richly grassed, with only an old tree here and there. A few sheep lay about, which as they ruminated looked quietly into the bedroom windows.

The situation of the house, prejudicial to humanity, was a stimulus to vegetation, on which account an endless shearing of the heavy-armed ivy went on, and a continual lopping of trees and shrubs. It was an edifice built in times when human constitutions were damp-proof, when shelter from the boisterous was all that men thought of in choosing a dwelling-place, the insidious being beneath their notice; and its hollow site was an ocular reminder by its unfitness for modern lives of the fragility to which these have declined.

The highest architectural cunning could have done nothing to make Little Hintock House dry and salubrious; and ruthless ignorance could have done little to make it unpicturesque. It was vegetable nature's own home; a spot to inspire the painter and poet of still life — if they did not suffer too much from the relaxing atmosphere — and to draw groans from the gregariously disposed.

The Woodlanders

Oxwell Hall:

As Anne moved forward the grey, weather-worn front of a building edged from behind the trees. It was Oxwell Hall, once the seat of a family now extinct, and of late years used as a farmhouse. . . .

The rambling and neglected dwelling had all the romantic excellencies and practical drawbacks which such mildewed places share in common with caves, mountains, wildernesses, glens, and other homes of poesy that people of taste wish to live and die in. Mustard and cress could have been raised on the inner plaster of the dewy walls at any height not exceeding three feet from the floor; and mushrooms of the most refined and thin-stemmed kinds grew up through the chinks of the larder paving. As for the outside, Nature, in the ample time that had been given her, had so mingled her filings and effacements with the marks of human wear and tear upon the house, that it was often hard to say in which of the two or if in both, any particular obliteration had its origin. The keenness was gone from the mouldings of the doorways, but whether worn out by the rubbing past of innumerable people's shoulders, and the moving of their heavy furniture, or by Time in a grander and more abstract form, did not appear. The iron stanchions inside the window-panes were eaten away to the size of wires at the bottom where they entered the stone, the condensed breathings of generations having settled there in pools and rusted them. The panes themselves had either lost their shine altogether or become iridescent as a peacock's tail. In the middle of the porch was a vertical sun-dial, whose gnomon swayed loosely about when the wind blew, and cast its shadow hither and thither, as much as to say "Here's your fine model dial; here's any time for any man; I am an old dial; and shiftiness is the best policy."

Anne passed under the arched gateway which screened the main front; over it was the porter's lodge, reached by a spiral staircase. Across the archway was fixed a row of wooden hurdles, one of which Anne opened and closed behind her. Their necessity was apparent as soon as she got inside. The quadrangle of the ancient pile was a bed of mud and manure, inhabited by calves, geese, ducks, and sow pigs surprisingly large, with young ones surprisingly small. In the enclosure some heifers were amusing themselves by stretching up their necks and licking the mouldings of any salient stonework.

The Trumpet-Major

Weatherbury Farm:

By daylight, the bower of Oak's new-found mistress, Bathsheba Everdene, presented itself as a hoary building, of the early stage of Classic Renaissance as regards its architecture, and of a proportion which told at a glance that, as is so frequently the case, it had once been the manorial hall upon a small estate around it, now altogether effaced as a distinct property, and merged in the vast tract of a non-resident landlord, which comprised several such modest demesnes.

Fluted pilasters, worked from the solid stone, decorated its front, and above the roof the chimneys were panelled or columnar, some coped gables with finials and like features still retaining traces of their Gothic extraction. Soft brown mosses, like faded velveteen, formed cushions upon the stone tiling, and tufts of the houseleek or sengreen[126] sprouted from the eaves of the low surrounding buildings. A gravel walk leading from the door to the road in front was encrusted at the sides with more moss — here it was a silver-green variety, the nut-brown of the gravel being visible to the width of only a foot or two in the centre. This circumstance, and the generally sleepy air of the whole prospect here, together with the animated and contrasting state of the reverse façade, suggested to the imagination that on the adaptation of the building for farming purposes the vital principle of the house had turned round inside its body to face the other way. Reversals of this kind, strange deformities, tremendous paralyses, are often seen to be inflicted by trade upon edifices — either individual or in the aggregate as streets and towns — which were originally planned for pleasure alone.

Lively voices were heard this morning in the upper rooms, the main staircase to which was of hard oak, the balusters, heavy as bed-posts, being turned and moulded in the quaint fashion of their century, the handrail as stout as a parapet-top, and the stairs themselves continually twisting round like a person trying to look over his shoulder. Going up, the floors above were found to have a very irregular surface, rising to ridges, sinking into valleys; and being just then uncarpeted, the face of the boards was seen to be eaten into innumerable vermiculations. Every window replied by a clang to the opening and shutting of every door, a tremble followed every bustling movement, and a creak accompanied a walker about the house, like a spirit, wherever he went.

Far from the Madding Crowd

The Great Barn:

The description, in Far from the Madding Crowd, *of the Great Barn is one of Hardy's finest pieces of writing about any country building. It is on page 230.*

SEVERAL KINDS OF INN

The Three Tranters, a fine medieval inn, was in time put out of business by the railway.[127]

"The inn called Peter's Finger was the church of Mixen Lane."[128]

It was at the Buck's Head, above Yalbury Wood, that Poorgrass suffered from the multiplying eye.[129]

Warren's Malthouse was "an alternative to the inn".[130]

The Three Mariners at Casterbridge:

This ancient house of accommodation for man and beast, now, unfortunately, pulled down, was built of mellow sandstone, with mullioned windows of the same material, markedly out of perpendicular from the settlement of foundations. The bay window projecting into the street, whose interior was so popular among the frequenters of the inn, was closed with shutters, in each of which appeared a heart-shaped aperture, somewhat more attentuated in the right and left ventricles than is seen in Nature. Inside these illuminated holes, at a distance of about three inches, were ranged at this hour, as every passer knew, the ruddy polls of Billy Wills the glazier, Smart the shoe-maker, Buzzford the general dealer, and others of a secondary set of worthies, of a grade somewhat below that of the diners at the King's Arms, each with his yard of clay.[131].... A long, narrow, dimly-lit passage gave access to the inn, within which passage the horses going to their stalls at the back, and the coming and departing human guests, rubbed shoulders indiscriminately, the latter running no slight risk of having their toes trodden upon by the animals. The good stabling and the good ale of the Mariners, though somewhat difficult to reach on account of there being but this narrow way to both, were nevertheless perseveringly sought out by the sagacious old heads who knew what was what in Casterbridge....

The accommodation of the Three Mariners was far from spacious, despite the fair area of ground it covered. The room demanded by intrusive beams and rafters, partitions, passages, staircases, disused ovens, settles, and four-posters, left comparatively small quarters for human beings. Moreover, this being at a time before home-brewing was abandoned by the smaller victuallers, and a house in which the twelve-bushel strength[132] was still religiously adhered to by the landlord in his ale, the quality of the liquor was the chief attraction of the premises, so that everything had to make way for utensils and operations in connection therewith.

The Mayor of Casterbridge

At Rolliver's — unofficially:

Rolliver's inn, the single alehouse at this end of the long and broken village, could only boast of an off-license; hence, as nobody could drink on the premises, the amount of overt accommodation for consumers was strictly limited to a little board about six inches wide and two yards long, fixed to the garden palings by pieces of wire, so as to form a ledge. On this board thirsty strangers deposited their cups as they stood in the road and drank, and threw the dregs on the dusty ground to the pattern of Polynesia, and wished they could have a restful seat inside.

Thus the strangers. But there were also local customers who felt the same wish; and where there's a will there's a way.

In a large bedroom upstairs, the window of which was thickly curtained with a great woollen shawl lately discarded by the landlady Mrs Rolliver, were gathered on this evening nearly a dozen persons, all seeking beatitude....

A gaunt four-post bedstead which stood in the room afforded sitting-space for several persons gathered round three of its sides; a couple more men had elevated themselves on a chest of drawers; another rested on the oak-carved "cwoffer"; two on the wash-stand; another on the stool; and thus all were, somehow, seated at their ease. The stage of mental comfort to which they had arrived at this hour was one wherein their souls expanded beyond their skins, and spread their personalities warmly through the room. In this process the chamber and its furniture grew more and more dignified and luxurious; the shawl hanging at the window took upon itself the richness of tapestry; the brass handles of the chest of drawers were as golden knockers; and the carved bed-posts seemed to have some kinship with the magnificent pillars of Solomon's temple.

Mrs Durbeyfield, having quickly walked hitherward after parting from Tess, opened the front door, crossed the downstairs room, which was in deep gloom, and then unfastened the stair-door like one whose fingers knew the tricks of the latches well. Her ascent of the crooked staircase was a slower process, and her face, as it rose into the light above the last stair, encountered the gaze of all the party assembled in the bedroom.

"— Being a few private friends I've asked in to keep up club-walking at my own expense," the landlady exclaimed at the sound of footsteps, as glibly as a child repeating the Catechism, while she peered over the stairs. "Oh, 'tis you, Mrs Durbeyfield — Lard — how you frightened me! — I thought it might be some gaffer[133] sent by Gover'ment."

Tess of the d'Urbervilles

Carpenter and nobleman drive through the night to stop a hated marriage:

When they entered Flychett it was about three.

"Now, where's the inn?" said Mountclere, yawning.

"Just on the knap,"[134] Sol answered. "'Tis a little small place, and we must do as well as we can."

They pulled up before a cottage, upon the white-washed front of which could be seen a square board representing the sign. After an infinite labour of rapping and shouting, a casement opened overhead, and a woman's voice inquired what was the matter. Sol explained, when she told them that the horses were away from home.

"Now we must wait till these have rested," growled Mountclere. "A pretty muddle!"

"It cannot be helped," answered Sol; and he asked the woman to open the door. She replied that her husband was away with the horses and van, and that they could not come in.

Sol was known to her, and he mentioned his name; but the woman only began to abuse him.

"Come, publican, you'd better let us in, or we'll have the law for 't," rejoined Sol, with more spirit. "You don't dare to keep nobility waiting like this."...

A few more words to the woman resulted in her agreeing to admit them if they would attend to themselves afterwards. This Sol promised, and the key of the door was let down to them from the bedroom window by a string. When they had entered,

Sol, who knew the house well, busied himself in lighting a fire, the driver going off with a lantern to the stable, where he found standing-room for the two horses. Mountclere walked up and down the kitchen, mumbling words of disgust at the situation, the few of this kind that he let out being just enough to show what a fearfully large number he kept in.

"A-calling up people at this time of morning!" the woman occasionally exclaimed down the stairs. "But folks show no mercy upon their flesh and blood — not one bit or mite."

"Now never be stomachy,[135] my good soul," cried Sol from the fireplace, where he stood blowing the fire with his breath. "Only tell me where the victuals bide, and I'll do all the cooking. We'll pay like princes — especially my mate."

"There's but little in house," said the sleepy woman from her bedroom. "There's pig's fry, a side of bacon, a conger eel, and pickled onions."...

"Well, then, tell me where the bacon is," shouted Sol to the woman.

"You must find it," came again down the stairs. " 'Tis somewhere up in chimley, but in which part I can't mind. Really I don't know whether I be upon my head or my heels, and my brain is all in a spin, wi' being rafted up in such a larry!"

"Bide where you be, there's a dear," said Sol. "We'll do it all. Just tell us where the tea-caddy is, and the grid-iron, and then you can go to sleep again."

The Hand of Ethelberta

6 Clothes

When Hardy's first published novel, Desperate Remedies, *appeared anonymously in 1871, some critics were at a loss to determine the sex of the writer; for although certain of its expressions were "so remarkably coarse" as to be surely unknown to a lady, on the other hand the writer seemed too familiar with "the mysteries of the female toilette" to be male. The enigma might have been solved had readers known that Hardy, working in London in the 1860s, had been in close contact not only with his first cousin, Martha Mary Sparks, but also, according to the evidence of a niece,*[136] *more or less formally engaged to a certain Eliza Nicholls; and both girls were ladies' maids.*

The three following passages exemplify something of the sensitivity to women's clothes, and their effect, which Hardy was always to show.

Cytherea Graye shelters from a storm in the porch of the new steward, Aeneas Manston:

At this moment, by reason of the narrowness of the porch, their clothing touched, and remained in contact.

His clothes are something exterior to every man; but to a woman her dress is part of her body. Its motions are all present to her intelligence if not to her eyes; no man knows how his coat-tails swing. By the slightest hyperbole it may be said that her dress has sensation. Crease but the very Ultima Thule[137] of fringe or flounce, and it hurts her as much as pinching her. Delicate antennae, or feelers, bristle on every outlying frill. Go to the uppermost: she is there: tread on the lowest: the fair creature is there almost before you.

Thus the touch of clothes, which was nothing to Manston, sent a thrill through Cytherea, seeing, moreover, that he was of the nature of a mysterious stranger. She looked out again at the storm, but still felt him.

Desperate Remedies

Anne Garland tries to stop her sailor lover from rejoining the fleet:

Anne saw these fluctuations of his mind between love and patriotism, and being terrified by what she had heard of sea-fights, used the utmost art of which she was capable to seduce him from his forming purpose. She came to him in the mill, wearing the very prettiest of her morning jackets — the one that only just passed the waist, and was laced so tastefully round the collar and bosom. Then she would appear in her new hat, with a bouquet of primroses on one side; and on the following Sunday she walked before him in lemon-coloured boots, so that her feet looked like a pair of yellow-hammers flitting under her dress.

The Trumpet-Major

In his "Trumpet-Major" Notebook, *Hardy made innumerable notes and sketches of both men and women's fashions from contemporary newspapers and "ladies'" magazines.*

Milkmaid Tess puts on her husband's heirloom diamonds, and is transformed:

As everybody knows, fine feathers make fine birds; a peasant girl but very moderately prepossessing to the casual observer in her simple condition and attire, will bloom as an amazing beauty if clothed as a woman of fashion with the aids that art can render; while the beauty of the midnight crush would often cut but a sorry figure if placed inside the field-woman's wrapper upon a monotonous acreage of turnips on a dull day.

Tess of the d'Urbervilles

The Milkmaid

Under a daisied bank
There stands a rich red ruminating cow,
And hard against her flank
A cotton-hooded milkmaid bends her brow.

The flowery river-ooze
Upheaves and falls; the milk purrs in the pail;
Few pilgrims but would choose
The peace of such a life in such a vale.

The maid breathes words — to vent,
It seems, her sense of Nature's scenery,
Of whose life, sentiment,
And essence, very part itself is she.

She bends a glance of pain,
And, at a moment, lets escape a tear;
Is it that passing train,
Whose alien whirr offends her country ear? —

Nay! Phyllis does not dwell
On visual and familiar things like these;
What moves her is the spell
Of inner themes and inner poetries:

Could but by Sunday morn
Her gay new gown come, meads might dry to dun,
Trains shriek till ears were torn,
If Fred would not prefer that Other One.

Poems of the Past and Present

CLOTHES FOR WORK

Lady Constantine hurries to catch St Cleeve before his ship sails:

She rang to tell Green to be ready with the pony to drive her to Warborne station in a quarter of an hour.... She was ready before Green, and urged on that factotum so wildly as to leave him no time to change his corduroys and "skitty-boots"[138] in which he had been gardening; he therefore turned himself into a coachman as far down as his waist merely — clapping on his proper coat, hat, and waistcoat, and wrapping a rug over his horticultural half below. In this compromise he appeared at the door, mounted, and reins in hand.

Two on a Tower

The village confirmation:

The Right Reverend Cuthbert Helmsdale, D.D., ninety-fourth occupant of the episcopal throne of the diocese, revealed himself to be a personage of dark complexion, whose darkness was thrown still further into prominence by the lawn protuberances that now rose upon his two shoulders like the Eastern and Western hemispheres. In stature he seemed to be tall and imposing, but something of this aspect may have been derived from his robes.

Two on a Tower

Dairying at Talbothays:

The dairymaids and men had flocked down from their cottages and out of the dairy-house with the arrival of the cows from the meads; the maids walking in pattens, not on account of the weather, but to keep their shoes above the mulch of the barton.... The male milkers, with hat-brims turned down, resting flat on their foreheads and gazing on the ground, did not observe her...; Tess... changed her bonnet for a hood....

Tess could then see [one of the milkers] at full length. He wore the ordinary white pinner and leather leggings of a dairy-farmer when milking, and his boots were clogged with the mulch of the yard; but this was all his local livery. Beneath it was something educated, reserved, subtle, sad, differing.

Tess of the d'Urbervilles

The haytrusser:

He wore a short jacket of brown corduroy, newer than the remainder of his suit, which was a fustian waistcoat with white horn buttons, breeches of the same, tanned leggings, and a straw hat overlaid with black glazed canvas.

Some twenty years later:

The same evening at dusk Henchard left the town, to whose development he had been one of the chief stimulants for many years. During the day he had bought a new tool-basket, cleaned up his old hay-knife and wimble, set himself up in fresh leggings, knee-naps and corduroys, and in other ways gone back to the working clothes of his young manhood, discarding for ever the shabby-genteel suit of cloth and rusty silk hat that since his decline had characterized him in the Casterbridge street as a man who had seen better days.

The Mayor of Casterbridge

The furze-cutter:

He was a somewhat solemn young fellow, and carried the hook and leather gloves of a furze-cutter, his legs, by reason of that occupation, being sheathed in bulging leggings as stiff as the Philistine's greaves of brass.

The Return of the Native

The field-woman:

Thus Tess walks on; a figure which is part of the landscape; a fieldwoman pure and simple, in winter guise; a gray serge cape, a red woollen cravat, a stuff skirt covered by a whitey-brown rough wrapper, and buff leather gloves. Every thread of that old attire has become faded and thin under the stroke of raindrops, the burn of sunbeams and the stress of winds.

Tess of the d'Urbervilles

The agricultural worker:

Henery appeared in a drab kerseymere[139] great-coat, buttoned over his smock-frock, the white skirts of the latter being visible to the distance of about a foot below the coat-tails, which, when you got used to the style of dress, looked natural enough, and even ornamental — it certainly was comfortable.

Far From The Madding Crowd

The hiring-fair of recent years presents an appearance unlike that of former times. A glance up the high street of the town on a Candlemas-fair day twenty or thirty years ago revealed a crowd whose general colour was whity-brown flecked with white. Black was almost absent, the few farmers who wore that shade hardly discernible. Now the crowd is as dark as a London crowd. This change is owing to the rage for cloth clothes which possesses the labourers of to-day. Formerly they came in smock-frocks and gaiters, the shepherds with their crooks, the carters with a zone of whipcord round their hats, thatchers with a straw tucked into the brim, and so on. Now, with the exception of the crook in the hands of an occasional old shepherd, there is no mark of speciality in the groups, who might be tailors or undertakers' men, for what they exhibit externally. Out of a group of eight, for example, who talk together in the middle of the road, only one wears corduroy trousers. Two wear cloth pilot-coats and black trousers, two patterned tweed suits with black canvas overalls, the remaining four suits being of faded broadcloth. To a great extent these are their Sunday suits; but the genuine white smock-frock of Russia duck and the whity-brown one of drabbet, are rarely seen now afield, except on the shoulders of old men. Where smocks are worn by the young and middle-aged, they are of blue material. The mechanic's "slop" has also been adopted; but a mangy old cloth coat is preferred; so that often a group of these honest fellows on the arable has the aspect of a body of tramps up to some mischief in the field, rather than its natural tillers at work there.

That peculiarity of the English urban poor (which M. Taine ridicules, and unfavourably contrasts with the taste of the Continental working-people) — their preference for the cast-off clothes of a richer class to a special attire of their own — has, in fact, reached the Dorset farm folk. Like the men, the women are, pictorially, less interesting than they used to be. Instead of the wing bonnet like the tilt of a waggon, cotton gown, bright-hued neckerchief, and strong flat boots and shoes, they (the younger ones at least) wear shabby millinery bonnets and hats with beads and feathers, "material" dresses, and boot-heels almost as foolishly shaped as those of ladies of highest education.

The Dorsetshire Labourer

CLOTHES FOR OCCASIONS

Clothes for Church

Tranter Dick and Miss Fancy Day, having moved her possessions to her new home at the school-house, find that the towel they need for their newly-washed hands is at the bottom of a box of clean clothes:

Dick managed by the aid of a knife and fork to extract a towel from under a muslin dress without wetting the latter; and for a moment he ventured to assume a tone of criticism.

"I fear for the dress," he said, as they wiped their hands together.

"What?" said Miss Day, looking into the box at the dress alluded to. "O, I know what you mean — that the vicar will never let me wear muslin?"

"Yes."

"Well, I know it is condemned by all orders in the church as flaunting, and unfit for common wear for girls who've their living to get, but we'll see."

"In the interest of the church I hope you don't speak seriously."

"Yes, I do; but we'll see." There was a comely determination on her lip, very pleasant to a beholder who was neither bishop, priest, nor deacon. "I think I can manage any vicar's views about me if he's under forty."

Dick rather wished she had never thought of managing vicars.

Under the Greenwood Tree

Fancy Day sets off for church to play, for the first time, the organ which is to supplant the Quire:

If ever a woman looked a divinity Fancy Day appeared one that morning as she floated down those school steps, in the form of a nebulous collection of colours inclining to blue. With an audacity unparalleled in the whole history of village-schoolmistresses at this date — partly owing, no doubt, to papa's respectable accumulation of cash, which rendered her profession not altogether one of necessity — she had actually donned a hat and feather and lowered her hitherto plainly looped-up hair, which now fell about her shoulders in a profusion of curls....

... Fancy proceeded to the church. The organ stood on one side of the chancel, close to and under the immediate eye of the vicar when he was in the pulpit and also in full view of the congregation. Here she sat down, for the first time in such a conspicuous position, her seat having previously been in a remote spot in the aisle.

"Good heavens — disgraceful! Curls and a hat and feather!" said the daughters of the small gentry, who had either only curly hair without a hat and feather, or a hat and feather without curly hair. "A bonnet for church always!" said sober matrons.

Under the Greenwood Tree

Clothes for courting:

Dick prepares to visit Fancy's father to ask her hand:

"Yes, and I'll put on my second-best suit and clean shirt and collar, and black my boots as if 'twas a Sunday. 'Twill have a good appearance, you see, and that's a great deal to start with."

"You won't wear that old waistcoat, will you, Dick?"

"Bless you, no! Why, I—"

"I didn't mean to be personal, dear Dick," she said, fearing she had hurt his feelings. " 'Tis a very nice waistcoat, but what I meant was, that though it is an excellent waistcoat for a settled-down man, it is not quite one for" (she waited, and a blush expanded over her face, and then she went on again) — "for going courting in."

"No, I'll wear my best winter one, with the leather lining, mother made. It is a beautiful, handsome waistcoat inside, yes, as ever anybody saw. In fact, only the other day, I unbuttoned it to show a chap that very lining, and he said it was the strongest, handsomest lining you could wish to see on the king's waistcoat himself."

"*I* don't quite know what to wear," she said.... "After all, I think that by wearing my gray [dress] Saturday, I can make the blue one do for Sunday. Yes, I will. A hat or a bonnet, which shall it be? Which do I look best in?"

"Well, I think the bonnet is nicest, more quiet and matronly."

"What's the objection to the hat? Does it make me look old?"

"O no; the hat is well enough; but it makes you look rather too — you won't mind me saying it, dear?"

"Not at all, for I shall wear the bonnet."

"— Rather too coquettish and flirty for an engaged young woman."

She reflected a minute. "Yes; yes. Still, after all, the hat would do best; hats *are* best, you see. Yes, I must wear the hat, dear Dicky, because I ought to wear a hat, you know."

Under the Greenwood Tree

Shepherd Oak similarly prepares to call on Bathsheba Everdene:

He had made a toilet of a nicely-adjusted kind — of a nature between the carefully neat and the carelessly ornate — of a degree between fine market-day and wet-Sunday selection. He thoroughly cleaned his silver watch-chain with whiting, put new lacing straps to his boots, looked to the brass eyelet-holes, went to the inmost heart of the plantation for a new walking-stick, and trimmed it vigorously on his way back; took a new handkerchief from the bottom of his clothes-box, put on the light waistcoat patterned all over with sprigs of an elegant flower uniting the beauties of rose and lily without the defects of either, and used all the hair-oil he possessed upon his usually dry, sandy, and inextricably curly hair, till he had deepened it to a splendidly novel colour, between that of guano and Roman cement, making it stick to his head like mace round a nutmeg, or wet seaweed round a boulder after the ebb.

Far from the Madding Crowd

The Old Gown

I have seen her in gowns the brightest,
  Of azure, green, and red,
And in the simplest, whitest,
  Muslined from heel to head;
I have watched her walking, riding,
  Shade-flecked by a leafy tree,
Or in fixed thought abiding
  By the foam-fingered sea.

In woodlands I have known her,
  When boughs were mourning loud,
In the rain-reek she has shown her
  Wild-haired and watery-browed.
And once or twice she has cast me
  As she pomped along the street
Court-clad, ere quite she had passed me,
  A glance from her chariot-seat.

But in my memoried passion
  For evermore stands she
In the gown of fading fashion
  She wore that night when we,
Doomed long to part, assembled
  In the snug small room; yea, when
She sang with lips that trembled,
  "Shall I see his face again?"

Late Lyrics and Earlier

Clothes (and hair) for a wedding:

Fancy was stationary upstairs, receiving her layers of clothes and adornments [from]... Mrs Dewy and Mrs Penny, who were assisting her at the toilet.... Mrs

Penny appeared with nine corkscrew curls on each side of her temples, and a back comb stuck upon her crown like a castle on a steep.

"Hark! Who's that?" exclaimed a small pupil-teacher, who also assisted this morning to her great delight. She ran half-way down the stairs and peeped round the banister. "O, you should, you should, you should!" she exclaimed, scrambling up to the room again.

"What?" said Fancy.

"See the bridesmaids! They've just a-come! 'Tis wonderful, really! 'tis wonderful how muslin can be brought to it. There, they don't look a bit like themselves, but like some very rich sisters o' theirs that nobody knew they had!"

Dick was advancing to the door in a painfully new coat of shining cloth, primrose-coloured waistcoat, hat of the same painful style of newness, and with an extra quantity of whiskers shaved off his face and hair cut to an unwonted shortness in honour of the occasion.

Under the Greenwood Tree

Clothes for entertainment — the Mummers:

The piece was the well-known play of "Saint George", and all who were behind the scenes assisted in the preparations, including the women of each household.... This class of assistance was not without its drawbacks....

It might be that Joe, who fought on the side of Christendom, had a sweetheart, and that Jim, who fought on the side of the Moslem, had one likewise. During the making of the costumes it would come to the knowledge of Joe's sweetheart that Jim's was putting brilliant silk scallops at the bottom of her lover's surcoat, in addition to the ribbons of the visor, the bars of which, being invariably formed of coloured strips about half an inch wide hanging before the face, were mostly of that material.

Joe's sweetheart straightway placed brilliant silk on the scallops of the hem in question, and, going a little further, added ribbon tufts to the shoulder pieces. Jim's not to be outdone, would affix bows and rosettes everywhere.

The result was that in the end the Valiant Soldier, of the Christian army, was distinguished by no peculiarity of accoutrement from the Turkish Knight; and what was worse, on a casual view Saint George himself might be mistaken for his deadly enemy, the Saracen.[140]

The Return of the Native

Clothes for mourning:

At the Draper's

"I stood at the back of the shop, my dear,
    But you did not perceive me.
Well, when they deliver what you were shown
    I shall know nothing of it, believe me!"

And he coughed and coughed as she paled and said,
    "O, I didn't see you come in there —
Why couldn't you speak?" — "Well, I didn't. I left
    That you should not notice I'd been there.

"You were viewing some lovely things. *'Soon required
    For a widow, of latest fashion;'*
And I knew 'twould upset you to meet the man
    Who had to be cold and ashen

"And screwed in a box before they could dress you
    'In the last new note in mourning,'
As they defined it. So, not to distress you,
    I left you to your adorning."

Satires of Circumstance

The Hatband

She held it out. "But you can't both have it," she said;
And hesitating they stood. The boom of the bell
For the maiden came across as her fond farewell:—
        That one was the friend of the dead,
The second her lover, there needed no words to tell.

They looked at the object — a hatband the parish folk
Would borrow at times of the well-to-do woman who spoke:
Its trailing two-yards' length had grown rusty and bare
        From much promiscuous wear.

"Decide between you," she added, and handed it over,
Whereon their faces appeared as much stressed at the choice
As the one at the loss of his friend, of his sweetheart the lover:
And still did the bell throb forth, as with querying voice,
Which head the crape symbol should cover?

"You take it," at last said the friend, standing back with a sigh:
"You were dearer to her than was I."
The streamer was tied on the hat with a love-knot of white,
And they hurried away, and shared in the last sad rite.

Next Sunday came; and pending the due church-hour
There stood, hot, playing at fives, by the western tower,
The ruddy young lover, as often aforetime there:
And the long black love-knotted hatband blew wild in the air
With his rushings everywhere.

Then murmured her friend, as he slowly drew near that day,
"I might just as well, truly, have had it! Alas, could not he
Refrain him for one little week, out of bare loyalty?
But young love is brief; let him play:
Yet never *this* sight, had the sad sign been worn here by me!"

Note: It should be remembered that hatbands were formerly worn hanging down behind to the waist, and tied with a bow of white ribbon when the deceased was a young unmarried woman. It was retained for the service on the Sunday following the funeral.

Uncollected Poems

COUNTRIFIED CLOTHES

On the Isle of Slingers:

He suddenly became aware of the presence of a lady still further ahead in the aisle, whose attire, though of black materials in the quietest form, was of a cut which rather suggested London than this *Ultima Thule*. . . .

The Well-Beloved

Mrs Dewy expresses some self-satisfaction:

"You never did look so well in a pair o' trousers as in them," she continued. . . . "Such a cheap pair as 'twas too. As big as any man could wish to have, and lined inside, and double-lined in the lower parts, and an extra piece of stiffening at the bottom. And 'tis a nice high cut that comes up right under your armpits, and there's enough turned down inside the seams to make half a pair more, besides a piece of cloth left that will make an honest waistcoat — all by my contriving in buying the stuff at a bargain, and having it made up under my eye. It only shows what may be done by taking a little trouble, and not going straight to the rascally tailors."

Under the Greenwood Tree

Margery the Milkmaid sets out across country:

It was half-past four o'clock on a May morning in the eighteen-forties. . . . The barton-gate slammed again, and in two or three minutes a something became visible, rising out of the fog in that quarter.

The shape revealed itself as that of a woman having a young and agile gait. The colours and other details of her dress were then disclosed — a bright pink cotton frock (because winter was over); a small woollen shawl of shepherd's plaid (because summer was not come); a white handkerchief tied over her head-gear, because it was so foggy, so damp, and so early; and a straw bonnet and ribbons peeping from under the handkerchief, because it was like to be a sunny May day.

The Romantic Adventures of a Milkmaid

Informal dress at a country rectory:

[Elfride] turned the handle and entered, throwing off the cloak which enveloped her, under which she appeared without hat or bonnet, and in the sort of half-toilette country people ordinarily dine in.

A Pair of Blue Eyes

The need for pattens:

Arrived at the entrance to a long flat lane, which had taken the spirit out of many a pedestrian in times when, with the majority, to travel meant to walk, he saw before him the trim figure of a young woman in pattens, journeying with that steadfast concentration which means purpose and not pleasure. . . . Click, click, click went the pattens; and she did not turn her head. . . .

"Why do you wear pattens, Marty? The turnpike is clean enough although the lanes are muddy."

"They save my boots."

"But twelve miles in pattens — 'twill twist your feet off. Come, get up and ride with me."

She hesitated, removed her pattens, knocked the gravel out of them against the wheel, and mounted.

The Woodlanders

"Whatever d'ye think?" said Susan Tall, "Gable Oak is coming it quite the dand. He now wears shining boots with hardly a hob in 'em, two or three times a-week, and a tall hat a-Sundays, and 'a hardly knows the name of smockfrock. When I see people strut enough to be cut up into bantam cocks, I stand dormant with wonder, and says no more!"

Far from the Madding Crowd

The vicar is summoned from his lowlier parishioners to the Great House:

Mr Torkingham seated himself. His boots, which had seemed elegant in the farmhouse, appeared rather clumsy here, and his coat, that was a model of tailoring when he stood amid the choir, now exhibited decidedly strained relations with his limbs.

Two on a Tower

Mrs Crick, the dairyman's wife . . . was too respectable to go out milking herself, and wore a hot stuff gown in warm weather because the dairymaids wore prints.

Tess of the d'Urbervilles

The village schoolmaster becomes aware of contrasts:

To further complicate his feeling tonight there was the sight, on the one hand, of the young lady with her warm rich dress and glowing future, and on the other of the weak little boys and girls — some only five years old, and none more than twelve, going off in their different directions in the pelting rain, some for a walk of more than two miles, with the certainty of being drenched to the skin, and with no change of clothes when they reached their home. He watched the rain spots thickening upon the faded frocks, worn-out tippets, yellow straw hats and bonnets, and coarse pinafores of his unprotected little flock as they walked down the path, and was thereby reminded of the hopelessness of his attachment, by perceiving how much more nearly akin was his lot to theirs than to hers.

An Indiscretion in the Life of an Heiress

7 Schooling

Hardy was more fortunate than many rural boys in the nineteenth century in having an ambitious, reading mother who encouraged him to read from an early age; and in living near Dorchester which in mid-century was well-provided with schools, in particular with an outstanding teacher, Isaac Last, to whose school Hardy went in 1849. Yet he left at sixteen to become an architect's apprentice, and much of his education was continued by his own efforts and the help of friends after this time – when, for example, he began to read Greek which he had never learnt at school.

The rural characters in his stories reflect the general lack of education of the time. Although the two religious voluntary bodies, the British and Foreign Society and the National Society, had from their inception in 1808 and 1811 provided literally thousands of schools, the Newcastle Commission of 1861 found that only one in seven children was attending day schools of any kind, the number attending schools that were "guaranteed efficient" dropping to one in twenty. It was not until the Mundella Act of 1880 that a system of universal compulsory education was established, nor till 1891 that free education was virtually assured; nor had any public body the right to build a secondary school until after the turn of the century.

Abel Whittle, who so loyally tended Michael Henchard till his death, could not read his will pinned up on the bedhead; of Susan Henchard, Michael himself said: "What advantages had she? None. She could write her own name, and no more."[141]

This was the secret of Anna's embarrassment and flutterings. She could neither read nor write. She had grown up under the care of an aunt by marriage, at one of the lonely hamlets on the Great Mid-Wessex Plain where, even in days of national education, there had been no school within a distance of two miles. Her aunt was an ignorant woman; there had been nobody to investigate Anna's circumstances, nobody to care about her learning the rudiments....

On the Western Circuit

Jude at the age of eleven was only able to go to night-school; the whole story of his and his teacher's failure to become undergraduates shows the great disadvantage of the rural poor. Tess had been luckier, as far as she had gone, in having "passed the Sixth Standard in the National School under a London-trained mistress".[142] *Sergeant Troy was said to have attended Casterbridge Grammar School,*[143] *and Swithin St Cleeve, in* Two on a Tower, *according to old Haymoss's vivid account,*[144] *Warborne Grammar School – "a place where they draw up young gam'sters' brains like rhubarb under a ninepenny pan, my lady". But Stephen Smith had to go further afield; and the more aristocratic Elfride is surprised at his humble educational beginnings:*

"Where do you think I went to school — I mean, to what kind of school?"
"Dr Somebody's academy," she said simply.
"No. To a dame school originally, then to a national school."
"Only to those! Well, I love you just as much, Stephen, dear Stephen," she murmured tenderly....

Stephen continues the story:

"Remember, I have not lived here since I was nine years old. I then went to live with my uncle, a builder, near Exonbury, in order to be able to attend a national school as a day scholar; there was none on this remote coast then. It was there I met with my friend Knight. And when I was fifteen and had been fairly educated by the schoolmaster — and more particularly by Knight — I was put as a pupil in an architect's office in that town, because I was skilful in the use of the pencil. A full premium[145] was paid by the efforts of my mother and father, rather against the wishes of Lord Luxellian, who likes my father, however, and thinks a great deal of him. There I stayed till six months ago, when I obtained a situation as improver,[146] as it is called, in a London office. That's all of me."

A Pair of Blue Eyes

The forerunners of today's "private schools" receive little mention. George Melbury the timber-merchant felt his own childhood ignorance so deeply that he paid nearly £100 a year to educate his daughter Grace as a lady – "Mrs Charmond herself is not better informed than my girl Grace." Clym Yeobright's first intention to run a night-school near Egdon, to dispel the superstitious ignorance of the scattered heath-dwellers, was met with scepticism from them. He modified it to the idea of a private school for farmers' sons; but his failing eyesight made this impossible, and he ended, after the tragic deaths of his mother and wife, as a kind of itinerant lecturer in adult education of the broadest moral kind.

Hardy was well aware that such further education for living, and the widening of horizons and experience through travel and social intercourse with people of varied backgrounds and types, was impossible for the majority of country dwellers who had neither the money nor the means of transport.[147]

Tess Durbeyfield's route on this memorable morning lay amid the north-eastern undulations of the Vale in which she had been born, and in which her life had unfolded. The Vale of Blackmoor was to her the world, and its inhabitants the races thereof. From the gates and stiles of Marlott she had looked down its length in the wondering days of infancy, and what had been mystery to her then was not much less than mystery to her now. She had seen daily from her chamber-window towers, villages, faint white mansions; above all the town of Shaston standing majestically on its height; its windows shining like lamps in the evening sun. She had hardly ever visited the place, only a small tract even of the Vale and its environs being known to her by close inspection. Much less had she been far outside the valley. Every contour of the surrounding hills was as personal to her as that of her relatives' faces; but for what lay beyond her judgment was dependent on the teaching of the village school, where she had held a leading place at the time of her leaving, a year or two before this date.

Tess of the d'Urbervilles

In this sense, the greatly increased annual migration of labourers, about which Hardy wrote in 1883, brought some benefit:

Change is also a certain sort of education.... The habitually-removing man... is much more wide awake than his fellow-worker, astonishing him with stories of the wide world comprised in a twenty-mile radius from their homes.

But:

A practical injury which this wandering entails on the children of the labourers should be mentioned here. In shifting from school to school, their education cannot possibly progress with that regularity which is essential to their getting the best knowledge in the short time available to them. It is the remark of village school-teachers of experience, that the children of the vagrant workfolk form the mass of those who fail to reach the ordinary standard of knowledge expected of their age. The rural schoolmaster or mistress enters the schoolroom on the morning of the sixth

of April, and finds that a whole flock of the brightest young people has suddenly flown away. In a village school which may be taken as a fair average specimen, containing seventy-five scholars, thirty-three vanished thus on the Lady Day of the present year. Some weeks elapse before the new comers drop in, and a longer time passes before they take root in the school, their dazed, unaccustomed mood rendering immediate progress impossible; while the original bright ones have by this time themselves degenerated into the dazed strangers of other districts.

The Dorsetshire Labourer

Aug 10. 86.
Feb. 13
94

8 Church

Something delayed the arrival of the Wesleyan minister, and a young man came temporarily in his stead. It was on the thirteenth of January 1839 that Mr Stockdale, the young man in question, made his humble entry into the village, unknown, and almost unseen. But when those of the inhabitants who styled themselves of his connection became acquainted with him, they were rather pleased with the substitute than otherwise, though he had scarcely as yet acquired ballast of character sufficient to steady the consciences of the hundred-and-forty Methodists of pure blood who, at this time, lived in Nether-Moynton, and to give in addition supplementary support to the mixed race which went to church in the morning and chapel in the evening, or when there was a tea — as many as a hundred-and-ten people more, all told, and including the parish-clerk in the winter-time, when it was too dark for the vicar to observe who passed up the street at seven o'clock — which, to be just to him, he was never anxious to do.

It was owing to this overlapping of creeds that the celebrated population-puzzle arose among the denser gentry of the district around Nether-Moynton: how could it be that a parish containing fifteen score of strong full-grown Episcopalians, and nearly thirteen score of well-matured Dissenters, numbered barely two-and-twenty score adults in all?

The Distracted Preacher

All his life Hardy was linked with the Church of England, and when young had close contacts with individual Baptists and Congregationalists. Not only did he, as a child of four or five, on wet Sundays don a tablecloth and recite Morning Prayer (with sermon) to his grandmother in the Bockhampton cottage, his cousin as Parish Clerk responding with loud Amens, but he sang in the church choir, taught for a time in the Sunday School, and went regularly to services for many years. Despite an increasingly critical attitude to the church, he still attended occasionally to the end of his active life, reading lessons (his balding head, according to Turnworth Church guide, steaming visibly at the lectern at the end of a long bicycle ride) and musing continually on old psalm and hymn tunes. In his 1922 preface to Late Lyrics and Earlier *he wrote of how "poetry and religion touch each other":*

It may indeed be a forlorn hope, a mere dream, that of an alliance between religion, which must be retained unless the world is to perish, and complete rationality, which must come, unless also the world is to perish, by means of the interfusing effect of poetry.

He hoped at this time that the projected revision of the Anglican Prayer Book might bring the church (as the chief representative of religion) nearer, as he thought, to rationality, by dispensing with those supernatural elements which he could not accept. When the revised Prayer Book was published – though never authorized since it failed to secure Parliamentary approval – he was so disappointed that "from that time he lost all expectation of seeing the Church representative of modern thinking minds".[148]

In his poetry the church appears mainly in nostalgic memories; in his prose many aspects of it are frequently discussed by his characters. Hardy rarely makes his own comments; when he does they are characteristically ironical.

Tess, in misery because her dying baby has not been baptized:

. . . thought of the child consigned to the nethermost corner of hell, as its double doom for lack of baptism and lack of legitimacy; saw the archfiend tossing it with his three-pronged fork, like the one they used for heating the oven on baking days;[149] to which picture she added many other quaint and curious details of torment sometimes taught the young in this Christian country.

Tess of the d'Urbervilles

In his stories he makes a few factual statements about the church as it was during the nineteenth century, and in 1922 places it in society by asking, for example:

What other purely English establishment . . . of such dignity and footing, with such strength of old association, such scope for transmutability, such architectural spell, is left in this country to keep the shreds of morality together?

Preface to *Late Lyrics and Earlier*

Even the interior of the sacred edifice was affected by the agitation of the times. The religion of the country had, in fact, changed from love of God to hatred of Napoleon Buonaparte; and, as if to remind the devout of this alteration, the pikes for the pikemen . . . were kept in the church of each parish.

The Trumpet-Major

By this time the Maumbrys had frequently listened to the preaching of the gentle if narrow-minded curate; for these light-natured, hit-or-miss rackety people went to church like others for respectability's sake.

A Changed Man

Now there arose a second reason for squeezing into an already over-crowded church. The persuasive and gentle eloquence of Mr Sainway operated like a charm upon those accustomed only to the higher and drier styles of preaching, and for a time the other churches of the town were thinned of their sitters.

At this point in the nineteenth century the sermon was the sole reason for churchgoing amongst a vast body of religious people. The liturgy was a formal preliminary, which, like the Royal proclamation in a court of assize, had to be got through before the real interest began; and on reaching home the question was simply: Who preached, and how did he handle his subject? Even had an archbishop officiated in the service proper nobody would have cared much about what was said or sung.

A Changed Man

Hardy also drew on his experiences as an architect working with church buildings during the Victorian Gothic revival.

"Active destruction under saving names" was Hardy's description of church restoration in a paper he wrote in 1906 for the Society for the Protection of Ancient Buildings. In this he gave some perceptive comments and interesting facts:

In respect of church conservation, the difficulty we encounter . . . at every turn, is the fact that the building is beheld in two contradictory lights, and required for two incompatible purposes. To the incumbent the church is a workshop or laboratory; to the antiquary it is a relic. To the parish it is a utility; to the outsider a luxury. How unite these incompatibles?

Apart from irregularities it was always a principle that anything later than Henry the Eighth was Anathema, and to be cast out. At Wimborne Minster fine Jacobean canopies were removed from Tudor stalls for the offence only of being Jacobean.

The protection of an ancient edifice against renewal in fresh materials is, in fact, even more of a social — I may say a humane — duty than an aesthetic one. It is the preservation of memories, history, fellowship, fraternities. Life, after all, is more than art. . . .

Memories of Church Restoration

"I look back in a contrite spirit at my own brief experience as a church-restorer", he wrote – but it was an experience that was to introduce him to his wife Emma, and give him the setting for the first novel to appear under his name.

"This tower of ours is, as you will notice, entirely gone beyond the possibility of restoration; but the church itself is well enough. You should see some of the churches in this county. Floors rotten: ivy lining the walls."

"Dear me!"

"Oh, that's nothing. The congregation of a neighbour of mine, whenever a storm

of rain comes on during service, open their umbrellas and hold them up till the dripping ceases from the roof. . . ."

The rector explained things as he went on: "The fact is, Mr Smith, I didn't want this bother of church restoration at all, but it was necessary to do something in self-defence, on account of those d---- dissenters: I use the word in its scriptual meaning, of course, not as an expletive."

A Pair of Blue Eyes

More about Dissenters:

[The Baptist Minister] "is single-mindedness itself. He gives away nearly all he has to the poor. He works among the sick, carrying them necessaries with his own hands. He teaches the ignorant men and lads of the village when he ought to be resting at home, till he is absolutely prostrate from exhaustion, and then he sits up at night writing encouraging letters to those poor people who formerly belonged to his congregation in the village, and have now gone away. He always offends ladies, because he can't help speaking the truth as he believes it; but he hasn't offended me!"

A Laodicean

"I believe ye to be a chapel-member, Joseph. That I do."

"Oh, no, no! I don't go so far as that."

"For my part," said Coggan, "I'm staunch Church of England."

"Ay, and faith, so be I," said Mark Clark.

"I won't say much for myself; I don't wish to," Coggan continued, with that tendency to talk on principles which is characteristic of the barleycorn. "But I've never changed a single doctrine: I've stuck like a plaster to the old faith I was born in. Yes; there's this to be said for the Church, a man can belong to the Church and bide in his cheerful old inn, and never trouble or worry his mind about doctrines at all. But to be a meetinger, you must go to chapel in all winds and weathers, and make yourself as frantic as a skit. Not but that chapel-members be clever chaps enough in their way. They can lift up beautiful prayers out of their own heads, all about their families and shipwracks in the newspaper."

"They can — they can," said Mark Clark, with corroborative feeling; "but we Churchmen, you see, must have it all printed aforehand, or, dang it all, we should no more know what to say to a great gaffer like the Lord than babes unborn."

"Chapel-folk be more hand-in-glove with them above than we," said Joseph thoughtfully.

"Yes," said Coggan. "We know very well that if anybody do go to heaven, they will. They've worked hard for it, and they deserve to have it, such as 'tis. I bain't such a fool as to pretend that we who stick to the Church have the same chance as they, because we know we have not. But I hate a feller who'll change his old ancient doctrines for the sake of getting to heaven. I'd as soon turn king's evidence for the few pounds you get. Why, neighbours, when every one of my taties were frosted, our

Pa'son Thirdly were the man who gave me a sack for seed, though he hardly had one for his own use and no money to buy 'em. If it hadn't been for him, I shouldn't hae had a tatie to put in my garden. D'ye think I'd turn after that? No. I'll stick to my side; and if we be in the wrong, so be it: I'll fall with the fallen!"

Far from the Madding Crowd

More about the Church – from the countryman's viewpoint:

"Is there soon to be a confirmation?"

"Yes... the first time in Welland church for twenty years...."

... "Confirmation was a sight different at that time," mused Biles. "The Bishops didn't lay it on so strong as they do now. Now-a-days, yer Bishop gives both hands to every Jack-rag and Tom-straw that drops the knee afore him; but 'twas six chaps to one blessing when we was boys. The Bishop o' that time would stretch out his palms and run his fingers over our row of crowns as off-hand as a bank gentleman telling money or a thimble-rigger at a fair. The great lords of the Church in them days wasn't particular to a soul or two more or less; and, for my part, I think living was easier for't."

Two on a Tower

"Well, sir, 'tis much as before wi' me," replied Nat. "One hour a week wi' God A'mighty and the rest with the devil, as a chap may say. And really, now yer poor father's gone, I'd as lief that that Sunday hour should pass like the rest; for Pa'son Tarkenham do tease a feller's conscience that much, that church is no hollerday at all to the limbs, as it was in your reverent father's time!"

Two on a Tower

"Ah, well, I was at church that day," said Fairway, "which was a very curious thing to happen."

"If 'twasn't my name's Simple," said the Grandfer emphatically. "I ha'n't been there to-year;[150] and now the winter is a-coming on I won't say I shall."

"I ha'n't been these three years," said Humphrey; "for I'm so dead sleepy of a Sunday; and 'tis so terrible far to get there; and when you do get there 'tis such a mortal poor chance that you'll be chose for up above, when so many bain't, that I bide at home and don't go at all."

The Return of the Native

Young Cainy Ball returns from the bright lights of Bath:

And I went to grand churches and chapels. And how the parson would pray! Yes; he would kneel down and put up his hands together, and make the holy gold rings on his fingers gleam and twinkle in yer eyes, that he'd earned by praying so excellent well! — Ah yes, I wish I lived there."

"Our poor Parson Thirdly can't get no money to buy such rings," said Matthew Moon thoughtfully. "And as good a man as ever walked. I don't believe poor Thirdly have a single one, even of humblest tin or copper. Such a great ornament as they'd be to him on a dull a'ternoon, when he's up in the pulpit lighted by the wax candles! But 'tis impossible, poor man. Ah, to think how unequal things be."

"Perhaps he's made of different stuff than to wear 'em," said Gabriel grimly. "Well, that's enough of this. Go on, Cainy — quick."

"Oh — and the new style of pa'sons wear moustaches and long beards," continued the illustrious traveller, "and look like Moses and Aaron complete, and make we fokes in the congregation feel all over like the children of Israel."

"A very right feeling — very," said Joseph Poorgrass.

"And there's two religions going on in the nation now — High Church and High Chapel. And, thinks I, I'll play fair; so I went to High Church in the morning, and High Chapel in the afternoon."

"A right and proper boy," said Joseph Poorgrass.

"Well, at High Church they pray singing, and worship all the colours of the rainbow; and at High Chapel they pray preaching, and worship drab and whitewash only."

Far from the Madding Crowd

The carter looks towards Christminster:

'Tis all learning there — nothing but learning, except religion. And that's learning too, for I never could understand it. Yes, 'tis a serious-minded place. Not but there's wenches in the streets o' nights . . . You know, I suppose, that they raise pa'sons there like radishes in a bed? And though it do take — how many years, Bob? — five years to turn a lirruping hobble-de-hoy chap into a solemn preaching man with no corrupt passions, they'll do it, if it can be done, and polish un off like the workmen they be, and turn un out wi' a long face, and a long black coat and waistcoat, and a religious collar and hat, same as they used to wear in the Scriptures, so that his own mother wouldn't know un sometimes. . . . There, 'tis their business, like anybody else's."

Jude the Obscure

Clergymen, in fact, crop up like radishes in Hardy's writings. Joshua and Cornelius Halborough, sons of a drunken millwright who has dissipated their mother's savings so that they cannot enter university, have to work their way through schoolmastering to ordination as "despised licentiates". It is they and Jude, who suffered similarly from poverty, who probably echo Hardy's views most harshly:

"If the Church is elastic, and stretches to the shape of the time, she'll last, I suppose," said Cornelius. "If not . . .".

"To succeed in the Church, people must believe in you, first of all, as a gentleman, secondly as a man of means, thirdly as a scholar, fourthly as a preacher, fifthly, perhaps, as a Christian — but always first as a gentleman, with all their heart and soul and strength."

"The Church is a poor forlorn hope for people without influence.... A social regenerator has a better chance outside, where he is unhampered by dogma and tradition. As for me, I would rather have gone on mending mills, with my crust of bread and liberty."

A Tragedy of Two Ambitions

After the tragic death of his little children, Jude in bitterness attacks the remote irrelevance of the clerics:

She sobbed again. "O, O my babies! They had done no harm! Why should they have been taken away, and not I!"

There was another stillness — broken at last by two persons in conversation somewhere without.

"They are talking about us, no doubt!" moaned Sue. "We are made a spectacle unto the world, and to angels, and to men!"

Jude listened — "No — they are not talking of us," he said. "They are two clergymen of different views, arguing about the eastward position.[151] Good God — the eastward position, and all creation groaning!"

Jude the Obscure

Hardy's criticism seems to be of the system more than individuals. Some of his clergy are eccentric and amusing, some snobs or bores; those whose characters are based on the Rev. Henry Moule of Fordington (Jack Maumbry the "Changed Man",[152] and the Rev. Mr Clare of Emminster – "a man of Apostolic simplicity in life and thought") – are respected.

Mr Clare "despite his narrowness, was far less starched and ironed than [his sons] and had to the full the gift of charity"[153] – to Hardy a most important quality. Unlike him was the Sidlinch parson, who insisted on the old Sergeant's coffinless burial at the crossroads, because of his suicide:

"Ay, as our pa'son says, 'tis a barbarous custom they keep up at Sidlinch, and ought to be done away wi'. The man a' old soldier, too. You see, our pa'son is not like yours at Sidlinch."

"He says it is barbarous, does he? So it is!" cried the soldier. "Now hearken, my friends." Then he proceeded to inquire if they would increase his indebtedness to them by undertaking the removal, privately, of the body of the suicide to the churchyard, not of Sidlinch, a parish he now hated, but of Chalk-Newton. He would give them all he possessed to do it....

Cattstock, the 'cello player, who was also the sexton, demurred, and advised the young soldier to sound the rector about it first. "Mid be he would object, and yet 'a midn't. The pa'son o' Sidlinch is a hard man, I own ye, and 'a said if folk will kill theirselves in hot blood they must take the consequences. But ours don't think like that at all, and might allow it."

"What's his name?"

"The honourable and reverent Mr Oldham, brother to Lord Wessex. But you needn't be afeard o' en on that account. He'll talk to 'ee like a common man, if so be you haven't had enough drink to gie 'ee bad breath."

The Grave by the Handpost

Undoubtedly Hardy's favourite parson is "that truly delightful personage" the basis for Parson Toogood, who was lured by the joys of the hunt to forget he had a pregnant bride and reluctant bridegroom locked up in the church tower all night waiting to be made man and wife:

"'Halloo!" cries the clerk. 'There he goes! Why, dammy, there's two foxes —'

"'Hush, clerk, hush! Don't let me hear that word again! Remember our calling.'

"True, sir, true. But really, good sport do carry away a man so, that he's apt to forget his high persuasion!' And the next minute the corner of the clerk's eye shot again into the corner of the pa'son's, and the pa'son's back again to the clerk's. 'Hee, hee!' said the clerk.

"'Ha, Ha!' said Pa'son Toogood.

"'Ah, sir,' says the clerk again, 'this is better than crying Amen to your Ever-and-ever on a winter's morning!'

"'Yes, indeed, clerk! To everything there's a season,' says Pa'son Toogood, quite pat, for he was a learned Christian man when he liked, and had chapter and ve'se at his tongue's end, as a pa'son should."

Audrey Satchel and the Parson and Clerk

In his preface Hardy continued the story of the real-life model:

One would like to tell of the second baptisms in old port which he used to perform on the squire's children at the christening dinner; of the bishop's descent one day upon the parsonage to convict Toogood of absenteeism, the latter's breakneck ride across country from a cocking party in consequence, and his breathless entry by his back door just in time to open his front to his visitor, whom he meeky received with a quill behind his ear, and a sermon outspread. He had several imitators in his composite calling of sportsman and divine, but no rival.

1896 Preface to *Life's Little Ironies*

Whispered at the Church-Opening

In the bran-new pulpit the bishop stands,
And gives out his text, as his gaze expands
To the people, the aisles, the roof's new frame,
And the arches, and ashlar with coloured bands.

"Why — he's the man," says one, "who came
To preach in my boyhood — a fashion then —
In a series of sermons to working-men

On week-day evenings, a novelty
Which brought better folk to hear and see.
They preached each one each week, by request:
Some were eloquent speakers, among the best
Of the lot being this, as all confessed."

"I remember now. And reflection brings
Back one in especial, sincerest of all;
Whose words, though unpicked, gave the essence of things; —
And where is he now, whom I well recall?"

"Oh, he'd no touches of tactic skill:
His mind ran on charity and good will:
He's but as he was, a vicar still."

Winter Words

Postscript:

Max Gate, Dorchester *Sunday, Aug. 8th, 1920*

Dear Mr Cockerell,

... We walked to Stinsford Church this morning — a delightful walk, as you know. The friendly Vicar, seeing T.H. there, read his favourite lesson, which he generally goes to hear on the evening of the 11th Sunday after Trinity — which we call "Small Voice Sunday", because of the lesson.[154] Last year when we went Mr Cowley made a mistake and read the wrong lesson, but this time he read it a week beforehand so that we should not miss it. And by a lucky chance they had also an old chant T.H. liked as a boy, and one of his favourite hymns — the old morning hymn. So it was a successful venture....

Yours very sincerely,

Florence Hardy

Max Gate, Dorchester *Feb. 6th, 1919*

Dear Mr Cockerell,

... We had another tea-party, of a kind you would *not* appreciate, the Rector of West Stafford and his wife, the Vicar of Stinsford and his wife, an elderly and religious peer, Lord Ellenborough, and our neighbours at Syward Lodge — all good Conservatives and staunch Anglicans. T.H. declares that he understands that type of person better than any other, and he prefers to know the rather narrow, churchy, conservative country person to the brilliant young writer who is always popping in and out of the divorce court. An interesting statement from the author of *Jude* and *The Dark-Eyed Gentleman*. . . .

Yours very sincerely,

Florence Hardy

9 News, Communications, and Distances

LETTERS

When Leslie Stephen, editor of the Cornhill, *wrote to Hardy in December 1872 asking for a serial for his magazine, it was only by good fortune that Hardy received the letter; for as the custom was in such a remote area, it had been given to one of the children at school in Lower Bockhampton to deliver when he went home to Higher Bockhampton. He dropped the letter in the lane, where it was later found in the mud by a passing labourer. Another contemporary author alleged that his MS. had been lost in the post; yet in August 1872, when Hardy was staying with his future wife Emma Gifford near Bodmin, the posts were reliable and speedy enough to enable the proofs of the first instalment of* A Pair of Blue Eyes *to be posted there, corrected, returned to London, and published within a week.*

For a description of the rural postman at work, *see page 201.* *The passage below shows something of the place of letters in the life of country people early in the century, as well as another current superstitious belief:*

"Miller," said the man, "a letter has been lying at the post-office for you for the last three days. If I had known that I should see 'ee here I'd have brought it along with me."

The miller thanked him for the news, and they parted, Loveday returning to the summit. "What a very strange thing!" he said to Mrs Garland, who had looked inquiringly at his face, now very grave. "That was Budmouth postmaster, and he says there's a letter for me. Ah, I now call to mind that there *was* a letter in the candle[155] three days ago this very night — a large red one; but foolish-like I thought nothing o't. Who *can* that letter be from?"

A letter at this time was such an event for hamleteers, even of the miller's respectable standing, that Loveday thenceforward was thrown into a fit of abstraction which prevented his seeing any more of the sham fight, or the people, or the King.

The Trumpet-Major

The Thing Unplanned

The white winter sun struck its stroke on the bridge,
    The meadow-rills rippled and gleamed
As I left the thatched post-office, just by the ridge,
And dropped in my pocket her long tender letter,
With: "This must be snapped! it is more than it seemed;
    And now is the opportune time!"

But against what I willed worked the surging sublime
    Of the thing that I did — the thing better!

Human Shows

THE TELEGRAPH

The part played by a private telegraph system in A Laodicean *may strike the modern reader as odd, or as untypical of Hardy the painter of rural life. Yet he was fascinated by the railway which had brought such far-reaching changes to the countryside, and liked to think of himself, and certain contemporaries, as people with "modern" minds. Early telegraphic experiments had been made at the end of the eighteenth century; after the Electric Telegraph Company was formed in 1845, the telegraph became available to the general public. The Telegraph Act of 1868 nationalized the system, though it was not unusual for private subscribers to have their own installations, until the telephone gradually displaced these from the 1880s onward.*

The little village inn at which Somerset intended to pass the night lay a mile further on, and retracing his way up to the stile he rambled along the lane, now beginning to be streaked like a zebra with the shadows of some young trees that edged the road. But his attention was attracted to the other side of the way by a hum as of a night-bee, which arose from the play of the breezes over a single wire of telegraph running parallel with his track on tall poles that had appeared by the road, he hardly knew when, from a branch route, probably leading from some town in the neighbourhood to the village he was approaching. He did not know the population of Sleeping-Green, as the village of his search was called, but the presence of this mark of civilization seemed to signify that its inhabitants were not quite so far in the rear of their age as might be imagined; a glance at the still ungrassed heap of earth round the foot of each post was, however, sufficient to show that it was at no very remote period that they had made their advance.

Aided by this friendly wire Somerset had no difficulty in keeping his course, till he reached a point in the ascent of a hill at which the telegraph branched off from the road, passing through an opening in the hedge, to strike up a slope, while the road wound round to the left. For a few moments Somerset doubted and stood still. The wire sang on overhead with dying falls[156] and melodious rises that invited him to

follow; while above the wire rode the stars in their courses, the low nocturn of the former seeming to be the voices of those stars,

Still quiring to the young-eyed cherubim[157]

Recalling himself from these reflections Somerset decided to follow the lead of the wire. It was not the first time during his present tour that he had found his way at night by the help of these musical threads which the post-office authorities had erected all over the country for quite another purpose than to guide belated travellers.

Somerset is led, however, not to the village, but to a mediaeval castle, where the wire "vanished through an arrow-slit into the interior".

The fossil of feudalism, then, was the journey's end of the wire, and not the village of Sleeping-Green.

There was a certain unexpectedness in the fact that the hoary memorial of a stolid antagonism to the interchange of ideas, the monument of hard distinctions in blood and race, of deadly mistrust of one's neighbour in spite of the Church's teaching, and of a sublime unconsciousness of any other force than a brute one, should be the goal of a machine which beyond everything may be said to symbolize cosmopolitan views and the intellectual and moral kinship of all mankind. In that light the little buzzing wire had a far finer significance to the student Somerset than the vast walls which neighboured it. But the modern fever and fret which consumes people before they can grow old was also signified by the wire; and this aspect of to-day did not contrast well with the fairer side of feudalism — leisure, light-hearted generosity, intense friendships, hawks, hounds, revels, healthy complexions, freedom from care, and such a living power in architectural art as the world may never again see.

A Laodicean

The following poem, where the telegraph wire calls up one of Hardy's most characteristic images, was written on the day when his second wife, Florence, came out of a London nursing-home after an operation, and was driven home to Dorchester. It is also a surprisingly "modern" poem.

Nobody Comes

Tree-leaves labour up and down,
And through them the fainting light
Succumbs to the crawl of night.
Outside in the road the telegraph wire
To the town from the darkening land
Intones to travellers like a spectral lyre
Swept by a spectral hand.

A car comes up, with lamps full-glare,
That flash upon a tree:
It has nothing to do with me,
And whangs along in a world of its own,
Leaving a blacker air;
And mute by the gate I stand again alone,
And nobody pulls up there.

9 October 1924 — *Human Shows*

THE RAILWAY

The "excursion train" — an absolutely new departure in the history of travel — was still a novelty on the Wessex line, and probably everywhere. Crowds of people had flocked to all the stations on the way up to witness the unwonted sight of so long a train's passage.... The seats for the humbler class of travellers in these early experiments in steam-locomotion, were open trucks, without any protection whatever from the wind and rain; and damp weather having set in with the afternoon, the unfortunate occupants of these vehicles were, on the train drawing up at the London terminus, found to be in a pitiable condition from their long journey; blue-faced, stiff-necked, sneezing, rain-beaten, chilled to the marrow, many of the men being hatless; in fact, they resembled people who had been out all night in an open boat on a rough sea, rather than inland excursionists for pleasure. The women had in some degree protected themselves by turning up the skirts of their gowns over their heads, but as by this arrangement they were additionally exposed about the hips, they were all more or less in a sorry plight.

The Fiddler of the Reels

The action of this story takes place around the time of the Great Exhibition of 1851, when the railway was still comparatively new in England. In the next decade, Mrs Swancourt in A Pair of Blue Eyes *is still being uncomplimentary about "the risk of being killed by excursion trains, which is not a little one at this time of the year if the papers are true";*[158] *and Stephen Smith takes the steamer from Bristol to Cornwall (as Hardy did from London), "the time saved by speed on the railway being wasted at junctions, and in following a devious course".*[159]

Hardy's attitude to the railway seems characteristic. First, he saw it as the arch-instrument of change:

Reddlemen of the old school are now but seldom seen. Since the introduction of railways Wessex farmers have managed to do without these Mephistophelian[160] visitants, and the bright pigment so largely used by shepherds in preparing sheep for the fair is obtained by other routes.

The Return of the Native

The Three Tranters Inn, a many-gabled, mediaeval building... was an uncommonly

characteristic and handsome specimen of the genuine roadside inn of bygone times; and standing on one of the great highways in this part of England, had in its time been the scene of as much of what is now looked upon as the romantic and genial experience of stage-coach travelling as any halting-place in the country. The railway had absorbed the whole stream of traffic which formerly flowed through the village and along by the ancient door of the inn, reducing the empty-handed landlord, who used only to farm a few fields at the back of the house, to the necessity of eking out his attenuated income by increasing the extent of his agricultural business if he would still maintain his social standing. Next to the general stillness pervading the spot, the long line of outbuildings adjoining the house was the most striking and saddening witness to the passed-away fortunes of the Three Tranters Inn. It was the bulk of the original stabling, and where once the hoofs of two-score horses had daily rattled over the stony yard, to and from the coaches without, thick grass now grew, whilst the line of roofs — once so straight — over the decayed stalls, had sunk into vast hollows till they seemed like the cheeks of toothless age.

* * *

"The railways have left you lonely here," [Cytherea] observed.... Save the withered old flies, which were quite tame from the solitude, not a being was in the house. Nobody seemed to have entered it since the last passenger had been called out to mount the last stage-coach that had run by.

"Yes, the Inn and I seem almost a pair of fossils," the farmer replied.

Desperate Remedies

Sometimes the railway is itself chief among many changes wrought by time:

Twenty-one years and six months do not pass without setting a mark even upon durable stone and triple brass; upon humanity such a period works nothing less than transformation.... Of inorganic differences the greatest was that a railway had invaded the town, tying it on to a main line at a junction a dozen miles off.

Fellow-Townsmen

Often Hardy shows the railway as being an intrusion upon the country and its life:

Boldwood looked at her — not slily, critically, or understandingly, but blankly at gaze, in the way a reaper looks up at a passing train — as something foreign to his element, and but dimly understood.

Far from the Madding Crowd

Jocelyn Pierston revisits his old home on the Isle of Slingers:

Since the days of his youth a railway had been constructed along the pebble bank, so that, except when the rails were washed away by the tides, which was rather often, the peninsula was quickly accessible. At two o'clock in the afternoon he was rattled along by this new means of locomotion, under the familiar monotonous line of bran-coloured stones, and he soon emerged from the station, which stood as a strange exotic among the black lerrets,[161] the ruins of the washed-away village, and the white cubes of oolite, just come to view after burial through unreckonable geologic years.

The Well-Beloved

Yet, though the railway represents the "clash between ancient and modern", it is also important for progress and the improvement of rural economic conditions.

Angel Clare and Tess drive the evening's milk to the station:

They crept along towards a point in the expanse of shade just at hand at which a feeble light was beginning to assert its presence, a spot where, by day, a fitful white streak of steam at intervals upon the dark green background denoted intermittent moments of contact between their secluded world and modern life. Modern life stretched out its steam feeler to this point three or four times a day, touched the native existences, and quickly withdrew its feeler again, as if what it touched had been uncongenial.

They reached the feeble light, which came from the smoky lamp of a little railway station; a poor enough terrestrial star, yet in one sense of more importance to Talbothays Dairy and mankind than the celestial ones to which it stood in such humiliating contrast.

Tess of the d'Urbervilles

And it has a beauty of its own:

Somerset looked down on the mouth of the tunnel. The popular commonplace that science, steam, and travel must always be unromantic and hideous, was not proven at this spot. On either slope of the deep cutting, green with long grass, grew drooping young trees of ash, beech, and other flexible varieties, their foliage almost concealing the actual railway which ran along the bottom, its thin steel rails gleaming like silver threads in the depths. The vertical front of the tunnel, faced with brick that had once been red, was now weather-stained, lichened, and mossed over in harmonious rusty-browns, pearly greys, and neutral greens, at the very base appearing a little blue-black spot like a mouse-hole — the tunnel's mouth.

A Laodicean

After a Romantic Day

The railway bore him through
An earthen cutting out from a city:
There was no scope for view,
Though the frail light shed by a slim young moon
Fell like a friendly tune.

Fell like a liquid ditty,
And the blank lack of any charm
Of landscape did no harm.
The bald steep cutting, rigid, rough,
And moon-lit, was enough
For poetry of place: its weathered face
Formed a convenient sheet whereon
The visions of his mind were drawn.[162]

Late Lyrics and Earlier

Midnight on the Great Western

In the third-class seat sat the journeying boy,
And the roof-lamp's oily flame
Played down on his listless form and face,
Bewrapt past knowing to what he was going,
Or whence he came.

In the band of his hat the journeying boy
Had a ticket stuck; and a string
Around his neck bore the key of his box,
That twinkled gleams of the lamp's sad beams
Like a living thing.

What past can be yours, O journeying boy
    Towards a world unknown,
Who calmly, as if incurious quite
On all at stake, can undertake
        This plunge alone?

Knows your soul a sphere, O journeying boy,
    Our rude realms far above,
Whence with spacious vision you mark and mete
This region of sin that you find you in,
        But are not of?

Moments of Vision

DISTANCES AND TRANSPORT

The poor man and the lady: two ways of looking at distances:

"How long does it take to go to Westcombe across this way?" she asked of him while they were bringing up the carriage.

"About two hours," he said.

"Two hours — so long as that, does it? How far is it away?"

"Eight miles."

"Two hours to drive eight miles — who ever heard of such a thing!"

"I thought you meant walking."

"Ah, yes; but one hardly means walking without expressly stating it."

"Well, it seems just the other way to me — that walking is meant unless you say driving."

That was the whole of their conversation. The remarks had been simple and trivial, but they brought a similar thought into the minds of both of them. On her part it spread a sudden gloom over her face, and it made him feel dead at heart. It was that horrid thought of their differing habits and of those contrasting positions which could not be reconciled.

An Indiscretion in the Life of an Heiress

Poor Margery stood before him.

She looked worn and weary, and her little shoes and the skirts of her dress were covered with dust. The weather was sultry, the sun being already high and powerful, and rain had not fallen for weeks. The Baron, who walked little, had thought nothing of the effects of this heat and drought in inducing fatigue.

The Romantic Adventures of a Milkmaid

Much of Tess's tragedy springs from her dependence on others for transport:

She was inexpressibly weary. She had risen at five o'clock every morning of that week, had been on foot the whole of each day, and on this evening had in addition walked the three miles to Chaseborough, waited three hours for her neighbours without eating or drinking, her impatience to start them preventing either; she had then walked a mile of the way home, and had undergone the excitement of the quarrel, till, with the slow progress of their steed, it was now nearly one o'clock. Only once, however, was she overcome by actual drowsiness. In that moment of oblivion her head sank gently against him.

Tess sets out for the valley of the Frome:

She went through Stourcastle without pausing, and onward to a junction of highways, where she could await a carrier's van that ran to the south-west; for the railways which engirdled this interior tract of country had never yet struck across it. While waiting, however, there came along a farmer in his spring cart, driving approximately in the direction that she wished to pursue. Though he was a stranger to her she accepted his offer of a seat beside him, ignoring that its motive was a mere tribute to her countenance. He was going to Weatherbury, and by accompanying him thither she could walk the remainder of the distance instead of travelling in the van by way of Casterbridge.

Tess did not stop at Weatherbury, after this long drive, further than to make a slight nondescript meal at noon at a cottage to which the farmer recommended her. Thence she started on foot, basket in hand, to reach the wide upland of heath dividing this district from the low-lying meads of a further valley in which the dairy stood that was the aim and end of her day's pilgrimage.

— and, in desperation, to see her unknown parents-in-law at Emminster:

To leave the farm on a week-day was not in her power; Sunday was the only possible opportunity. Flintcomb-Ash being in the middle of the cretaceous tableland over which no railway had climbed as yet, it would be necessary to walk. And the distance being fifteen miles each way she would have to allow herself a long day for the undertaking by rising early.

A fortnight later, when the snow had gone, and had been followed by a hard black frost, she took advantage of the state of the roads to try the experiment. At four o'clock that Sunday morning she came downstairs and stepped out into the starlight. The weather was still favourable, the ground ringing under her feet like an anvil.

Tess of the d'Urbervilles

For Jude, too, poverty and distance combine:

His fixed idea was to get away to some obscure spot and hide, and perhaps pray; and the only spot which occurred to him was Marygreen. He called at his lodging in Christminster, where he found awaiting him a note of dismissal from his employer; and having packed up he turned his back upon the city that had been such a thorn in his side, and struck southward into Wessex. He had no money left in his pocket, his small savings, deposited at one of the banks in Christminster, having fortunately been left untouched. To get to Marygreen, therefore, his only course was walking; and the distance being nearly twenty miles, he had ample time to complete on the way the sobering process begun in him.

At some hour of the evening he reached Alfredston. Here he pawned his waistcoat, and having gone out of the town a mile or two, slept under a rick that night. At dawn he rose, shook off the hayseeds and stems from his clothes, and started again, breasting the long white road up the hill to the downs, which had been visible to him a long way off, and passing the milestone at the top, whereon he had carved his hopes years ago.

He reached the ancient hamlet while the people were at breakfast.

Jude the Obscure

Mid-century: the end of an era:

The railway to south Wessex was in process of construction, but it was not as yet opened for traffic; and Hipcroft reached the capital by a six days' trudge on foot, as many a better man had done before him. He was one of the last of the artisan class who used that now extinct method of travel to the great centres of labour, so customary then from time immemorial.

The Fiddler of the Reels

Country distances curtailed certain activities:

Distances on Egdon Heath increased the isolation of its inhabitants.[163] *When Thomasin and Venn married, the usual custom of walking to the church together had to be abandoned, for "the church was too remote for a walking bridal-party." So it was too with Tess and Angel Clare.*[164] *Mr Torkingham's parish, which includes Welland House, is similarly widespread:*

"Mr Torkingham has been here this afternoon," said his grandmother: "and he wants me to let him meet some of the choir here tonight for practice. They who live at this end of the parish won't go to his house to try over the tunes, because 'tis so far, they say; and so 'tis, poor men. So he's going to see what coming to them will do."

Two on a Tower

Ice on the Highway

Seven buxom women abreast, and arm in arm,
        Trudge down the hill, tip-toed,
                And breathing warm;
They must perforce trudge thus, to keep upright
        On the glassy ice-bound road,
And they must get to market whether or no,
        Provisions running low
        With the nearing Saturday night,
While the lumbering van wherein they mostly ride
                Can nowise go:
Yet loud their laughter as they stagger and slide!

Yell'ham Hill

Human Shows

The Milestone by the Rabbit-Burrow

(On Yell'ham Hill)

In my loamy nook
As I dig my hole
I observe men look
At a stone, and sigh
As they pass it by
To some far goal.

Something it says
To their glancing eyes
That must distress
The frail and lame,
And the strong of frame
Gladden or surprise.

Do signs on its face
Declare how far
Feet have to trace
Before they gain
Some blest champaign
Where no gins are?

Late Lyrics and Earlier

At this time in the history of Overcombe one solitary newspaper occasionally found its way into the village. It was lent by the postmaster at Budmouth (who, in some mysterious way, got it for nothing through his connexion with the mail) to Mr Derriman at the Hall, by whom it was handed on to Mrs Garland when it was not more than a fortnight old. . . .

Mrs Martha Garland, as a respectable widow, occupied a twilight rank between the benighted villagers and the well-informed gentry, and kindly made herself useful to the former as letter-writer and reader, and general translator from the printing tongue. It was not without satisfaction that she stood at her door of an evening, newspaper in hand, with three or four cottagers standing round, and poured down their open throats any paragraph that she might choose to select from the stirring ones of the period. When she had done with the sheet Mrs Garland passed it on to the miller, the miller to the grinder, and the grinder to the grinder's boy, in whose hands it became subdivided into half pages, quarter pages, and irregular triangles, and ended its career as a paper cap, a flagon bung, or a wrapper for his bread and cheese.

The Trumpet-Major

This was of course in the first decade of the nineteenth century; but even in the mid-1820s newspapers were still comparatively rare for country people. Another, older, method of disseminating news was more commonly used:

There was at this time [between 1820–29] but one county paper, and that [Farmer Lodge] only occasionally borrowed. But old-fashioned days had old-fashioned means, and news was extensively conveyed by word of mouth from market to market, or from fair to fair, so that, whenever such an event as an execution was about to take place, few within a radius of twenty miles were ignorant of the coming sight.

The Withered Arm

"I am afeard your labour in keeping it close will be throwed away," said Coggan, as they walked along. "Labe Tall's old woman will horn it all over parish in half-an-hour."

Far from the Madding Crowd

The dangerous illness and miscarriage of Mrs Farfrae was soon rumoured through the town. . . .

The Mayor of Casterbridge

While [Arabella and Jude] sat without speaking she suddenly observed: "You seem all in a brood, old man. I'm sorry for you."

"I am all in a brood."

"It is about her, I know. It's no business of mine, but I could find out all about the wedding — if it really did take place — if you wanted to know."

"How could you?"

"I wanted to go to Alfredston to get a few things I left there. And I could see Anny, who'll be sure to have heard all about it, as she has friends at Marygreen."

Jude the Obscure

In the passing of news by mouth, rumour and distortion inevitably played their part:

The story of the deaths of Eustacia and Wildeve was told throughout Egdon, and far beyond, for many weeks and months. All the known incidents of their love were enlarged, distorted, touched up, and modified, till the original reality bore but a slight resemblance to the counterfeit presentation by surrounding tongues.

The Return of the Native

Sergeant Troy becomes a paragon:

"What kind of person is he?"

"O! miss — I blush to name it — a gay man! But I know him to be very quick and trim, who might have made his thousands, like a squire. Such a clever young dand as he is! He's a doctor's son by name, which is a great deal; and he's an earl's son by nature!"

"Which is a great deal more. Fancy! Is it true?"

"Yes. And he was brought up so well, and sent to Casterbridge Grammar School for years and years. Learnt all languages while he was there; and it was said he got on so far that he could take down Chinese in shorthand; but that I don't answer for, as it was only reported. . . ."

Far from the Madding Crowd

Opportunities for exchanging news between one place and another had always centred on market or fair or highway; now, by mid-century, the old order was beinning to change:

At length [Henchard] obtained employment at his own occupation of hay-trusser, work of that sort being in demand at this autumn time. The scene of his hiring was a pastoral farm near the old western highway, whose course was the channel of all such communications as passed between the busy centres of novelty and the remote Wessex boroughs. He had chosen the neighbourhood of this artery from a sense that, situated here, though at a distance of fifty miles, he was virtually nearer to her whose welfare was so dear than he would be at a roadless spot only half as remote. . . .

He often kept an eager ear upon the conversation of those who passed along the road — not from a general curiosity by any means — but in the hope that among these travellers between Casterbridge and London some would, sooner or later, speak of the former place. The distance, however, was too great to lend much probability to his desire; and the highest result of his attention to wayside words was that he did indeed hear the name "Casterbridge" uttered one day by the driver of a road-waggon. Henchard ran to the gate of the field he worked in, and hailed the speaker, who was a stranger.

"Yes — I've come from there, maister," he said, in answer to Henchard's inquiry. "I trade up and down, ye know; though, what with this travelling without horses that's getting so common, my work will soon be done."

"Anything moving in the old place, mid I ask?"

"All the same as usual."

... "But yes, John — you forget," said a woman inside the waggon-tilt. "What were them packages we carr'd there at the beginning o' the week? Surely they said a wedding was coming off soon — on Martin's Day?"

The carrier's tells him more:

Part of the distance he travelled by carrier, seating himself in the darkest corner at the back of that trader's van; and as the other passengers, mainly women going short journeys, mounted and alighted in front of Henchard, they talked over much local news, not the least portion of this being the wedding then in course of celebration at the town they were nearing.

The Mayor of Casterbridge

Life and Death at Sunrise

(Near Dogbury Gate, 1867)

The hills uncap their tops
Of woodland, pasture, copse,
And look on the layers of mist
At their foot that still persist:
They are like awakened sleepers on one elbow lifted,
Who gaze around to learn if things during night have shifted.

A waggon creaks up from the fog
With a laboured leisurely jog;
Then a horseman from off the hill-tip
Comes clapping down into the dip;
While woodlarks, finches, sparrows, try to entune at one time,
And cocks and hens and cows and bulls take up the chime.

With a shouldered basket and flagon
A man meets the one with the waggon,
And both the men halt of long use.
"Well," the waggoner says, "what's the news?"
"— 'Tis a boy this time. You've just met the doctor trotting back.
She's doing very well. And we think we shall call him 'Jack'.

"And what have you got covered there?"
He nods to the waggon and mare.
"Oh, a coffin for old John Thinn:
We are just going to put him in."
"— So he's gone at last. He always had a good constitution."
"— He was ninety-odd. He could call up the French Revolution."

Human Shows

10 Class, Power, Poverty — and Escape

POVERTY

"Poverty separates chiefest friends",[165] *wrote Hardy's grandmother Elizabeth Hand (née Swetman) who was too poor to travel from Melbury Osmond to Higher Bockhampton to visit her young grandchild. A yeoman farmer's daughter who had married a mere servant, she was disowned by her father, and later widowed, with seven children (including Hardy's mother Jemima) who were brought up as paupers on Poor Law relief. The bitterness of this experience was never forgotten, though Hardy in his extreme sensitiveness about poverty and class referred to it only most obliquely.*

He remained aware of poverty all his life (and, personally, exceedingly loth to part with money even when a very rich man). He takes the trouble, for example, to record in his notebook in middle age an extract from an old Dorset County Chronicle of 1830 about the people of Portland Bill who "during the memory of man" had been too poor to maintain a doctor. He knows, with Henchard, that "self-respect [is] the last mental prop under poverty"; and that the struggle to survive in these conditions can be self-defeating. Poverty, and its denial of opportunity and the full life, is a dominant theme in many of his novels and stories.

Christophe: Coney wonders why Farfrae should exile himself to Casterbridge:

"We be bruckle folk here — the best of us hardly honest sometimes, what with hard winters, and so many mouths to fill, and God-a'mighty sending his little taties so terrible small to fill 'em with. We don't think about flowers and fair faces, not we — except in the shape o' cauliflowers and pigs' chaps."

The Mayor of Casterbridge

So many mouths. . . .

All these young souls were passengers in the Durbeyfield ship — entirely dependent on the judgment of the two Durbeyfield adults for their pleasures, their necessities, their health, even their existence. If the heads of the Durbeyfield household chose to sail into difficulty, disaster, starvation, disease, degradation, death, thither were these half-dozen little captives under hatches compelled to sail with them — six helpless creatures, who had never been asked if they wished for life on any terms, much less if they wished for it on such hard conditions as were involved in being of the shiftless house of Durbeyfield.

Tess of the d'Urbervilles

The workfolk discuss at length how they have seen (and smelt) the ghost of Sir Blount Constantine in his old fur coat ("The skins that old coat was made of," ruminated Swithin):

"Well, well; I've not held out against the spectre o' starvation these five-and-twenty year on nine shillings a week, to be afeard of a walking vapour, sweet or savoury," said Hezzy. "So here's home-along."

Two on a Tower

The disadvantaged life:

The sight of the girl made her mother sad — not vaguely, but by logical inference. They both were in that strait-waistcoat of poverty from which she had tried so many times to be delivered for the girl's sake. The woman had long perceived how zealously and constantly the young mind of her companion was struggling for enlargement; and yet now, in her eighteenth year, it still remained but little unfolded. The desire — sober and repressed — of Elizabeth-Jane's heart was indeed to see, to hear, and to understand. How could she become a woman of wider knowledge, higher repute — "better", as she termed it — this was her constant inquiry of her mother. She sought further into things than other girls in her position ever did, and her mother groaned as she felt she could not aid in the search.

The Mayor of Casterbridge

Jude addresses the crowd watching the Commemoration procession:

". . . it was my poverty and not my will that consented to be beaten. It takes two or three generations to do what I tried to do in one; and my impulses — affections — vices perhaps they should be called — were too strong not to hamper a man without disadvantages; who should be as cold-blooded as a fish and as selfish as a pig to have a really good chance of being one of his country's worthies. You may ridicule me — I am quite willing that you should — I am a fit subject, no doubt. But I think if you knew what I have gone through these last few years you would rather pity me."

Jude the Obscure

The Workhouse

By the 1834 Poor Laws, the 15,000 parishes of England and Wales were organized into a few hundred Poor Law Unions, each of which was to set up a "well-regulated workhouse". To discourage would-be entrants, the regime was purposely repellent and based on the idea that poverty deserved stigma. Inmates were deprived of their civil and political rights and had to wear pauper uniforms, and married couples were separated. By 1852 an experienced lawyer, Robert Pashley, wrote: "The Workhouse as now organized is a reproach and disgrace peculiar to England: nothing corresponding to it is to be found throughout the whole Continent of Europe."

After the extension of the franchise in 1884, a new approach to the poor began slowly to make itself felt (though it was not until 1918 that inmates' votes were restored). The Royal Commission of 1909 found the state of the workhouses deplorable, and unanimously recommended their abolition; though this was not achieved, reforms continued, and after this date married couples were allowed to live together.

Hardy's references to the workhouse are surprisingly few — perhaps the pauper status of his grandmother's family, receiving "outdoor relief", was too deep a wound for him to dare to probe.

Bathsheba Everdene, distraught by her love for the notorious Sergeant Troy, exclaims revealingly:

"Dear, dear — I don't know what I am doing since this miserable ache o' my heart has weighted and worn upon me so! What shall I come to! I suppose I shall get further and further into troubles. I wonder sometimes if I am doomed to die in the Union. I am friendless enough, God knows!"

Far from the Madding Crowd

Fanny Robin's memorable odyssey to reach the Casterbridge Union ends with a brief description only of its exterior:

Originally it had been a mere case to hold people. The shell had been so thin, so devoid of excrescence, and so closely drawn over the accommodation granted, that the grim character of what was beneath showed through it, as the shape of a body is visible under a winding-sheet.

Then Nature, as if offended, lent a hand. Masses of ivy grew up, completely covering the walls, till the place looked like an abbey....

This stone edifice consisted of a central mass and two wings, whereon stood as sentinels a few slim chimneys, now gurgling sorrowfully to the slow wind. In the wall was a gate, and by the gate a bell-pull formed of a hanging wire. The woman raised herself as high as possible upon her knees, and could just reach the handle. She moved it and fell forwards in a bowed attitude, her face upon her bosom.

Far from the Madding Crowd

The Curate's Kindness

A Workhouse Irony

I

I thought they'd be strangers aroun' me,
    But she's to be there!
Let me jump out o' waggon and go back and drown me
    At Pummery or Ten-Hatches Weir.

II

I thought: "Well, I've come to the Union —
    The workhouse at last —
After honest hard work all the week, and Communion
    O'Zundays, these fifty years past.

III

"'Tis hard; but," I thought, "never mind it:
There's gain in the end:
And when I get used to the place I shall find it
A home, and may find there a friend.

IV

"Life there will be better than t'other,
For peace is assured.
The men in one wing and their wives in another
Is strictly the rule of the Board."

V

Just then one young Pa'son arriving
Steps up out of breath
To the side o' the waggon wherein we were driving
To Union; and calls out and saith:

VI

"Old folks, that harsh order is altered,
Be not sick of heart!
The Guardians they poohed and they pished and they paltered
When urged not to keep you apart.

VII

"'It is wrong,' I maintained, 'to divide them,
Near forty years wed.'
'Very well, sir. We promise, then, they shall abide them
In one wing together,' they said."

VIII

Then I sank — knew 'twas quite a foredone thing
That misery should be
To the end!... To get freed of her there was the one thing
Had made the change welcome to me.

IX

To go there was ending but badly;
'Twas shame and 'twas pain;
"But anyhow," thought I, "thereby I shall gladly
Get free of this forty years' chain."

X

I thought they'd be strangers aroun' me,
But she's to be there!
Let me jump out o' waggon and go back and drown me
At Pummery or Ten-Hatches Weir.

Time's Laughingstocks

Class and the Social Hierarchy

Hardy succeeded, as Jude never did, in what was in Victorian Dorset the Herculean feat of moving up to a "higher" class than that of his birth. A mason's son, he married the daughter of a solicitor; and he remained obsessed with the problems of class all his life. His first novel, The Poor Man and the Lady, *was too radical (as well as too deficient in plot) to achieve publication; but parts of it resurfaced in* Desperate Remedies, Under the Greenwood Tree, *and particularly a later short novel called* An Indiscretion in the Life of an Heiress. *It was a theme that reappeared in one form or another in many of his stories and poems; that "vision of social breakers ahead" which Christine Everard (in "The Waiting Supper") was led to forget by the joys of the dance was also ignored by Geraldine Allenville:*

It plainly had not crossed her young mind that she was on the verge of committing the most horrible social sin — that of loving beneath her, and owning that she so loved.

An Indiscretion in the Life of an Heiress

The class-consciousness of the time:

When the sick Squire Dornell, told of his daughter's enterprising flight from the suitor both he and she disliked, laughed uproariously at her courage and his wife's discomfiture, and collapsed dead with the words: "Well done, Bet! – haw! haw! Hurrah!" the neighbours' recorded action was simply this:

People said there had not been such an ungenteel death in a good county family for years.

The First Countess of Wessex

At "the miller's little entertainment":

Loveday apologized in a whisper to Mrs Garland for the presence of the inferior villagers. "But as they are learning to be brave defenders of their country, ma'am, as fast as they can master the drill, and have worked for me off and on these many years, I've asked 'em in, and thought you'd excuse it."

The Trumpet-Major

As Grace and Fitzpiers watch Winterborne and his cider-makers, he says:

"I dare say I am inhuman, and supercilious, and contemptibly proud of my poor old ramshackle family; but I do honestly confess to you that I feel as if I belonged to a different species from the people who are working in that yard."

The Woodlanders

"What does Luxellian write for, I wonder?" Mr Swancourt had said simultaneously with her words. He handed Stephen his letter, and took his own, putting on his countenance a higher class of look than was customary, as became a poor gentleman who was going to read a letter from a peer connected with his family.

A Pair of Blue Eyes

The fixed hierarchy

At the Three Mariners:

The young Scotchman had just joined the guests. These, in addition to the respectable master-tradesmen occupying the seats of privilege in the bow-window and its neighbourhood, included an inferior set at the unlighted end, whose seats were mere benches against the wall, and who drank from cups instead of from glasses. . . .

The Mayor of Casterbridge

Mrs Martha Garland, as a respectable widow, occupied a twilight rank between the benighted villagers and the well-informed gentry, and kindly made herself useful to the former as letter-writer and reader, and general translator from the printing tongue.

The Trumpet-Major

Mr Swancourt rejects Stephen as a son-in-law:

"It is not enough that I have been deluded by having him here, — the son of one of my village peasants, — but now I am to make him my son-in-law! . . . It is impossible; no father in England would hear of such a thing."

"But he is the same man, papa; the same in every particular; and how can he be less fit for me than he was before?"

"He appeared a young man with well-to-do friends, and a little property; but having neither, he is another man."

A Pair of Blue Eyes

Cytherea, maid to Miss Aldclyffe:

. . . called then on the two gentleman-farmers' wives, who soon transacted their business with her, frigidly indifferent to her personality. A person who socially is nothing is thought less of by people who are not much than by those who are a great deal.

Desperate Remedies

Problems of social mobility

Ethelberta's father, a butler, sends her some advice:

"Much lies in minding this, that your best plan for lightness of heart is to raise yourself a little higher than your old mates, but not so high as to be quite out of their reach. All human beings enjoy themselves from the outside, and so getting on a *little* has this good in it, you still keep in your old class where your feelings are, and are thoughtfully treated by this class: while by getting on *too much* you are sneered at by your new acquaintance, who don't know the skill of your rise, and you are parted from and forgot by the old ones who do...."

The Hand of Ethelberta

Stephen Smith returns from India to his home, where the pig-killer is busy cutting up:

It must be owned that the gentlemanly son of the house looked rather out of place in the course of these operations. Nor was his mind quite philosophic enough to allow him to be comfortable with the old-established persons his father's friends. He had never lived long at home — scarcely at all since his childhood. The presence of William Worm was the most awkward feature of the case, for, though Worm had left the house of Mr Swancourt, the being hand-in-glove with a *ci-devant* servitor reminded Stephen too forcibly of the rector's classification of himself before he went from England. Mrs Smith was conscious of the defect in her arrangements which had brought about the undesired conjunction. She spoke to Stephen privately.

"I am above having such people here, Stephen; but what could I do? And your father is so rough in his nature that he's more mixed up with them than need be."

"Never mind, mother," said Stephen; "I'll put up with it now."

"When we leave my lord's service, and get further up the country — as I hope we shall soon — it will be different. We shall be among fresh people, and in a larger house, and shall keep ourselves up a bit, I hope."

A Pair of Blue Eyes

George Somerset reflects about Paula Power, daughter of a wealthy Baptist railway contractor, who has bought Stancy Castle:

He thought of her wealth and the social position into which she had drifted. Somerset, being of a solitary and studious nature, was not quite competent to estimate precisely the disqualifying effect, if any, of her nonconformity, her newness of blood, and other things, among the old county families established around her; but the toughest prejudices, he thought, were not likely to be long invulnerable to such cheerful beauty and brightness of intellect as Paula's.

A Laodicean

Humbug and hypocrisy

"... the abnormal, almost morbid, development of the passion for position in present-day society...."

"I must get a Herald to invent an escutcheon of my family, and throw a genealogical tree into the bargain in consideration of my taking a few second-hand heirlooms of a pawn broking friend of his. I must get up sham ancestors, and find out some notorious name to start my predigree from. It does not matter what his character was; either villain or martyr will do, provided that he lived five hundred years ago. It would be considered far more creditable to make good my descent from Satan in the age when he went to and fro on the earth than from a ministering angel under Victoria."

The Hand of Ethelberta

The happiness of a class can rarely be estimated aright by philosophers who look down upon that class from the Olympian heights of society. Nothing, for instance, is more common than for some philanthropic lady to burst in upon a family, be struck by the apparent squalor of the scene, and to straightway mark down that household in her note-book as a frightful example of the misery of the labouring classes. There are two distinct probabilities of error in forming any such estimate. The first is that the apparent squalor is no squalor at all. I am credibly informed that the conclusion is nearly always based on *colour.* A cottage in which the walls, the furniture, and the dress of the inmates reflect the brighter rays of the solar spectrum is read by these amiable visitors as a cleanly, happy home while one whose prevailing hue happens to be dingy russet, or a quaint old leather tint, or any of the numerous varieties of mud colour, is thought necessarily the abode of filth and Giant Despair. "I always kip a white apron behind the door to slip on when the gentle knock, for if so be they see a white apron they think ye be clane," said an honest woman one day, whose bedroom floors could have been scraped with as much advantage as a pigeon-loft; but who, by a judicious use of high lights, shone as a pattern of neatness in her patrons' eyes.

The Dorsetshire Labourer

One Who Married Above Him

"'Tis you, I think? Back from your week's work, Steve?"

"It is I. Back from work this Christmas Eve."

"But you seem off again? — in this night-rime?"

"I am off again, and thoroughly off this time."

"What does that mean?"

"More than may first be seen . . .
Half an hour ago I footed homeward here,
No wife found I, nor child, nor maid, indoors or near.
She has, as always, gone with them to her mother's at the farm,
Where they fare better far than here, and, maybe, meet less harm.
She's left no fire, no light, has cooked me nothing to eat,
Though she had fuel, and money to get some Christmas meat.
Christmas with them is grand, she knows, and brings good victual,
Other than how it is here, where it's but lean and little.
But though not much, and rough,
If managed neat there's enough.
She and hers are too highmade for me;
But she's whimmed her once too often, she'll see!
Farmer Bollen's daughter should never have married a man that's poor;
And I can stand it no longer; I'm leaving; you'll see me no more, be sure."

"But nonsense: you'll be back again ere bedtime, and lighting a fire,
And sizzling your supper, and vexing not that her views of supper are higher."

"Never for me."

"Well, we shall see."

The sceptical neighbour and Stephen then followed their foredesigned ways,
And their steps dimmed into white silence upon the slippery glaze;
And the trees went on with their spitting amid the icicled haze.

The evening whiled, and the wife with the babies came home,
But he was not there, nor all Christmas Day did he come.
Christmastide went, and likewise went the New Year,
But no husband's footfall revived.
And month after month lapsed, graytime to green and to sere,
And other new years arrived,
And the children grew up: one husbanded and one wived. —
She wept and repented,
But Stephen never relented.
And there stands the house, and the sycamore-tree and all,
With its roots forming steps for the passers who care to call,
And there are the mullioned windows, and Ham-Hill door,
Through which Steve's wife was brought out, but which Steve re-entered
no more.

Human Shows

This house, which also features in "Interlopers at the Knap" (Wessex Tales) *appears to have a significant connection with Hardy's grandmother's family at Melbury Osmond.*[166]

Fear seized upon the shepherd boy: the Duke was Jove himself to the rural population, whom to offend was starvation, homelessness, and death, and whom to look at was to be mentally scathed and dumbfoundered.

What the Shepherd Saw

When the frost glittered under the Christmas moon, the shepherd boy involuntarily witnessed an act of murder by the Duke — and his whole life was changed thereafter. Old Andrew, who merely borrowed a fiddle and pretended to be one of the choir playing at the manor-house one Christmas, for the sake of the good supper that followed, nearly suffered disastrous consequences at the hand of the outraged Squire:

This revealed everything; the Squire's mother had Andrew turned out of the house as a vile impostor, and there was great interruption to the harmony of the proceedings, the Squire declaring he should have notice to leave his cottage that day fortnight. However, when we got to the servants' hall there sat Andrew, who had been let in at the back door by the orders of the Squire's wife, after being turned out at the front by the orders of the Squire, and nothing more was heard about his leaving his cottage. . . .

Old Andrey's Experience as a Musician

For another humourless Squire see "Absentmindedness in a Parish Choir" on page 40. Certainly in Hardy's writings the ruling class — even when dispossessed as Miss de Stancy was — seemed to think nothing of turning a tenant out of his house for some personal reason:

"Would you believe it, the man who preached so bitterly is a tenant of hers? I said, 'Surely you will turn him out of his house?' — But she answered, in her calm, deep, nice way, that she supposed he had a perfect right to preach against her, that she could not in justice molest him at all. I wouldn't let him stay if the house were mine."

A Laodicean

The lord of the manor's rights over property meant power to alter the whole course of somebody's life, and power in very personal areas of it. Mrs Charmond coveted Marty South's hair — and Barber Percomb, to obtain it, pointed out the dangers of thwarting the lady:

"No, no, no!" she cried, beginning to be much agitated.... "I don't want your money, and won't agree. Why did you come? I said when you got me into your shop and urged me so much that I didn't mean to sell my hair!"

"Marty, now hearken. The lady that wants it wants it badly. And, between you and me, you'd better let her have it. 'Twill be bad for you if you don't.... You see, Marty, as you are in one of this lady's cottages, and your father is ill, and wouldn't like to turn out, it would be as well to oblige her. I say that as a friend."

The Woodlanders

Sometimes the whole topography and structure of village life was changed by the squire (as, in the eighteenth century, the first Earl of Dorchester moved a whole village merely for greater privacy. Hardy told the story in "The Doctor's Legend").

The heavy, many-chevroned church . . . stood close to her grounds, as in many other parishes, though the village of which it was formerly the nucleus had become quite depopulated: its cottages had been demolished to enlarge the park, leaving the old building to stand there alone, like a standard without an army.

Two on a Tower

To be fair, Lady Constantine's drive was, democratically, a common highway:

The parishioners looked upon the park avenue as their natural thoroughfare, particularly for christenings, weddings, and funerals. . . . Hence the house of Constantine, when going out from its breakfast, had been continually crossed on the doorstep for the last two hundred years by the houses of Hodge and Giles in full cry to dinner.

Two on a Tower

Not all power was exercised selfishly. But Ethelberta's mother laments her family's loss of "character as simple country folk who know nothing, which are the only class of poor people that squires will give any help to".

Many simple country folk, however, suffered from the lifehold system of house tenure, a theme of great importance in all Hardy's thinking and stories. His birthplace at Higher Bockhampton, built by his great-grandfather for his son Thomas, Hardy's grandfather, was held for the duration of his life and those of his two sons, James and Thomas II, after which it should have reverted to the owner. Few families were as lucky as the Hardys in being allowed to keep the cottage after the death of Thomas II in 1892.

"It almost seems wrong that houses should be leased for lives. . . ."

The news was true. The life — the one fragile life — that had been used as a measuring-tape of time by law, was in danger of being frayed away. It was the last of a group of lives which had served this purpose, at the end of whose breathings the small homestead occupied by South himself, the larger one of Giles Winterborne, and half a dozen others that had been in the possession of various Hintock village families for the previous hundred years, and were now Winterborne's, would fall in and become part of the encompassing estate.

Winterborne walked up and down his garden next day thinking of the contingency. The sense that the paths he was pacing, the cabbage-plots, the apple-trees, his dwelling, cider-cellar, wring-house,[167] stables, weathercock, were all slipping away over his head and beneath his feet as if they were painted on a magic-lantern slide, was curious. In spite of John South's late indisposition he had not anticipated danger.

... His heart sank within him when he perceived that, despite all the legal reciprocities and safeguards prepared and written, the upshot of the matter was that it depended upon the mere caprice of the woman he had met the day before, in such an unfortunate way,[168] whether he was to possess his houses for life or no.

The Woodlanders

All Giles Winterborne's tragedy stems from the loss of his houses; much of Tess Durbeyfield's from her father's sudden death and the loss of theirs:

The news meant even more than it sounded. Her father's life had a value apart from his personal achievements, or perhaps it would not have had much. It was the last of the three lives for whose duration the house and premises were held under a lease; and it had long been coveted by the tenant-farmer for his regular labourers, who were stinted in cottage accommodation. Moreover, "liviers" were disapproved of in villages almost as much as little freeholders, because of their independence of manner, and when a lease determined it was never renewed.

Thus the Durbeyfields, once d'Urbervilles, saw descending upon them the destiny which, no doubt, when they were among the Olympians of the county, they had caused to descend many a time, and severely enough, upon the heads of such landless ones as they themselves were now. So do flux and reflux — the rhythm of change — alternate and persist in everything under the sky.

Tess of the d'Urbervilles

Even where another home could be found, Hardy was quick to see the personal tragedy:

Were the house and farm which his grandfather had occupied so long to be taken away, Egbert knew it would affect his life to a degree out of all proportion to the seriousness of the event. The transplanting of old people is like the transplanting of old trees; a twelvemonth usually sees them wither and die away.

An Indiscretion in the Life of an Heiress

"The Damocles' sword of the poor is the fear of being turned out of their houses by the farmer or squire", Hardy wrote in "The Dorsetshire Labourer"[169] *but he saw too the far-reaching social results of the lifeholds falling into hand:*

All the mutations so increasingly discernible in village life did not originate entirely in the agricultural unrest. A depopulation was also going on. The village had formerly contained, side by side with the agricultural labourers, an interesting and better-informed class, ranking distinctly above the former — the class to which Tess's father and mother had belonged — and including the carpenter, the smith, the shoemaker, the huckster, together with nondescript workers other than farm-labourers; a set of people who owed a certain stability of aim and conduct to the fact of their being lifeholders like Tess's father, or copyholders, or, occasionally, small freeholders. But as the long holdings fell in they were seldom again let to similar tenants, and were mostly pulled down, if not absolutely required by the farmer for his hands. Cottagers who were not directly employed on the land were looked upon with disfavour, and the banishment of some starved the trade of others, who were thus obliged to follow. These families, who had formed the backbone of the village life in the past, who were the depositaries of the village traditions, had to seek refuge in the large centres; the process, humorously designated by statisticians as "the tendency of the rural population towards the large towns", being really the tendency of water to flow uphill when forced by machinery.

Tess of the d'Urbervilles

Too long to include here, one of Hardy's most amusing (if characteristically macabre) stories turns upon this theme. It is called "Netty Sargent's Copyhold", and is part of the group of stories called A Few Crusted Characters, *and collected in* Life's Little Ironies.

EMIGRATION

"Selina, I am thinking of giving up the army. Will you emigrate with me to New Zealand? I've an uncle out there doing well, and he'd soon help me to making a larger income. The English army is glorious, but it ain't altogether enriching."

Enter a Dragoon

That [Arabella] had grown tired of [Jude] she frankly admitted. He was such a slow old coach, and she did not care for the life he led. There was no prospect of his ever bettering himself or her. She further went on to say that her parents had, as he knew, for some time considered the question of emigrating to Australia, the pig-jobbing business being a poor one nowadays. They had at last decided to go and she proposed to go with them, if he had no objection. A woman of her sort would have more chance over there than in this stupid country.

Jude the Obscure

There is hardly a story of Hardy's which has not a reference to emigration. (Some of his close relations emigrated to Australia and Canada.) Both Donald Farfrae and Gabriel Oak thought of going to America, and in "The Fiddler of the Reels" it was local opinion that the magnetic Ollamoor had spirited his little daughter away there. Two of Ethelberta's sisters married farmers and went to Queensland; and in "Destiny and a Blue Cloak" poor Agatha is sacrificed by her uncle to marry his elderly creditor:

"Well, I don't want to force you to do anything against your will, Agatha, but... you know I am a little behind-hand in my dealings with Lovill — nothing serious, you know, if he gives me time — but I want to be free of him quite in order to go to Australia."

"Australia!"

"Yes. There's nothing to be done here. I don't know what business is coming to — can't think. But... if you will marry Farmer Lovill, he offers to clear off the debt... in short, away I can go."

Destiny and a Blue Cloak

It was not always poverty that drove the natives abroad: for some it was a timely escape from an unhappy situation. But emigration was not always successful. There were, Angel Clare was told, "discouraging reports of some farm-labourers who had emigrated [to Brazil] and returned home within the twelve months." When he himself was there, his days were:

... by no means free from trial. At this moment he was lying ill of fever in the clay lands near Curitiba in Brazil, having been drenched with thunderstorms and persecuted by other hardships, in common with all the English farmers and farm-labourers who, just at this time, were deluded into going thither by the promises of the Brazilian Government, and by the baseless assumption that those frames which, ploughing and sowing on English uplands, had resisted all the weathers to whose moods they had been born, could resist equally well all the weathers by which they were surprised on Brazilian plains.

Tess of the d'Urbervilles

Sometimes the returning émigré found he had no real home in either hemisphere:

"I am not very rich," Mr Lackland said. "Even in new countries, you know, there are failures. The race is not always to the swift, nor the battle to the strong; and even if it sometimes is, you may be neither swift nor strong."

... He walked on, looking at this chimney and that old wall, till he came to the churchyard, which he entered.

The headstones, whitened by the moon, were easily decipherable; and now for the first time Lackland began to feel himself amid the village community that he had left behind him five-and-thirty years before.... It is now a dozen or fifteen years since his visit was paid, and his face has not again been seen.

A Few Crusted Characters

11 Rural Occupations

ENCOUNTERS WITH FIRE AND WATER

Weirs and Waterways

Growing up in a house where water came from a well, and where a favourite haunt all his life was the Frome valley visible from the heights of Rainbarrows behind his home, with its rushing weirs and its multitude of "carrier" streams criss-crossing the water-meadows, Hardy might be expected to value water; and indeed to concur in the Chinese concept cf landscape, made up of the two characters "hill, water". The chapter in The Return of the Native *where Clym Yeobright helps to retrieve a lost bucket from the depths of the well shows first-hand knowledge of such an event, and of the "strange humid leaves, which knew nothing of the seasons of the year, and quaint-natured mosses [which] were revealed on the well-side as the lantern descended".*[170] *The following passages illustrate something of his special knowledge of the waterways of the country around him.*

Returning from one of these dark walks they reached a great gravel-cliff immediately over the levels, where they stood still and listened. The water was now high in the streams, squirting through the weirs, and tinkling under culverts; the smallest gullies were all full; there was no taking short cuts anywhere, and foot-passengers were compelled to follow the permanent ways. From the whole extent of the invisible vale came a multitudinous intonation; it forced upon their fancy that a great city lay below them, and that the murmur was the vociferation of its populace.

"It seems like tens of thousands of them," said Tess; "holding public-meetings in their market-places, arguing, preaching, quarrelling, sobbing, groaning, praying, and cursing."

Tess of the d'Urbervilles

Men were at work here and there — for it was the season for "taking up" the meadows, or digging the little waterways clear for the winter irrigation, and mending their banks where trodden down by the cows. The shovelfuls of loam, black as jet, brought there by the river when it was as wide as the whole valley, were an essence of soils, pounded champaigns of the past, steeped, refined, and subtilized to extraordinary richness, out of which came all the fertility of the mead, and of the cattle grazing there.

Tess of the d'Urbervilles

Instead of leaving the spot by the gate, he flung himself over the fence, and pursued a direction towards the river under the trees. And it was now, in his lonely progress, that he showed for the first time outwardly that he was not altogether unworthy of her. He wore long water-boots reaching above his knees, and, instead of making a circuit to find a bridge by which he might cross the Froom — the river aforesaid — he made straight for the point whence proceeded the low roar that was at this hour the only evidence of the stream's existence. He speedily stood on the verge of the waterfall which caused the noise, and stepping into the water at the top of the fall, waded through with the sure tread of one who knew every inch of his footing, even though the canopy of trees rendered the darkness almost absolute, and a false step would have precipitated him into the pool beneath. Soon reaching the boundary of the grounds, he continued in the same direct line to traverse the alluvial valley, full of brooks and tributaries to the main stream — in former times quite impassable, and impassable in winter, now. Sometimes he would cross a deep gully on a plank not wider than the hand; at another time he ploughed his way through beds of spear-grass, where at a few feet to the right or left he might have been sucked down into a morass. At last he reached firm land on the other side of this watery tract, and came to his house on the rise behind.

The Waiting Supper

The drunken Halborough falls into the weir — and drifts into the culvert:

Below the foot-bridge of the weir the stream suddenly narrowed to half its width, to pass under the barrel arch or culvert constructed for waggons to cross into the middle of the mead in haymaking time. It being at present the season of high water the arch was full to the crown, against which the ripples clucked every now and then. At this point he had just caught sight of a pale object slipping under. In a moment it was gone....

It was summer-time, six months later, and mowers and haymakers were at work in the meads.... Now, in June, when they were mowing the meads, the hatches had to be drawn and the water let out of its channels for the convenience of the mowers. It was thus that the discovery was made. A man, stooping low with his scythe, caught a view of the culvert lengthwise, and saw something entangled in the recently bared weeds of its bed. A day or two after there was an inquest; but the body was unrecognizable. Fish and flood had been busy with the millwright... and a verdict of the accidental drowning of a person unknown settled the matter.

A Tragedy of Two Ambitions

The jaws of death:

Only one sound rose above this din of weather, and that was the roaring of a ten-hatch weir to the southward.... Shadwater Weir had at its foot a large circular pool, fifty feet in diameter, into which the water flowed through ten huge hatches, raised and lowered by a winch and cogs in the ordinary manner. The sides of the pool were of masonry, to prevent the water from washing away the bank; but the force of the stream in winter was sometimes such as to undermine the retaining wall and precipitate it into the hole. Clym reached the hatches, the framework of which was shaken to its foundations by the velocity of the current. Nothing but the froth of the waves could be discerned in the pool below. He got upon the plank bridge over the race, and holding to the rail, that the wind might not blow him off, crossed to the other side of the river. There he leant over the wall and lowered the lamp, only to behold the vortex at the curl of the returning current....

Wildeve meanwhile had arrived on the former side, and the light from Yeobright's lamp shed a flecked and agitated radiance across the weir-pool, revealing to the ex-engineer the tumbling courses of the currents from the hatches above. Across this gashed and puckered mirror a dark body was slowly borne by one of the backward currents.

Yeobright could now also discern the floating body, though but indistinctly; and imagining from Wildeve's plunge that there was life to be saved he was about to leap after. Bethinking himself of a wiser plan he placed the lamp against a post to make it stand upright, and running round to the lower part of the pool, where there was no wall, he sprang in and boldly waded upwards towards the deeper portion. Here he was taken off his legs, and in swimming was carried round into the centre of the basin, where he perceived Wildeve struggling....

Diggory, having returned to the brink of the pool, observed that the small upper hatches or floats were withdrawn. He found one of these lying upon the grass, and taking it under one arm, and with his lantern in his hand, entered at the bottom of the pool as Clym had done. As soon as he began to be in deep water he flung himself across the hatch; thus supported he was able to keep afloat as long as he chose, holding the lantern aloft with his disengaged hand. Propelled by his feet he steered round and round the pool, ascending each time by one of the back streams and descending in the middle of the current.

At first he could see nothing. Then amidst glistening of the whirlpools and the white clots of foam he distinguished a woman's bonnet floating alone.

The Return of the Native

Before My Friend Arrived

I sat on the eve-lit weir,
Which gurgled in sobs and sighs;
I looked across the meadows near
To the towered church on the rise.
Overmuch cause had my look!
I pulled out pencil and book,
And drew a white chalk mound,
Outthrown on the sepulchred ground.

Why did I pencil that chalk?
It was fetched from the waiting grave,
And would return there soon,
Of one who had stilled his walk
And sought oblivion's cave.
He was to come on the morrow noon
And take a good rest in the bed so hewn.

He came, and there he is now, although
This was a wondrous while ago.
And the sun still dons a ruddy dye;
The weir still gurgles nigh;
The tower is dark on the sky.[171]

Human Shows

This poem commemorates Hardy's friend Horace Moule, brother of Henry and son of the Vicar of Fordington — the part of Dorchester called "Durnover" in Hardy's novels, and containing his notorious "Mixen Lane". Horace Moule committed suicide in Cambridge in September 1873, and his body was brought home to Fordington St George for burial.

Human Shows, *the last volume of Hardy's verse to be published during his lifetime, appeared in 1925 —* Winter Words *posthumously in 1928.*

FIRES IN THE COUNTRY

Fire plays an important part in several of Hardy's novels (and in the first poem he ever had publiished.)[172] *In three of them he pauses to describe at length how different fires burn. The account of the smouldering fire of couch-grass in* Desperate Remedies *which has such far-reaching consequences extends over several pages – too long to quote in full here, as is the rick-yard fire in* Far from the Madding Crowd; *and an early chapter in* The Return of the Native *is devoted to the weird glow behind the dancing figures who celebrate with November bonfires all over the heath. The passages quoted below show again the special knowledge Hardy had acquired through long familiarity and observation.*

Farmers and horticulturists well know that it is in the nature of a heap of couch-grass, when kindled in calm weather, to smoulder for many days, and even weeks, until the whole mass is reduced to a powdery charcoal ash, displaying the while scarcely a sign of combustion beyond the volcano-like smoke from its summit; but the continuance of this quiet process is throughout its length at the mercy of one particular whim of Nature; that is, a sudden breeze, by which the heap is liable to be fanned into a flame so brisk as to consume the whole in an hour or two.

Had the farmer narrowly watched the pile when he went to close the door, he would have seen, besides the familiar twine of smoke from its summit, a quivering of the air around the mass, showing that a considerable heat had arisen inside.

As the railway-porter turned the corner of the row of houses adjoining the Three Tranters, a brisk new wind greeted his face, and spread past him into the village. He walked along the high-road till he came to a gate, about three hundred yards from the inn. Over the gate could be discerned the situation of the building he had just quitted. He carelessly turned his head in passing, and saw behind him a clear red glow indicating the position of the couch-heap: a glow without a flame, increasing and diminishing in brightness as the breeze quickened or fell, like the coal of a newly-lighted cigar. If those cottages had been his, he thought, he should not care to have a fire so near them as that — and the wind rising. But the cottages not being his, he went on his way to the station.

Desperate Remedies

Town fires and country fires:

A feature in the decline of town fires was noticeably absent here — steam. There was present what is not observable in towns — incandescence.

Desperate Remedies

Gabriel Oak saves Bathsheba's wheat:

The fire was issuing from a long straw-stack, which was so far gone as to preclude a possibility of saving it. A rick burns differently from a house. As the wind blows the fire inwards, the portion in flames completely disappears like melting sugar, and the outline is lost to the eye. However, a hay or a wheat rick, well put together, will resist combustion for a length of time if it begins on the outside.

This before Gabriel's eyes was a rick of straw, loosely put together, and the flames darted into it with lightning swiftness. It glowed on the windward side, rising and falling in intensity like the coal of a cigar. Then a superincumbent bundle rolled down with a whisking noise; flames elongated, and bent themselves about with a quiet roar, but no crackle. Banks of smoke went off horizontally at the back like passing clouds, and behind these burned hidden pyres, illuminating the semi-transparent sheet of smoke to a lustrous yellow uniformity. Individual straws in the foreground were consumed in a creeping movement of ruddy heat, as if they were knots of red worms, and above shone imaginary fiery faces, tongues hanging from lips, glaring eyes, and other impish forms, from which at intervals sparks flew in clusters like birds from a nest.... Other figures now appeared... among the smoke....

"Stop the draught under the wheat-rick!" cried Gabriel to those nearest to him. The corn stood on stone saddles,[173] and between these, tongues of yellow hue from the burning straw licked and darted playfully. If the fire once got *under* this stack, all would be lost.

"Get a tarpaulin — quick!" said Gabriel.

A rick-cloth was brought, and they hung it like a curtain across the channel. The flames immediately ceased to go under the bottom of the corn-stack, and stood up vertical.

"Stand here with a bucket of water and keep the cloth wet," said Gabriel again.

The flames, now driven upwards, began to attack the angles of the huge roof covering the wheat-stack.

"A ladder," cried Gabriel

"The ladder was against the straw-rick and is burnt to a cinder," said a spectre-like form in the smoke.

Oak seized the cut ends of the sheaves, as if he were going to engage in the operation of "reed-drawing",[174] and digging in his feet, and occasionally sticking in the stem of his sheep-crook, he clambered up the beetling face. He at once sat astride the very apex, and began with his crook to beat off the fiery fragments which had lodged thereon, shouting to the others to get him a bough and a ladder and some water.

... The smoke at this corner was stifling, and Clark, a nimble fellow, having been handed a bucket of water, bathed Oak's face and sprinkled him generally, whilst Gabriel, now with a long beech-bough in one hand, in addition to his crook in the other, kept sweeping the stack and dislodging all fiery particles....

"D'ye think the barn is safe, Jan Coggan?"...

"Safe now. — leastwise I think so. If this rick had gone the barn would have followed. 'Tis that bold shepherd up there that have done the most good — he sitting on the top o' rick, whizzing his great long arms about like a windmill."

Far from the Madding Crowd

Bonfires on the heath:

The bonfire was by this time beginning to sink low, for the fuel had not been of that substantial sort which can support a blaze long. Most of the other fires within the wide horizon were also dwindling weak. Attentive observation of their brightness, colour, and length of existence would have revealed the quality of the material burnt; and through that, to some extent the natural produce of the district in which each bonfire was situated. The clear, kingly effulgence that had characterized the majority expressed a heath and furze country like their own, which in one direction extended an unlimited number of miles: the rapid flares and extinctions at other points of the compass showed the lightest of fuel — straw, beanstalks, and the usual waste from arable land. The most enduring of all — steady unaltering eyes like planets — signified wood, such as hazel-branches, thorn-faggots, and stout billets. Fires of the last-mentioned materials were rare, and, though comparatively small in magnitude beside the transient blazes, now began to get the best of them by mere long-continuance. The great ones had perished, but these remained.

The Return of the Native

SMUGGLING

Loveday the soldier was . . . bestirring himself to get the ladies some of the best liquor the house afforded, which had, as a matter of fact, crossed the Channel as privately as Buonaparte wished his army to do, and had been landed on a dark night over the cliff.

The Trumpet-Major

Mrs Lizzy Newberry, secretly a smuggling partner, takes her innocent lodger to a cache of barrels in the church-tower:

"Now, will you roll out one of the tubs?"

"What to do with it?" said the minister.

"To draw a little from it to cure your cold," she answered. "It is so 'nation strong that it drives away that sort of thing in a jiffy. . . ."

"I will, to oblige you, since you have a right to it," murmured the minister; and though he was not quite satisfied with his part in the performance, he rolled one of the "tubs" out from the corner into the middle of the tower floor.

"How do you wish me to get it out — with a gimlet, I suppose?"

"No, I'll show you," said his interesting companion; and she held up with her other hand a shoemaker's awl and a hammer. "You must never do these things with a gimlet, because the wood-dust gets in; and when the buyers pour out the brandy that would tell them that the tub had been broached. An awl makes no dust, and the hole nearly closes up again. Now tap one of the hoops forward."

Stockdale took the hammer and did so.

"Now make the hole in the part that was covered by the hoop."

He made the hole as directed. "It won't run out," he said.

"O yes it will," said she. "Take the tub between your knees, and squeeze the heads, and I'll hold the cup."

Stockdale obeyed; and the pressure taking effect upon the tub, which seemed to be thin, the spirit spirted out in a stream. When the cup was full he ceased pressing, and the flow immediately stopped. "Now we must fill up the keg with water," said Lizzy, "or it will cluck like forty hens when it is handled, and show that 'tis not full."

"But they tell you you may take it?"

"Yes, the *smugglers*; but the *buyers* must not know that the smugglers have been kind to me at their expense."

"I see," said Stockdale doubtfully. "I much question the honesty of this proceeding."

By her direction he held the tub with the hole upwards, and while he went through the process of alternately pressing and ceasing to press, she produced a bottle of water, from which she took mouthfuls, conveying each to the keg by putting her pretty lips to the hole, where it was sucked in at each recovery of the cask from pressure. When it was again full he plugged the hole, knocked the hoop down to its place, and buried the tub in the lumber as before.

"Aren't the smugglers afraid that you will tell?" he asked, as they recrossed the churchyard.

"O no; they are not afraid of that. I couldn't do such a thing."

The Distracted Preacher

Lizzy tells how the stuff is landed:

"I only went to-night to burn the folks off,[175] because we found that the

Preventive-men knew where the tubs were to be landed."

Lizzy slowly murmured the particulars of their plan, the chief of which were that they meant to try their luck at some other point of the shore the next night; that three landing-places were always agreed upon before the run was attempted, with the understanding that, if the vessel was "burnt off" from the first point, which was Ringsworth, as it had been by her to-night, the crew should attempt to make the second, which was Lulwind Cove, on the second night; and if there, too, danger threatened, they should on the third night try the third place, which was behind a headland further west.

"Suppose the officers hinder them landing there, too?" he said, his attention to this interesting programme displacing for a moment his concern at her share in it.

"Then we shan't try anywhere else all this dark — that's what we call the time between moon and moon — and perhaps they'll string the tubs to a stray-line, and sink 'em a little-ways from shore, and take the bearings; and then when they have a chance they'll go to creep for 'em."

"What's that?"

"O, they'll go out in a boat and drag a creeper — that's a grapnel — along the bottom till it catch hold of the stray-line."

The Distracted Preacher

More inside information:

Among the many devices for concealing smuggled goods in caves and pits of the earth, that of planting an apple-tree in a tray or box which was placed over the mouth of the pit is, I believe, unique, and it is detailed in "The Distracted Preacher" precisely as described by an old carrier of "tubs" — a man who was afterwards in my father's employ for over thirty years. I never gathered from his reminiscences what means were adopted for lifting the tree, which, with its roots, earth, and receptacle, must have been of considerable weight. There is no doubt, however, that the thing was done through many years. My informant often spoke, too, of the horribly suffocating sensation produced by the pair of spirit-tubs slung upon the chest and back, after stumbling with the burden of them for several miles inland over a rough country and in darkness. He said that though years of his youth and young manhood were spent in this irregular business, his profits from the same, taken all together, did not average the wages he might have earned in a steady employment, whilst the fatigues and risks were excessive.

I may add that the action of this story is founded on certain smuggling exploits that occurred between 1825 and 1830. . . .

Preface to *Wessex Tales*

Postscript: Lady Constantine shows Swithin round her mansion:

She showed him . . . the wardrobe of some member of the family who had died young early in the century, when muslin reigned supreme, when waists were close to armpits, and muffs as large as smugglers' tubs....

Two on a Tower

Hardy's close interest in smugglers is also explained by the long note made in an early notebook about the use made by smugglers of his birthplace;[176] *see too the poem "Winter Night in Woodland".*[177]

POACHING

Like smuggling, poaching was widely practised in the Dorset of Hardy's youth. (In extreme poverty, often a man would prefer to poach for a living than to go to the workhouse.) Only a few weeks before Hardy died he was telling his wife about various poaching families he had known when a boy; and he remembered the finding of two swingels under the thatch of a Bockhampton house when it was demolished.

His notebooks contain a fair amount of information about poaching. He quotes a local landowner's account of how poachers used to drug pheasants with the fumes from a pan of brimstone (sulphur) held up under their roosts — see the poem "Winter Night in Woodland".[177] *The same friend told of keepers making dummy pheasants and hiding nearby to catch the poachers who were lured to shoot them: and of how a poacher, convicted at Quarter Sessions, told him he had asked for time to pay his £5 fine — so that he could earn it by poaching on the Justice's grounds, which he did within a week.*

[1884] *Dec.* Poachers' iron swingels.
A strip of iron ran down 3 or 4 sides of the flail part and the two flails were united by 3 or 4 links of chain, the keepers carrying cutlasses which would cut off the ordinary eel-skin hinge of a flail.

Memoranda I

At the inn called Peter's Finger:

The settles on which they sat down were thin and tall, their tops being guyed by pieces of twine to hooks in the ceiling; for when the guests grew boisterous the settles would rock and overturn without some such security. The thunder of bowls echoed from the backyard; swingels hung behind the blower of the chimney; and ex-poachers and ex-gamekeepers, whom squires had persecuted without a cause, sat elbowing each other — men who in past times had met in fights under the moon, till lapse of sentences on the one part, and loss of favour and expulsion from service on the other, brought them here together to a common level, where they sat calmly discussing old times.

The Mayor of Casterbridge

Poaching affrays were common:

Keeper [Day] entered from the garden. . . . His nose had been thrown backwards by a blow in a poaching fray, so that when the sun was low and shining in his face people could see far into his head.

Under the Greenwood Tree

In the same novel, brief reference is made to the notorious man-trap:

"Ay, I've knowed times when the wedding had to be put off through [the bridegroom's] not appearing, being tired of the woman. And another case I knowed was when the man was catched in a man-trap crossing Oaker's Wood, and the three months had run out before he got well, and the banns had to be published over again."

When subsequently, in the 1880s, Hardy's friend Henry Moule, founder of the Dorset County Museum, was collecting man-traps, Hardy learnt more about them — and used his knowledge in The Woodlanders:

Mrs Charmond was at the end of a gallery opening from the hall when Miss Melbury was announced. . . .

"Ah! you have noticed those," she said, seeing that Grace's eyes were attracted by some curious objects against the walls. "They are man-traps. My husband was a connoisseur in man-traps and spring-guns and such articles, collecting them from all his neighbours. He knew the histories of all these — which gin had broken a man's leg, which gun had killed a man."

The trap in the outhouse:

Were the inventors of automatic machines to be ranged according to the excellence of their devices for producing sound artistic torture, the creator of the man-trap would occupy a very respectable, if not a very high, place.

It should rather, however, be said, the inventor of the particular form of man-trap of which this found in the keeper's outhouse was a specimen. For there were other shapes and other sizes, instruments which, if placed in a row beside one of the type disinterred by Tim, would have worn the subordinate aspect of the bears, wild boars, or wolves in a travelling menagerie as compared with the leading lion or tiger. In short, though many varieties had been in use during those centuries which we are accustomed to look back upon as the true and only period of merry England — in the rural districts more especially — and onward down to the third decade of the nineteenth century, this model had borne the palm, and had been most usually followed when the orchards and estates required new ones.

There had been the toothless variety used by the softer-hearted landlords — quite contemptible in their clemency. The jaws of these resembled the jaws of an old woman to whom time has left nothing but gums. There were also the intermediate or half-toothed sorts, probably devised by the middle-natured squires, or those under the influence of their wives: two inches of mercy, two inches of cruelty, two inches of mere nip, two inches of probe, and so on, through the whole extent of the jaws. There were also, as a class apart, the bruisers, which did not lacerate the flesh, but only crushed the bone.

The sight of one of these gins, when set, produced a vivid impression that it was endowed with life. It exhibited the combined aspects of a shark, a crocodile, and a scorpion. Each tooth was in the form of a tapering spine two and a quarter inches long, which, when the jaws were closed, stood in alternation from this side and from that. When they were open the two halves formed a complete circle between two and three feet in diameter, the plate or treading-place in the midst being about a foot square, while from beneath extended in opposite directions the soul of the apparatus, the pair of springs, each one having been in its prime of a stiffness to render necessary a lever or the whole weight of the body when forcing it down, though rust had weakened it somewhat now.

There were men at this time still living at Hintock who remembered when the gin and others like it were in use. Tim Tangs's great-uncle has endured a night of six hours in this very trap, which lamed him for life. Once a keeper of Hintock woods set it on the track of a poacher, and afterwards coming back that way forgetful of what he had done walked into it himself. The wound brought on lockjaw, of which he died. This event occurred during the thirties, and by the year 1840 the use of such implements was well-nigh discontinued in the neighbourhood. But being made entirely of iron they by no means disappeared, and in almost every village one could be found in some nook or corner as readily as this was found by Tim. It had indeed been a fearful amusement of Tim and other Hintock lads — especially those who had a dim sense of becoming renowned poachers when they reached their prime — to drag out this trap from its hiding, set it, and throw it with billets of wood, which were penetrated by the teeth to the depth of near an inch.

The Woodlanders

POSTILIONS AND MAIL-COACHES

The church was a long way off, and they were obliged to drive, particularly as it was winter. A close carriage was ordered from a roadside inn, a vehicle which had been kept there ever since the old days of post-chaise travelling. It had stout wheel-spokes, and heavy felloes,[178] a great curved bed, immense straps and springs, and a pole like a battering-ram. The postilion was a venerable "boy" of sixty — a martyr to rheumatic gout, the result of excessive exposure in youth, counteracted by strong liquors — who had stood at inn-doors doing nothing for the whole five-and-twenty years that had elapsed since he had no longer been required to ride professionally, as if expecting the old times to come back again. He had a permanent running wound on the outside of his right leg, originated by the constant bruisings of aristocratic carriage-poles during the many years that he had been in regular employ at the King's Arms, Casterbridge.

Inside this cumbrous and creaking structure, and behind this decayed conductor, the *partie carrée*[179] took their seats — the bride and bridegroom and Mr and Mrs Crick.

Tess of the d'Urbervilles

Post-chaises — the fast method of travel in the eighteenth and early nineteenth century, by means of carriage or horses hired at certain stages on a journey — were gradually displaced after the railway's development in mid-century.

This reference to a postilion is extremely rare in any of Hardy's novels; yet he made extensive notes on the subject in his first notebook.

[1881] *July 23. Old Postilions.* Hired a wagonette at the *George* and drove with E. and K.[180] to Badbury Rings — William Young, who drove us, had been a postilion since he was 16 till he got too old and there was no posting to do. His work lay mostly in the saddle — not at the reins — suffers now from rheumatic gout, brought on by exposure and hard work. Has ridden along the Blandford Rd. on nights so dark that he had to feel his way by touching the hedge with his whip — the lights of the coach not showing far enough forward to light the postboy (though he told how a lamp was sometimes fixed in the middle for that purpose.) Had often gone with the coach, tho not as driver, but as postboy to the 2 extra horses which were hitched on when the coach was overladen, and could not proceed.

Memoranda I

This note continues with many stories told to Hardy by the same postilion, William Young. It and the following note about the Mailcoach Guards are the longest in the Notebook.

[1874] *March.* Kenfield, the mailcoach guard from London to Dorchester, lived at Higher Bockhampton in the eighteen thirties, the reason probably being that the spot lay near the London Road, so that he could take small packages to London on his own account, by collusion with the coachman. He used to have butter brought to him by old Hedditch the dairyman, also eggs. Also game, which he bought of poachers — old Critchel for one. The provisions were packed into a box, the box into a hamper, and the whole put into the boot of the coach with the letter-bags, the boot being under the guard's seat, and opening behind with a door on which were "G R", a crown, and "Royal Mail".

He carried 2 pistols, a cutlass, and a blunderbus in a long tin box, "like a candle-box", in front of him; also a ball of tar-twine, and a screw-hammer (in case of a break down). Also "a little time-piece strapped on to him in a leather pouch", which when he got home he placed on his mantelpiece.

He kept a pony and gig to drive to Dorchester (2½ miles) to take his seat on the mail coach, putting on his red uniform before starting, and his dog's-hair hat with a gold band round it. He was on the coach two nights out of three.

Meanwhile John Downton, a youth of the village whom he employed, would carry the packed hamper in the evening about 5 down through the plantation separating Higher Bockhampton from the turnpike road, and knowing the exact time the coach would pass wait at the plantation gate for it, which pulled up for a moment to receive the hamper, and rolled on again.

Although Kenfield went right through to London, there were two or three coachmen to the journey. Whether they all knew of this butter and game business cannot be said. Oliver of Dorchester, who horsed the mail coach, horsed it only as far as Blandford, where another contractor took on.

In bitter weather Kenfield drank mulled ale rather than spirits, saying that spirits would not keep out the cold so long as the ale would. When he retired from guarding the mail he took "The Coach and Snow" Inn, Dorchester....

When it had rained all the way from London he, in common with the whole mail, looked much weatherbeaten. In winter he wore a drab greatcoat over his red uniform.

John Downton was always charged to be punctual in meeting the coach. Kenfield used to jump off, catch up the hamper, and be in his seat again in a moment. On the return journey he would fling the empty hamper down without stopping.

It should have been mentioned that his uniform was a red frock coat, with blue flaps to the pockets, and a blue collar. In very cold weather he was buskin-legged, i.e. wrapped up round the legs like a bantam hen; and wrapped round the neck. There were three guards employed between London and Dorchester in shifts, each going the whole way when his turn came; and three below, from Dorchester to Exeter. The other two guards in Kenfield's seat drank hard, and Kenfield sometimes had to do extra duty: e.g. return to London again on the day of his arrival from the city. All the three, Kenfield, Preedy, and Churchill, died in middle age, the exposure, etc. trying them severely.

The guard used to blow his horn at every place where a mail-bag was to be taken up, e.g. Puddletown. When the mail arrived the first thing the guard did was to take out the letter-bags and carry them into the Post Office (at that time the house below the King's Arms, Dorchester). He would then hand down blunderbus and tools.

Memoranda I

CARTERS, WAGGONERS, CARRIERS, AND ROAD-TRAFFIC

As the inexperienced Tess drives her one-horse cart with its load of beehives through the dead dark hours before the dawn, she falls asleep, her candle-lantern goes out, and there is a disaster:

In consternation Tess jumped down, and discovered the dreadful truth. The groan

had proceeded from her father's poor horse Prince. The morning mail-cart, with its two noiseless wheels, speeding along these lanes like an arrow, as it always did, had driven into her slow and unlighted equipage. The pointed shaft of the cart had entered the breast of the unhappy Prince like a sword, and from the wound his life's blood was spouting in a stream, and falling with a hiss into the road.

Tess of the d'Urbervilles

Road traffic was a problem even before the population explosion and the internal combustion engine. One of Hardy's notebooks contains three stories of such night-time collisions drawn from old copies of the Dorset County Chronicle, and later reflected in several of his novels.

In a lingering fog before dawn, Giles sets out with a load of timber:

The horses wore their bells that day. There were sixteen to the team, carried on a frame above each animal's shoulders, and tuned to scale, so as to form two octaves, running from the highest note on the right or off-side of the leader to the lowest on the left or nearside of the shaft-horse. Melbury was among the last to retain horse-bells in that neighbourhood; for living at Little Hintock, where the lanes yet remained as narrow as before the days of turnpike roads, these sound-signals were still as useful to him and his neighbours as they had ever been in former times. Much backing was saved in the course of a year by the warning notes they cast ahead; moreover, the tones of all the teams in the district being known to the carters of each, they could tell a long way off on a dark night whether they were about to encounter friends or strangers....

So they rumbled on, shaking the foundations of the roadside cottages by the weight of their progress, the sixteen bells chiming harmoniously over all, till they had risen out of the valley, and were descending towards the more open route, sparks rising from their creaking skid[181] as if they would set fire to the dead leaves alongside.

Then occurred one of the very incidents against which the bells were an endeavour to guard. Suddenly there beamed into their eyes, quite close to them, the two lamps of a carriage, haloed by the fog. Its approach had been quite unheard by reason of their own noise. The carriage was a covered one, while behind it could be discerned another vehicle laden with luggage.

Winterborne went to the head of the team, and heard the coachman telling the carter that he must turn back. The carter declared that this was impossible.

"You can turn if you unhitch your string-horses," said the coachman.

"It is much easier for you to turn than for us," said Winterborne. "We've five ton of timber on these wheels if we've an ounce."

"But I've another carriage with luggage at my back."

Winterborne admitted the strength of the argument. "But even with that," he said, "you can back better than we. And you ought to for you could hear our bells half a mile off."

"And you could see our lights."

"We couldn't, because of the fog."

"Well, our time's precious," said the coachman haughtily. "You are only going to some trumpery little village or other in the neighbourhood, while we are going straight to Italy."

"Driving all the way, I suppose?" said Winterborne sarcastically.

The Woodlanders

Reckless driving in a dog-cart could be terrifying:

Down, down, they sped, the wheels humming like a top, the dog-cart rocking right and left, its axis acquiring a slightly oblique set in relation to the line of progress; the figure of the horse rising and falling in undulations before them. Sometimes a wheel was off the ground, it seemed, for many yards; sometimes a stone was sent spinning over the hedge, and flinty sparks from the horse's hoofs outshone the daylight. The aspect of the straight road enlarged with their advance, the two banks dividing like a splitting stick; one rushing past at each shoulder....

"Don't touch my arm! We shall be thrown out if you do!"

Tess of the d'Urbervilles

Safer travel could usually be assured with the carrier. Hardy himself had travelled in the local carrier's van at Bockhampton, surrounded by bacon and other village provisions.[182]

Presently a slight noise of labouring wheels, and the steady dig of a horse's shoe-tips became audible; and there loomed in the notch of sky and plantation a carrier's van drawn by a single horse.

The vehicle was half full of passengers, mostly women. He held up his stick at its approach, and the woman who was driving drew rein. . . .

This van was rather a movable attachment of the roadway than an extraneous object, to those who knew it well. The old horse, whose hair was of the roughness and colour of heather, whose leg-joints, shoulders, and hoofs were distorted by harness and drudgery from colthood — though if all had their rights he ought, symmetrical in outline, to have been picking the herbage of some Eastern plain instead of tugging here — had trodden this road almost daily for twenty years. Even his subjection was not made congruous throughout, for the harness being too short, his tail was not drawn through the crupper, and the breeching slipped awkwardly to one side. He knew every subtle incline of the ten miles of ground between Abbot's Cernel and Sherton — the market town to which he journeyed — as accurately as any surveyor could have learnt it by a Dumpy level.[183]

The vehicle had a square black tilt[184] which nodded with the motion of the wheels, and at a point in it over the driver's head was a hook to which the reins were hitched at times, forming a catenary curve from the horse's shoulders. Somewhere about the axles was a loose chain, whose only known function was to clink as it went. Mrs Dollery, having to hop up and down many times in the service of her passengers, wore, especially in windy weather, short leggings under her gown for modesty's sake; and instead of a bonnet a felt hat tied down with a handkerchief, to guard against an ear-ache to which she was frequently subject. In the rear of the van was a glass window, which she cleaned with her pocket-handkerchief every market-day before starting. Looking at the van from the back the spectator could thus see, through its interior, a square piece of the same sky and landscape that he saw without, but intruded on by the profiles of the seated passengers, who, as they rumbled onward, their lips moving and heads nodding in animated private converse, remained in cheerful unconsciousness that their mannerisms and facial peculiarities were sharply defined to the public eye.

This hour of coming home from market was the happy one, if not the happiest, of the week for them. Snugly ensconced under the tilt they could forget the sorrows of the world without, and survey life and discuss the incidents of the day with placid smiles.

The Woodlanders

The life of carters was familiar to Hardy — the gathering at Warren's Malthouse in Far from the Madding Crowd *included:*

Matthew Moon, Joseph Poorgrass, and other carters and waggoners who followed at his heels, with great lanterns dangling from their hands, which showed that they had just come from the cart-horse stables, where they had been busily engaged since four o'clock that morning.

– and when he came to describe the great annual migration of farmworkers to new jobs on Lady Day, he noted the special arrangements for carters:

Should the migrant himself be a carter there is a slight modification in the arrangement, for carters do not fetch carters, as they fetch shepherds and general hands. In this case the man has to transfer himself. He relinquishes charge of the horses of the old farm in the afternoon of April 5, and starts on foot the same afternoon for the new place. There he makes the acquaintance of the horses which are to be under his care for the ensuing year, and passes the night sometimes on a bundle of clean straw in the stable, for he is as yet a stranger here, and too indifferent to the comforts of a bed on this particular evening to take much trouble to secure one. From this couch he uncurls himself about two o'clock, a.m. (for the distance we have assumed), and, harnessing his new charges, moves off with them to his old home, where, on his arrival, the packing is already advanced by the wife, and loading goes on as before mentioned.

The Dorsetshire Labourer

The Carrier

"There's a seat, I see, still empty?"
    Cried the hailer from the road;
"No, there is not!" said the carrier,
    Quickening his horse and load.

"— They say you are in the grave, Jane;
    But still you ride with me!"
And he looked towards the vacant space
    He had kept beside his knee.

And the passengers murmured: " 'Tis where his wife
    In journeys to and fro,
Used always to sit; but nobody does
    Since those long years ago."

Rumble-mumble went the van
    Past Sidwell Church and wall,
Till Exon Towers were out of scan,
    And night lay over all.[185]

Human Shows

THE MASON

Hardy's father and grandfather were masons:

Old James (grandfather on the maternal side)... being by trade a mason... wore a long linen apron reaching almost to his toes, corduroy breeches and gaiters, which, together with his boots, graduated in tints of whitish-brown by constant friction against lime and stone. He also wore a very stiff fustian coat, having folds at the elbows and shoulders as unvarying in their arrangement as those in a pair of bellows: the ridges and the projecting parts of the coat collectively exhibiting a shade different from that of the hollows, which were lined with small ditch-like accumulations of stone and mortar-dust. The extremely large side-pockets, sheltered beneath wide flaps, bulged out convexly whether empty or full; and as he was often engaged to work at buildings far away — his breakfasts and dinners being eaten in a strange chimney-corner, by a garden wall, on a heap of stones, or walking along the road — he carried in these pockets a small tin canister of butter, a small canister of sugar, a small canister of tea, a paper of salt, and a paper of pepper; the bread, cheese and meat, forming the substance of his meals, hanging up behind him in his basket among the hammers and chisels. If a passer-by looked hard at him when he was drawing forth any of these, "My buttery," he said, with a pinched smile.

Under the Greenwood Tree

John Smith — brown as autumn as to skin, white as winter as to clothes — was a satisfactory specimen of the village artificer in stone. In common with most rural mechanics, he had too much individuality to be a typical "working-man" — a resultant of that beach-pebble attrition with his kind only to be experienced in large towns, which metamorphoses the unit Self into a fraction of the unit Class.

There was not the speciality in his labour which distinguishes the handicraftsmen of towns. Though only a mason, strictly speaking, he was not above handling a brick, if bricks were the order of the day; or a slate or tile, if a roof had to be covered before the wet weather set in, and nobody was near who could do it better. Indeed, on one or two occasions in the depth of winter, when frost peremptorily forbids all use of the trowel, making foundations to settle, stones to fly, and mortar to crumble, he had taken to felling and sawing trees. . . .

Probably our countryman was not such an accomplished artificer in a particular direction as his town brethren in the trades. But he was, in truth . . . much more the artist nevertheless.[186]

A Pair of Blue Eyes

The Old Workman

"Why are you so bent down before your time,
Old mason? Many have not left their prime
So far behind at your age, and can still
        Stand full upright at will."

He pointed to the mansion-front hard by,
And to the stones of the quoin against the sky;

"Those upper blocks," he said, "that there you see,
It was that ruined me."

There stood in the air up to the parapet
Crowning the corner height, the stones as set
By him — ashlar whereon the gales might drum
For centuries to come.

"I carried them up," he said, "by a ladder there;
The last was as big a load as I could bear;
But on I heaved; and something in my back
Moved, as 'twere with a crack.

"So I got crookt. I never lost that sprain;
And those who live there, walled from wind and rain
By freestone that I lifted, do not know
That my life's ache came so.

"They don't know me, or even know my name,
But good I think it, somehow, all the same
To have kept 'em safe from harm, and right and tight,
Though it has broke me quite.

"Yes; that I fixed it firm up there I am proud,
Facing the hail and snow and sun and cloud,
And to stand storms for ages, beating round
When I lie underground."

Late Lyrics and Earlier

The title on Hardy's original manuscript of this poem is "The Old Mason".

THE TRANTER

A mood of blitheness rarely experienced even by young men was Dick's on the following Monday morning. It was the week after the Easter holidays, and he was journeying along with Smart the mare and the light spring cart, watching the damp slopes of the hill-sides as they streamed in the warmth of the sun. . . . His errand was to fetch Fancy, and some additional household goods, from her father's house in the neighbouring parish to her dwelling at Mellstock.

Under the Greenwood Tree

"Dick," said his father, coming in from the garden at that moment — in each hand a hive of bees tied in a cloth to prevent their egress — "I think you'd better take these two swarms of bees to Mrs Maybold's to-morrow, instead o' me, and I'll go wi' Smiler and the wagon."

It was a relief; for Mrs Maybold, the vicar's mother, who had just taken into her head a fancy for keeping bees (pleasantly disguised under the pretence of its being an economical wish to produce her own honey), lived near the watering-place of Budmouth Regis, ten miles off, and the business of transporting the hives thither would occupy the whole day.... The best spring-cart was washed throughout, the axles oiled, and the bees placed therein for the journey.

Under the Greenwood Tree

"You see, sir," continued the ingenuous Dick, " 'twill be better in one sense. I shall by that time be the regular manager of a branch o' father's business which we think of starting elsewhere. It has very much increased lately, and we expect next year to keep a' extra couple of horses. We've already our eye on one — brown as a berry, neck like a rainbow, fifteen hands, and not a gray hair in her — offered us at twenty-five want a crown.[187] And to kip pace with the times I have had some cards prented, and I beg leave to hand you one, sir."

"Certainly," said the vicar, mechanically taking the card that Dick offered him....

DEWY AND SON,
TRANTERS AND HAULIERS,
MELLSTOCK.

N.B. — Furniture, Coals, Potatoes, Live and Dead Stock
removed to any distance on the shortest notice.

Under the Greenwood Tree

COUNTRY BARBER

Percomb was the chief of his trade in Sherton Abbas. He had the patronage of such county off-shoots as had been obliged to seek the shelter of small houses in that venerable town, of the local clergy, and so on; for some of whom he had made wigs, while others among them had compensated for neglecting him in their lifetime by patronizing him when they were dead, and letting him shave their corpses. On the strength of all this he had taken down his pole and called himself "Perruquier to the aristocracy".

Nevertheless, this sort of support did not quite fill his children's mouths, and they had to be filled. So behind his house there was a little yard, reached by a passage from the back street, and in that yard was a pole, and under the pole a shop of quite another description than the ornamental one in the front street. Here on Saturday nights from seven till ten he took an almost innumerable succession of twopences from the farm-labourers who flocked thither in crowds from the country. And thus he lived.[188]

The Woodlanders

COUNTRY POSTMAN[189]

It was a raw, damp, uncomfortable morning. . . . He heard the market-house clock strike five, and soon afterwards, quick hard footsteps smote upon the pavement. . . . They were those of the postman for the Tolchurch beat. He reached the bottom of the street, gave his bags a final hitch-up, stepped off the pavement, and struck out for the country with a brisk shuffle. . . .

In two minutes a flickering light shone upon his form, and the postman overtook him.

The new-comer was a short, stooping individual of above five-and-forty, laden on both sides with leather bags large and small, and carrying a little lantern strapped to his breast, which cast a tiny patch of light upon the road ahead. . . .

Besides the small private bags of the county families, which were all locked, the postman bore the large general budget for the remaining inhabitants along his beat. At each village or hamlet they came to, the postman searched for the packet of letters destined for that place, and thrust it into an ordinary letter-hole cut in the door of the receiver's cottage — the village post-offices being mostly kept by old women who had not yet risen, though lights moving in other cottage windows showed that such people as carters, woodmen, and stablemen, had long been stirring. . . .

It frequently happened that the houses of farmers, clergymen, &c., lay a short distance up or down a lane or path branching from the direct track of the postman's journey. To save time and distance, at the point of junction of some of these paths with the main road the gate-post was hollowed out to form a letter-box, in which the postman deposited his missives in the morning, looking in the box again in the evening to collect those placed there for the return post. . . .

The letter-box was scooped in an oak gate-post about a foot square. There was no slit for inserting the letters, by reason of the opportunity such a lonely spot would have afforded mischievous peasant-boys of doing damage had such been the case; but at the side was a small iron door, kept close by an iron reversible strap locked across it. One side of this strap was painted black, the other white, and white or black outwards implied respectively that there were letters inside, or none.

Desperate Remedies

Reaching the opposite side of the park there appeared before her for the third time that little old man, the foot-post. As the turnpike-road ran, the postman's beat was twelve miles a day; six miles out from the town, and six miles back at night. But what with zigzags, devious ways, offsets to country seats, curves to farms, looped courses, and triangles to outlying hamlets, the ground actually covered by him was nearer one-and-twenty miles.

The Romantic Adventures of a Milkmaid

FURZE-CUTTING ON EGDON HEATH

The very next day Yeobright went to Humphrey's cottage, and borrowed of him leggings, gloves, a whetstone, and a hook, to use till he should be able to purchase some for himself. Then he sailed forth with his new fellow-labourer and old acquaintance, and selecting a spot where the furze grew thickest he struck the first blow in his adopted calling.... He found that when a little practice should have hardened his palms against blistering he would be able to work with ease.

Day after day he rose with the sun, buckled on his leggings, and went off to the rendezvous with Humphrey. His custom was to work from four o'clock in the morning till noon; then, when the heat of the day was at its highest, to go home and sleep for an hour or two; afterwards coming out again and working till dusk at nine.

This man from Paris was now so disguised by his leather accoutrements, and by the goggles he was obliged to wear over his eyes, that his closest friend might have passed by without recognizing him. He was a brown spot in the midst of an expanse of olive-green gorse.

The Return of the Native

What they did with the furze:

On fine days at this time of the year, and earlier, certain ephemeral operations were apt to disturb, in their trifling way, the majestic calm of Egdon Heath. They were activities which, beside those of a town, a village, or even a farm, would have appeared as the ferment of stagnation merely, a creeping of the flesh of somnolence. But here, away from comparisons, shut in by the stable hills, among which mere walking had the novelty of pageantry, and where any man could imagine himself to be Adam without the least difficulty, they attracted the attention of every bird within eyeshot, every reptile not yet asleep, and set the surrounding rabbits curiously watching from hillocks at a safe distance.

The performance was that of bringing together and building into a stack the furze-faggots which Humphrey had been cutting for the captain's use during the foregoing fine days. The stack was at the end of the dwelling, and the men engaged in building it were Humphrey and Sam, the old man looking on.

The Return of the Native

THE REDDLEMAN[190]

When he drew nearer he perceived it to be a spring van, ordinary in shape, but singular in colour, this being a lurid red. The driver walked beside it; and, like his van, he was completely red. One dye of that tincture covered his clothes, the cap upon his head, his boots, his face, and his hands. He was not temporarily overlaid with the colour: it permeated him.

The old man knew the meaning of this. The traveller with the cart was a reddleman — a person whose vocation it was to supply farmers with redding for their sheep. He was one of a class rapidly becoming extinct in Wessex, filling at present in the rural world the place which, during the last century, the dodo occupied in the world of animals. He is a curious, interesting, and nearly perished link between obsolete forms of life and those which generally prevail.

The Return of the Native

The date at which the [above] events are assumed to have occurred may be set down as between 1840 and 1850. . . .

1895 Preface to *The Return of the Native*

THE LIME-BURNER

A novel attraction about this young man, which a glancing stranger would know nothing of, was a rare and curious freshness of atmosphere that appertained to him, to his clothes, to all his belongings, even to the room in which he had been sitting. It might almost have been said that by adding him and his implements to an over-crowded apartment you made it healthful. This resulted from his trade. He was a lime-burner; he handled lime daily; and in return the lime rendered him the incarnation of salubrity. His hair was dry, fair, and frizzled, the latter possibly by the operation of the same caustic agent.

At the senior lime-burner's:

With due regard to the principle that a man's surroundings should bear the impress of that man's life and occupation, the chief ornaments of the dwelling were a curious collection of calcinations, that had been discovered from time to time in the lime-kiln — misshapen ingots of strange substance, some of them like Pompeian remains.

The Romantic Adventures of a Milkmaid

MILLS AND MILLING

Sounds and substance:

She lived with her widowed mother in a portion of an ancient building formerly a manor-house, but now a mill, which, being too large for his own requirements, the miller had found it convenient to divide and appropriate in part to these highly respectable tenants. In this dwelling Mrs Garland's and Anne's ears were soothed morning, noon, and night by the music of the mill, the wheels and cogs of which, being of wood, produced notes that might have borne in their minds a remote resemblance to the wooden tones of the stopped diapason in an organ. Occasionally, when the miller was bolting,[191] there was added to these continous sounds the cheerful clicking of the hopper,[192] which did not deprive them of rest except when it was kept going all night; and over and above all this they had the pleasure of knowing that there crept in through every crevice, door, and window of their dwelling, however tightly closed, a subtle mist of superfine flour from the grinding-room, quite invisible, but making its presence known in the course of time by giving a pallid and ghostly look to the best furniture. The miller frequently apologized to his tenants for the intrusion of this insidious dry fog; but the widow was of a friendly and thankful nature, and she said that she did not mind it at all, being as it was, not nasty dirt, but the blessed staff of life.

The Trumpet-Major

She followed him along the dark passage, in the side of which he opened a little trap, when she saw a great slimy cavern, where the long arms of the mill-wheel flung themselves slowly and distractedly round, and splashing water-drops caught the little light that strayed into the gloomy place, turning it into stars and flashes. A cold mist-laden puff of air came into their faces, and the roar from within made it necessary for Anne to shout as she said, "It is dismal! let us go on."

Bob shut the trap, the roar ceased, and they went on to the inner part of the mill, where the air was warm and nutty, and pervaded by a fog of flour. Then they ascended the stairs, and saw the stones lumbering round and round, and the yellow corn running down through the hopper. They climbed yet further to the top stage, where the wheat lay in bins, and where long rays like feelers stretched in from the sun through the little window, got nearly lost among cobwebs and timber, and completed their course by marking the opposite wall with a glowing patch of gold.

In his earnestness as an exhibitor Bob opened the bolter, which was spinning rapidly round, the result being that a dense cloud of flour rolled out in their faces, reminding Anne that her complexion was probably much paler by this time than when she had entered the mill. She thanked her companion for his trouble, and said she would now go down.

The Trumpet-Major

The Second Visit

Clack, clack, clack, went the mill-wheel as I came,
And she was on the bridge with the thin hand-rail,
And the miller at the door, and the ducks at mill-tail;
I come again years after, and all there seems the same.

And so indeed it is: the apple-tree'd old house,
And the deep mill-pond, and the wet wheel clacking,
And a woman on the bridge, and white ducks quacking,
And the miller at the door, powdered pale from boots to brows.

But it's not the same miller whom long ago I knew,

Nor are they the same apples, nor the same drops that dash
Over the wet wheel, nor the ducks below that splash,
Nor the woman who to fond plaints replied, "You know I do!"

Winter Words

THE VILLAGE SHOEMAKER

Mr Penny's was the last house in that part of the parish, and stood in a hollow by the roadside; so that cart-wheels and horses' legs were about level with the sill of his shop-window. This was low and wide, and was open from morning till evening, Mr Penny himself being invariably seen working inside like a framed portrait of a shoemaker by some modern Moroni.[193] He sat facing the road, with a boot on his knees and the awl in his hand, only looking up for a moment as he stretched out his arms and bent forward at the pull', when his spectacles flashed in the passer's face with a shine of flat whiteness, and then returned again to the boot as usual. Rows of lasts, small and large, stout and slender, covered the wall which formed the background, in the extreme shadow of which a kind of dummy was seen sitting, in the shape of an apprentice with a string tied round his hair (probably to keep it out of his eyes). He smiled at remarks that floated in from without, but was never known to answer them in Mr Penny's presence. Outside the window the upper-leather of a Wellington-boot was usually hung, pegged to a board as if to dry. No sign was over his door; in fact — as with old banks and mercantile houses — advertising in any shape was scorned, and it would have been felt as beneath his dignity to paint up, for the benefit of strangers, the name of an establishment whose trade came solely by connection based on personal respect.

Under the Greenwood Tree

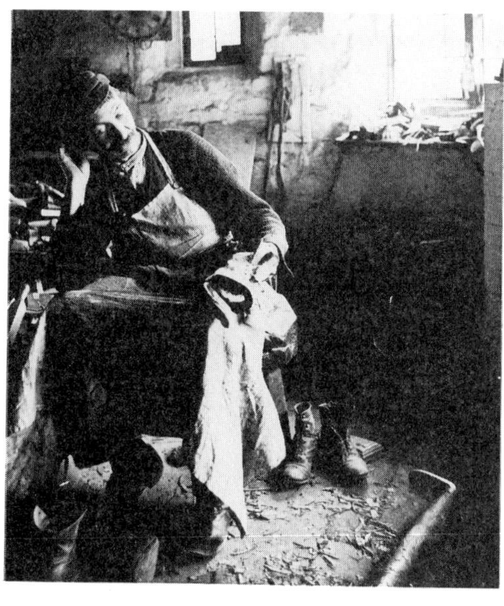

Mr Penny tells his friends in the Quire a thing or two about his trade:

He drew forth a last, and placed it on a table at his elbow. The eyes of three or four followed it.

"Well," said the shoemaker, seeming to perceive that the interest the object had excited was greater than he had anticipated, and warranted the last's being taken up again and exhibited; "Now, whose foot do ye suppose this last was made for? It was made for Geoffrey Day's father, over at Yalbury Wood. Ah, many's the pair o' boots he've had off the last! Well, when 'a died, I used the last for Geoffrey, and have ever since, though a little doctoring was wanted to make it do. Yes, a very queer natured last it is now, 'a b'lieve," he continued, turning it over caressingly. "Now, you notice that there" (pointing to a lump of leather bradded[194] to the toe), "that's a very bad bunion that he've had ever since 'a was a boy. Now, this remarkable large piece" (pointing to a patch nailed to the side), "shows a' accident he received by the tread of a horse, that squashed his foot a'most to a pomace.[195] The horse-shoe came full-butt on this point, you see. And so I've just been over to Geoffrey's, to know if he wanted his bunion altered or made bigger in the new pair I'm making."...

He now drew forth and placed upon the table a boot — small, light, and prettily shaped — upon the heel of which he had been operating.

"The new schoolmistress's!"

"Ay, no less, Miss Fancy Day; as neat a little figure of fun as ever I see, and just husband-high."

"Never Geoffrey's daughter Fancy?" said Bowman, as all glances present converged like wheel-spokes upon the boot in the centre of them.

"Yes, sure," resumed Mr Penny, regarding the boot as if that alone were his auditor; "'tis she that's come here schoolmistress."...

"And that's the boot, then," continued its mender imaginatively, "that she'll walk to church in to-morrow morning. I don't care to mend boots I don't make; but there's no knowing what it may lead to, and her father always comes to me."

There, between the cider-mug and the candle, stood this interesting receptacle of the little unknown's foot; and a very pretty boot it was. A character, in fact — the flexible bend at the instep, the rounded localities of the small nestling toes, scratches from careless scampers now forgotten — all, as repeated in the tell-tale leather, evidencing a nature and a bias. Dick surveyed it with a delicate feeling that he had no right to do so without having first asked the owner of the foot's permission.

"Now, neighbours, though no common eye can see it," the shoemaker went on, "a man in the trade can see the likeness between this boot and that last, although that is so deformed as hardly to recall one of God's creatures, and this is one of as pretty a pair as you'd get for ten-and-sixpence in Casterbridge. To you, nothing; but 'tis father's voot and daughter's voot to me, as plain as houses."

Mr Penny adjusted his spectacles.

"Now, I'll tell ye what happened to me once on this very point. You used to know Johnson the dairyman, William?"

"Ay, sure; I did."

"Well, 'twasn't opposite his house, but a little lower down — by his paddock, in front o' Parkmaze Pool. I was a-bearing across towards Bloom's End, and lo and behold, there was a man just brought out o' the Pool, dead; he had un'rayed[196] for a dip, but not being able to pitch it just there had gone in flop over his head. Men looked at en; women looked at en; children looked at en; nobody knowed en. He was covered wi' a sheet; but I catched sight of his voot, just showing out as they carried en along. 'I don't care what name that man went by,' I said, in my way, 'but he's John Woodward's brother; I can swear to the family voot.' At that very moment up comes John Woodward, weeping and teaving,[197] 'I've lost my brother! I've lost my brother!'"

"Only to think of that!" said Mrs Dewy.

Under the Greenwood Tree

THE SEXTON

The Sexton at Longpuddle

He passes down the churchyard track
    On his way to toll the bell;
And stops, and looks at the graves around,
And notes each finished and greening mound
        Complacently,
        As their shaper he,
    And one who can do it well,
And, with a prosperous sense of his doing,
        Thinks he'll not lack
Plenty such work in the long ensuing
        Futurity.
    For people will always die,
    And he will always be nigh
        To shape their cell.

Human Shows

HIRING-FAIRS AND WORKING CONDITIONS

Merryn Williams, in her Thomas Hardy and Rural England, *has made a detailed study of agricultural conditions – much reflected in Hardy's writings – in the nineteenth century. It should be remembered that the scene of the Tolpuddle Martyrs in 1834 was a neighbouring village to Hardy's home; and that a survey in 1837 showed that agricultural labourers' wages were highest in Cheshire (13 shillings a week) and lowest in Dorset (7 shillings and 6 pence a week). Conditions were probably worst in about mid-century, at the time when Hardy usually set his novels. They began to improve after Joseph Arch founded his National Agricultural Labourers' Union in 1872.*

To see the Dorset labourer at his worst and saddest time, he should be viewed when attending a wet hiring-fair at Candlemas, in search of a new master. . . .

The Dorsetshire Labourer

Among these, carters and waggoners were distinguished by having a piece of whip-cord twisted round their hats; thatchers wore a fragment of woven straw; shepherds held their sheep-crooks in their hands; and thus the situation required was known to the hirers at a glance.

Far from the Madding Crowd

The fair without the windows was now raging thick and loud. It was the chief hiring fair of the year, and differed quite from the market of a few days earlier. In substance it was a whitey-brown crowd flecked with white — this being the body of labourers waiting for places. The long bonnets of the women, like waggon-tilts,[198] their cotton gowns and checked shawls, mixed with the carters' smock-frocks; for they, too, entered into the hiring. Among the rest, at the corner of the pavement, stood an old shepherd, who attracted the eyes of Lucetta and Farfrae by his stillness. He was evidently a chastened man. The battle of life had been a sharp one with him, for, to begin with, he was a man of small frame. He was now so bowed by hard work and years that, approaching from behind, a person could hardly see his head. He had planted the stem of his crook in the gutter and was resting upon the bow, which was polished to silver brightness by the long friction of his hands. He had quite forgotten where he was, and what he had come for, his eyes being bent on the ground. A little way off negotiations were proceeding which had reference to him; but he did not hear them, and there seemed to be passing through his mind pleasant visions of the hiring successes of his prime, when his skill laid open to him any farm for the asking.

The negotiations were between a farmer from a distant county and the old man's son. In these there was a difficulty. The farmer would not take the crust without the crumb of the bargain, in other words, the old man without the younger; and the son had a sweetheart on his present farm, who stood by, waiting the issue with pale lips.

"I'm sorry to leave ye, Nelly," said the young man with emotion. "But, you see, I can't starve father, and he's out o' work at Lady-day. 'Tis only thirty-five mile."

The girl's lips quivered. "Thirty-five mile!" she murmured. "Ah! 'tis enough! I shall never see 'ee again!" It was, indeed, a hopeless length of traction for Dan[199] Cupid's magnet; for young men were young men at Casterbridge as elsewhere.

"O! no, no — I never shall," she insisted, when he pressed her hand; and she turned her face to Lucetta's wall to hide her weeping. The farmer said he would give the young man half-an-hour for his answer, and went away, leaving the group sorrowing.

The Mayor of Casterbridge

A glimpse of child labour:

A shepherd lad, young for his occupation . . . stood within a wheeled hut of the kind commonly in use among sheep-keepers during the early lambing season. . . .

An old shepherd presently entered the hut from the direction of the ewes, and looked around in the gloom. "Be ye sleepy?" he asked in cross accents of the boy.

The lad replied rather timidly in the negative.

"Then," said the shepherd. "I'll get me home-along, and rest for a few hours. . . . The ewes can want no more tending till daybreak — 'tis beyond the bounds of reason that they can. But as the order is that one of us must bide, I'll leave 'ee, d'ye hear? You can sleep by day, and I can't. And you can be down to my house in ten minutes if anything should happen. I can't afford 'ee candle; but, as 'tis Christmas week, and the time that folks have hollerdays, you can enjoy yerself by falling asleep a bit in the chair instead of biding awake all the time. But mind, not longer at once than while the shade of the Devil's Door moves a couple of spans, for you must keep an eye upon the ewes."

What the Shepherd Saw

Our Exploits at West Poley,[200] *a serial story for boys written in 1883, shows a miller desperately clinging to his "right over his 'prentice, body and soul!" In "The Dorsetshire Labourer" . . .*

The result of [Joseph Arch's] agitation, so far, upon the income of the labourers, has been testified by independent witnesses with a unanimity which leaves no reasonable doubt of its accuracy. It amounts to an average rise of three shillings a week in wages nearly all over the country. The absolute number of added shillings seems small; but the increase is considerable when we remember that it is three shillings on eight or nine — i.e. between thirty and forty per cent. And the reflection is forced upon everyone who thinks of the matter, that if a farmer can afford to pay thirty per cent more wages in times of agricultural depression than he paid in times of agricultural prosperity, and yet live, and keep a carriage, while the landlord still thrives on the reduced rent which has resulted, the labourer must have been greatly wronged in those prosperous times.

. . . It is hardly necessary to observe that the quoted wages never represent the labourer's actual income. Beyond the weekly payment — now standing at eleven or twelve shillings — he invariably receives a lump sum of 2/- of 3/- for harvest work. A cottage and garden is almost as invariably provided, free of rent, with, sometimes, an extra piece of ground for potatoes in some field near at hand. Fuel, too, is frequently furnished, in the form of wood faggots. At springtime, on good farms, the shepherd receives a shilling for every twin reared, while a carter gets what is called journey-money, that is, a small sum, mostly a shilling, for every journey taken beyond the bounds of the farm. Where all these supplementary trifles are enjoyed together, the weekly wage in no case exceeds eleven shillings at the present time.

The question of enough or not enough often depends less upon the difference of two or three shillings a week in the earnings of the head of a family than upon the nature of his household. With a family of half a dozen children, the eldest of them delicate girls, nothing that he can hope to receive for the labour of his one pair of hands can save him from many hardships during a few years. But with a family of strong boys, of ages from twelve to seventeen or eighteen, he enjoys a season of prosperity. . . .

The mother of the same goodly row of sons can afford to despise the farmer's request for female labour; she stays genteelly at home, and looks with some superciliousness upon wives who, having no useful children, are obliged to work in the fields like their husbands.

The Dorsetshire Labourer

Farming and the Agricultural Community

The agricultural and pastoral character of the people on whom [Casterbridge] depended for its existence was shown by the class of objects displayed in the shop windows. Scythes, reap-hooks, sheep-shears, bill-hooks, spades, mattocks, and hoes at the ironmonger's; bee-hives, butter-firkins, churns, milking-stools and pails, hay-rakes, field-flagons, and seed-lips at the cooper's; cart-ropes and plough-harness at the saddler's; carts, wheel-barrows, and mill-gear at the wheelwright's and machinist's; horse-embrocations at the chemist's; at the glover's and leather-cutter's, hedging-gloves, thatchers' knee-caps, ploughmen's leggings, villagers' pattens and clogs.

Casterbridge was in most respects but the pole, focus, or nerve-knot of the surrounding country life; differing from the many manufacturing towns which are as foreign bodies set down, like boulders on a plain, in a green world with which they have nothing in common. Casterbridge lived by agriculture at one remove further from the fountain-head than the adjoining villages — no more. The townsfolk understood every fluctuation in the rustic's condition, for it affected their receipts as much as the labourer's; they entered into the troubles and joys which moved the aristocratic families ten miles round — for the same reason. And even at the dinner-parties of the professional families the subjects of discussion were corn, cattle-disease, sowing and reaping, fencing and planting.

The Mayor of Casterbridge

In the latter quarter of each year cattle were at once the mainstay and the terror of families about Casterbridge and its neighbourhood, where breeding was carried on with Abrahamic success. The head of stock driven into and out of the town at this season to be sold by the local auctioneer was very large; and all these horned beasts, in travelling to and fro, sent women and children to shelter as nothing else could do. In the main the animals would have walked along quietly enough; but the Casterbridge tradition was that to drive stock it was indispensable that hideous cries, coupled with Yahoo antics[201] and gestures, should be used, large sticks flourished, stray dogs called in, and in general everything done that was likely to infuriate the viciously disposed and terrify the mild. Nothing was commoner than for a householder on going out of his parlour to find his hall or passage full of little children, nursemaids, aged women, or a ladies' school, who apologized for their presence by saying, "A bull passing down street from the sale."

Lucetta and Elizabeth regarded the animal in doubt, he meanwhile drawing vaguely towards them. It was a large specimen of the breed, in colour rich dun, though disfigured at present by splotches of mud about his seamy sides. His horns were thick and tipped with brass; his two nostrils like the Thames Tunnel as seen in the perspective toys[202] of yore. Between them, through the gristle of his nose, was a stout copper ring, welded on, and irremovable as Gurth's collar of brass.[203] To the ring was attached an ash staff about a yard long, which the bull with the motions of his head flung about like a flail.

It was not till they observed this dangling stick that the young women were really alarmed; for it revealed to them that the bull was an old one, too savage to be driven, which had in some way escaped, the staff being the means by which the drover controlled him and kept his horns at arms' length.

They looked round for some shelter or hiding-place, and though of the barn hard by....

It was closed save as to one of the usual pair of doors facing them, which had been propped open by a hurdle-stake, and for this opening they made. The interior had been cleared by a recent bout of threshing except at one end, where there was a stack of dry clover. Elizabeth-Jane took in the situation. "We must climb up there," she said.

But before they had even approached it they heard the bull scampering through the pond without, and in a second he dashed into the barn, knocking down the hurdle-stake in passing; the heavy door slammed behind him; and all three were imprisoned in the barn together.

... The pursuit went on, the hot air from his nostrils blowing over them like a sirocco.... What might have happened had their situation continued cannot be said; but in a few moments a rattling of the door distracted their adversary's attention, and a man appeared. He ran forward towards the leading-staff, seized it, and wrenched the animal's head as if he would snap it off. The wrench was in reality so violent that the thick neck seemed to have lost its stiffness and to become half-paralysed, whilst the nose dropped blood. The premeditated human contrivance of the nose-ring was too cunning for impulsive brute force, and the creature flinched....

Coming out [Elizabeth] paused to look for a moment at the bull, now rather to be pitied with his bleeding nose, having perhaps intended a practical joke rather than a murder.

The Mayor of Casterbridge

Rural solidarity — and the vital harvest:

Nearly the whole town had gone into the fields. The Casterbridge populace still retained the primitive habit of helping one another in time of need; and thus, though the corn belonged to the farming section of the little community — that inhabiting the Durnover quarter — the remainder was no less interested in the labour of getting it home.

The Mayor of Casterbridge

The time was in the years immediately before foreign competition had revolutionized the trade in grain; when still, as from the earliest ages, the wheat quotations from month to month depended entirely upon the home harvest. A bad harvest, or the prospect of one, would double the price of corn in a few weeks; and the promise of a good yield would lower it as rapidly. Prices were like the roads of the period, steep in gradient, reflecting in their phases the local conditions, without engineering, levellings, or averages.

The farmer's income was ruled by the wheat-crop within his own horizon, and the wheat-crop by the weather. Thus, in person, he became a sort of flesh-barometer, with feelers always directed to the sky and wind around him. The local atmosphere was everything to him; the atmospheres of other countries a matter of indifference. The people, too, who were not farmers, the rural multitude, saw in the god of the weather a more important personage than they do now. Indeed, the feeling of the peasantry in this matter was so intense as to be almost unrealizable in these equable days. Their impulse was well-nigh to prostrate themselves in lamentation before untimely rains and tempests, which came as the Alastor[204] of those households whose crime it was to be poor.

After midsummer they watched the weather-cocks as men waiting in antechambers watch the lackey. Sun elated them; weeks of watery tempest stupefied them. That aspect of the sky which they now regard as disagreeable they then beheld as maleficent.

It was June, and the weather was very unfavourable.

The Mayor of Casterbridge

The passing of the old order:

The morning was exceptionally bright for the time of year. The sun fell so flat on the houses and pavement opposite Lucetta's residence that they poured their brightness into her rooms. Suddenly, after a rumbling of wheels, there were added to this steady light a fantastic series of circling irradiations upon the ceiling, and the companions turned to the window. Immediately opposite a vehicle of strange description had come to a standstill, as if it had been placed there for exhibition.

It was the new-fashioned agricultural implement called a horse-drill, till then unknown, in its modern shape, in this part of the country, where the venerable seed-lip[205] was still used for sowing as in the days of the Heptarchy.[206] Its arrival created about as much sensation in the corn-market as a flying machine would create at Charing Cross. The farmers crowded round it, women drew near it, children crept under and into it. The machine was painted in bright hues of green, yellow, and red, and it resembled as a whole a compound of hornet, grasshopper, and shrimp, magnified enormously. Or it might have been likened to an upright musical instrument with the front gone. That was how it struck Lucetta. "Why, it is a sort of agricultural piano," she said.

"It has something to do with corn," said Elizabeth.

"I wonder who thought of introducing it here?"

... They examined it curiously; observing the rows of trumpet-shaped tubes one within the other, the little scoops, like revolving salt-spoons, which tossed the seed into the upper ends of the tubes that conducted it to the ground....

"We are looking at the wonderful new drill," Mrs Templeman said. "But practically it is a stupid thing — is it not?" she added, on the strength of Henchard's information.

"Stupid? O no!" said Farfrae gravely. "It will revolutionize sowing heerabout! No more sowers flinging their seed about broadcast, so that some falls by the wayside and some among thorns, and all that. Each grain will go straight to its intended place, and nowhere else whatever!"

"Then the romance of the sower is gone for good," observed Elizabeth-Jane, who felt herself at one with Farfrae in Bible-reading at least. "'He that observeth the wind shall not sow,' so the Preacher said; but his words will not be to the point any more. How things change!"

"Ay; ay.... It must be so!" Donald admitted, his gaze fixing itself on a blank point far away. "But the machines are already very common in the East and North of England," he added apologetically.

The Mayor of Casterbridge

"'Twas verily Fortune sent him to Henchard. His accounts were like a bramble-wood when Mr Farfrae came. He used to reckon his sacks by chalk strokes all in a row like garden-pailings, measure his ricks by stretching with his arms, weigh his trusses by a lift, judge his hay by a chaw,[207] and settle the price with a curse. But now this accomplished young man does it all by ciphering and mensuration. Then the wheat — that sometimes used to taste so strong o' mice when made into bread that people could fairly tell the breed — Farfrae has a plan for purifying, so that nobody would dream the smallest four-legged beast had walked over it once. O yes, everybody is full of him. . . ."

Henchard's stores, which had remained in a paralysed condition during the settlement of his bankruptcy, were stirred into activity again when the new tenant had possession. Thenceforward the full sacks, looped with the shining chain, went scurrying up and down under the cathead,[208] hairy arms were thrust out from the different door-ways, and the grain was hauled in; trusses of hay were tossed anew in and out of the barns, and the wimbles creaked; while the scales and steel-yards[209] began to be busy where guess-work had formerly been the rule.

The Mayor of Casterbridge

Life-style was changing for farmers too — a group to whom Hardy was not particularly attracted:[210]

Beside the farmers there were present several professional men of the town, who found it desirable to dine here on market-days for the opportunity it afforded them of increasing their practice among the agriculturists, many of whom were men of large balances, even luxurious livers, who drove to market in elegant phaetons drawn by horses of supreme blood, bone, and action, in a style never anticipated by their fathers when jogging thither in light carts, or afoot with a butter basket on each arm.

A Laodicean

They sat . . . looking out upon the market, which formed an animated scene . . . The farmers as a rule preferred the open *carrefour* for their transactions, despite its inconvenient jostlings and the danger from crossing vehicles, to the gloomy sheltered market-room provided for them. Here they surged on this one day of the week, forming a little world of leggings, switches, and sample-bags; men of extensive stomachs, sloping like mountain sides; men whose heads in walking swayed as the trees in November gales; who in conversing varied their attitudes much, lowering themselves by spreading their knees, and thrusting their hands into the pockets of remote inner jackets. Their faces radiated tropical warmth; for though when at home their countenances varied with the seasons, their market-faces all the year round were glowing little fires.

All over-clothes here were worn as if they were an inconvenience, a hampering necessity. Some men were well-dressed; but the majority were careless in that respect, appearing in suits which were historical records of their wearer's deeds, sun-scorchings, and daily struggles for many years past. Yet many carried ruffled cheque-books in their pockets which regulated at the bank hard by a balance of never less than four figures. In fact, what these gibbous human shapes specially represented was ready money — money insistently ready — not ready next year like a nobleman's —

often not merely ready at the bank like a professional man's, but ready in their large plump hands.

The Mayor of Casterbridge

THE FIELD-WOMEN

We Field-Women

How it rained
When we worked at Flintcomb-Ash,
And could not stand upon the hill
Trimming swedes for the slicing-mill.
The wet washed through us — plash, plash, plash:
How it rained!

How it snowed
When we crossed from Flintcomb-Ash
To the Great Barn for drawing reed,
Since we could nowise chop a swede. —
Flakes in each doorway and casement-sash:
How it snowed!

How it shone
When we went from Flintcomb-Ash
To start at dairywork once more
In the laughing meads, with cows three-score,
And pails, and songs, and love — too rash:
How it shone!

Winter Words

Women's labour, too, is highly in request, for a woman who, like a boy, fills the place of a man at half the wages, can be better depended on for steadiness. Thus where a boy is useful in driving a cart or a plough, a woman is invaluable in work which, though somewhat lighter, demands thought.

The Dorsetshire Labourer

Reaping –

Of all ruddy things that morning the brightest were two broad arms of painted wood, which rose from the margin of a yellow cornfield hard by Marlott village. They, with two others below, formed the revolving Maltese cross of the reaping-machine, which had been brought to the field on the previous evening to be ready for operations this day. The paint with which they were smeared, intensified in hue by the sunlight, imparted to them a look of having been dipped in liquid fire.

The field had already been "opened", that is to say, a lane a few feet wide had been hand-cut through the wheat along the whole circumference of the field, for the first passage of the horses and machine.

Two groups, one of men and lads, the other of women, had come down the lane just at the hour when the shadows of the eastern hedge-top struck the west hedge midway, so that the heads of the groups were enjoying sunrise while their feet were still in the dawn. They disappeared from the lane between the two stone posts which flanked the nearest field-gate.

Presently there arose from within a ticking like the love-making of the grasshopper. The machine had begun, and a moving concatenation of three horses and the aforesaid long rickety machine was visible over the gate, a driver sitting upon one of the hauling horses, and an attendant on the seat of the implement. Along one side of the field the whole train went, the arms of the mechanical reaper revolving slowly, till it passed down the hill quite out of sight. In a minute it came up on the other side of the field at the same equable pace; the glistening brass star in the forehead of the fore horse first catching the eye as it rose into view over the stubble, then the bright arms, and then the whole machine.

— and binding:

The reaping-machine left the fallen corn behind it in little heaps, each heap being of the quantity for a sheaf; and upon these the active binders in the rear laid their hands — mainly women, but some of them men in print shirts, and trousers supported round their waists by leather straps, rendering useless the two buttons behind, which twinkled and bristled with sunbeams at every movement of each wearer, as if they were a pair of eyes in the small of his back.

But those of the other sex were the most interesting of this company of binders, by reason of the charm which is acquired by woman when she becomes part and parcel of outdoor nature, and is not merely an object set down therein as at ordinary times.

A field man is a personality afield; a field-woman is a portion of the field; she has somehow lost her own margin, imbibed the essence of her surrounding, and assimilated herself with it.

The women — or rather girls, for they were mostly young — wore drawn cotton bonnets with great flapping curtains to keep off the sun, and gloves to prevent their hands being wounded by the stubble. There was one wearing a pale pink jacket, another in a cream-coloured tight-sleeved gown, another in a petticoat as red as the arms of the reaping-machine; and others, older, in the brown-rough "wropper" or over-all — the old-established and most appropriate dress of the field-woman, which the young ones were abandoning. . . .

[Tess's] binding proceeds with clock-like monotony. From the sheaf last finished she draws a handful of ears, patting their tips with her left palm to bring them even. Then stooping low she moves forward, gathering the corn with both hands against her knees, and pushing her left gloved hand under the bundle to meet the right on the other side, holding the corn in an embrace like that of a lover. She brings the ends of the bond together, and kneels on the sheaf while she ties it, beating back her skirts now and then when lifted by the breeze. A bit of her naked arm is visible between the buff leather of the gauntlet and the sleeve of her gown; and as the day wears on its feminine smoothness becomes scarified by the stubble, and bleeds.

. . . The movements of the other women were more or less similar to Tess's, the whole bevy of them drawing together like dancers in a quadrille at the completion of a sheaf by each, every one placing her sheaf on end against those of the rest, till a shock, or "stitch", as it was here called, of ten or a dozen was formed.

Tess of the d'Urbervilles

Swede-hacking and trimming:

The swede-field in which she and her companion were set hacking was a stretch of a hundred odd acres, in one patch, on the highest ground of the farm, rising above stony lanchets or lynchets — the outcrop of siliceous veins in the chalk formation, composed of myriads of loose white flints in bulbous, cusped, and phallic shapes. The upper half of each turnip had been eaten off by the live-stock, and it was the business of the two women to grub up the lower or earthy half of the root with a hooked fork called a hacker, that it might be eaten also. Every leaf of the vegetable having already been consumed, the whole field was in colour a desolate drab; it was a complexion without features, as if a face, from chin to brow, should be only an expanse of skin. The sky wore, in another colour, the same likeness; a white vacuity of countenance with the lineaments gone. So these two upper and nether visages confronted each other all day long, the white face looking down on the brown face, and the brown face looking up at the white face, without anything standing between them but the two girls crawling over the surface of the former like flies.

Nobody came near them, and their movements showed a mechanical regularity; their forms standing enshrouded in Hessian "wroppers" — sleeved brown pinafores, tied behind to the bottom, to keep their gowns from blowing about — scant skirts revealing boots that reached high up the ankles, and yellow sheepskin gloves with gauntlets. The pensive character which the curtained hood lent to their bent heads would have reminded the observer of some early Italian conception of the two Marys.

They worked on hour after hour, unconscious of the forlorn aspect they bore in the landscape, not thinking of the justice or injustice of their lot. Even in such a position as theirs it was possible to exist in a dream. In the afternoon the rain came on again, and Marian said that they need not work any more. But if they did not work they would not be paid; so they worked on. It was so high a situation, this field, that the rain had no occasion to fall, but raced along horizontally upon the yelling wind, sticking into them like glass splinters till they were wet through. Tess had not known till now what was really meant by that. There are degrees of dampness, and a very little is called being wet through in common talk. But to stand working slowly in a field, and feel the creep of rain-water, first in legs and shoulders, then on hips and head, then at back, front and sides, and yet to work on till the leaden light diminishes and marks that the sun is down, demands a distinct modicum of stoicism, even of valour.

Amid this scene Tess slaved in the morning frosts and in the afternoon rains. When it was not swede-grubbing it was swede-trimming, in which process they sliced off the earth and the fibres with a bill-hook before storing the roots for future use. At this occupation they could shelter themselves by a thatched hurdle if it rained; but if it was frosty even their thick leather gloves could not prevent the frozen masses they handled from biting their fingers.

Tess of the d'Urbervilles

Threshing:

It is the threshing of the last wheat-rick at Flintcomb-Ash Farm.... Close under the eaves of the stack, and as yet barely visible, was the red tyrant that the women had come to serve — a timber-framed construction, with straps and wheels appertaining — the threshing-machine which, whilst it was going, kept up a despotic demand upon the endurance of their muscles and nerves.

A little way off there was another indistinct figure; this one black, with a sustained hiss that spoke of strength very much in reserve. The long chimney running up beside an ash-tree, and the warmth which radiated from the spot, explained without the necessity of much daylight that here was the engine which was to act as the *primum mobile* of this little world. By the engine stood a dark motionless being, a sooty and grimy embodiment of tallness, in a sort of trance, with a heap of coals by his side: it was the engineman....

What he looked he felt. He was in the agricultural world, but not of it. He served fire and smoke; these denizens of the fields served vegetable, weather, frost, and sun. He travelled with his engine from farm to farm, from county to county, for as yet the stream threshing-machine was itinerant in this part of Wessex....

The long strap which ran from the driving-wheel of his engine to the red thresher under the rick was the sole tie-line between agriculture and him.... The rick was unhaled by full daylight; the men then took their places, the women mounted, and the work began. Farmer Groby — or, as they called him, "he" — had arrived ere this, and by his orders Tess was placed on the platform of the machine, close to the man who fed it, her business being to untie every sheaf of corn handed on to her by Izz Huett, who stood next, but on the rick; so that the feeder could seize it and spread it over the revolving drum, which whisked out every grain in one moment.

They were soon in full progress, after a preparatory hitch or two, which rejoiced the hearts of those who hated machinery. The work sped on till breakfast-time, when the thresher was stopped for half an hour; and on starting again after the meal the whole supplementary strength of the farm was thrown into the labour of constructing the straw-rick, which began to grow beside the stack of corn. A hasty lunch was eaten as they stood, without leaving their positions, and then another couple of hours brought them near to dinner-time; the inexorable wheels continuing to spin, and the penetrating hum of the thresher to thrill to the very marrow all who were near the revolving wire-cage....

The perspiring ones at the machine, including Tess, could not lighten their duties by the exchange of many words. It was the ceaselessness of the work which tried her so severely, and began to make her wish that she had never come to Flintcomb-Ash. The women on the corn-rick... could stop to drink ale or cold tea from the flagon now and then, or to exchange a few gossiping remarks while they wiped their faces or cleared the fragments of straw and husk from their clothing; but for Tess there was no respite; for, as the drum never stopped, the man who fed it could not stop, and she, who had to supply the man with untied sheaves, could not stop either....

Groby gave as his motive in selecting Tess that she was one of those who best combined strength with quickness in untying, and both with staying power, and this may have been true. The hum of the thresher, which prevented speech, increased to a raving whenever the supply of corn fell short of the regular quantity.

... Dinner-time came, and the whirling ceased; whereupon Tess left her post, her knees trembling so wretchedly with the shaking of the machine that she could scarcely walk.

Tess of the d'Urbervilles

Not a woman in the county but hates the threshing-machine.... I am not sure whether, at the present time, women are employed to feed the machine, but some years ago... a thin saucer-eyed woman of fifty-five, who had been feeding the machine all day, declared on one occasion that in crossing a field on her way home in the fog after dusk, she was so dizzy from the work as to be unable to find the opposite gate, and there she walked round and round the field, bewildered and terrified, till three o'clock in the morning, before she could get out. The farmer said that the ale had got into her head, but she maintained that it was the spinning of the machine. The point was never clearly settled between them; and the poor woman is now dead and buried.

The Dorsetshire Labourer

Reed-drawing:

"Well, as for the weather, it won't hurt us in the wheat-barn; but reed-drawing is fearful hard work — worse than swede-hacking. I can stand it because I'm stout; but you be slimmer than I. I can't think why maister should have set 'ee at it."...

Putting on their gloves all set to work in a row in front of the press, an erection formed of two posts connected by a cross-beam, under which the sheaves to be drawn from were laid ears outward, the beam being pegged down by pins in the uprights, and lowered as the sheaves diminished.

They continued for some long time in a reverie, as they went on seizing the ears of corn, drawing out the straw, gathering it under their arms, and cutting off the ears with their bill-hooks, nothing sounding in the barn but the swish of the straw and the crunch of the hook. Then Tess suddenly flagged, and sank down upon the heap of wheat-ears at her feet....

Just then the farmer entered.... "I want it finished," he said doggedly, as he crossed the barn and went out at the other door.

"Don't 'ee mind him, there's a dear," said Marian. "I've worked here before. Now you go and lie down there, and Izz and I will make up your number."

"I don't like to let you do that. I'm taller than you, too."

However, she was so overcome that she consented to lie down awhile, and reclined on a heap of pull-tails — the refuse after the straight straw had been drawn — thrown up at the further side of the barn.

Tess of the d'Urbervilles

The other side to the picture, as conditions improved:

To be just, however, to the farmers, they do not enforce the letter of the Candlemas agreement in relation to the woman, if she makes any reasonable excuse for breaking it; and indeed, many a nervous farmer is put to flight by a matron who has a tongue with a tang, and who chooses to assert, without giving any reason whatsover, that, though she had made fifty agreements, "be cust if she will come out unless she is minded" — possibly terrifying him with accusations of brutality at asking her, when he knows "how she is just now." A farmer of the present essayist's acquaintance, who has a tendency to blush in the presence of beauty... says that when the ladies of his farm are all together in the field, and he is the single one of the male sex present, he would as soon put his head into a hornet's nest as utter a word of complaint, or even a request beyond the commonest.

The Dorsetshire Labourer

Tess arrives in the Vale of Great Dairies:

Suddenly there arose from all parts of the lowland a prolonged and repeated call —
"Waow! waow! waow!"

From the furthest east to the furthest west the cries spread as if by contagion, accompanied in some cases by the barking of a dog. It was not the expression of the valley's consciousness that beautiful Tess had arrived, but the ordinary announcement of milking-time — half-past four o'clock, when the dairymen set about getting in the cows....

They were the less restful cows that were stalled. Those that would stand still of their own will were milked in the middle of the yard, where many of such better behaved ones stood waiting now — all prime milchers, such as were seldom seen out of this valley, and not always within it; nourished by the succulent feed which the water-meads supplied at this prime season of the year. Those of them that were spotted with white reflected the sunshine in dazzling brilliancy, and the polished brass knobs on their horns glittered with something of military display. Their large-veined udders hung ponderous as sandbags, the teats sticking out like the legs of a gipsy's crock; and as each animal lingered for her turn to arrive the milk oozed forth and fell in drops to the ground.

Tess of the d'Urbervilles

The majority of dairymen have a cross manner at milking-time, but it happened that Mr Crick was glad to get a new hand — for the days were busy ones now — and he received her warmly.

Tess of the d'Urbervilles

In general the cows were milked as they presented themselves, without fancy or choice. But certain cows will show a fondness for a particular pair of hands, sometimes carrying this predilection so far as to refuse to stand at all except to their favourite, the pail of a stranger being unceremoniously kicked over.

It was Dairyman Crick's rule to insist on breaking down these partialities and aversions by constant interchange, since otherwise, in the event of a milk-man or maid going away from the dairy, he was placed in a difficulty. The maids' private aims, however, were the reverse of the dairyman's rule, the daily selection by each damsel of the eight or ten cows to which she had grown accustomed rendering the operation on their willing udders surprisingly easy and effortless.

Tess of the d'Urbervilles

Work and rest:

Not a human being was out of doors at the dairy. The denizens were all enjoying the usual afternoon nap of an hour or so which the exceedingly early hours kept in summer-time rendered a necessity. At the door the wood-hooped pails sodden and bleached by infinite scrubbings, hung like hats on a stand. . . .

Tess of the d'Urbervilles

. . . a many-forked stand made as usual of the peeled limb of an oak-tree, set upright in the earth, and resembling a colossal antlered horn.

The Withered Arm

Milking, skimming, cheesemaking were done. Her father was asleep in the settle, the milkmen and maids were gone home to their cottages, and the clock showed a quarter to eight.

The Romantic Adventures of a Milkmaid

The beginning of November. . . . This was mostly a journey to the farmhouse on the slopes above the vale, to inquire how the advanced[211] cows were getting on in the straw-barton to which they were relegated. For it was a time of the year that brought great changes to the world of kine. Batches of the animals were sent away daily to this lying-in hospital, where they lived on straw till their calves were born, after which event, and as soon as the calf could walk, mother and offspring were driven back to the dairy. In the interval which elapsed before the calves were sold there was, of course, little milking to be done, but as soon as the calf had been taken away the milkmaids would have to set to work as usual.

Tess of the d'Urbervilles

The milkers formed quite a little battalion of men and maids, the men operating on the hard-teated animals, the maids on the kindlier natures. It was a large dairy. There were nearly a hundred milchers under Crick's management, all told; and of the herd the master-dairyman milked six or eight with his own hands, unless away from home. These were the cows that milked hardest of all; for his journey-milkmen[212] being more or less casually hired, he would not entrust this half-dozen to their treatment, lest, from indifference, they should not milk them fully; nor to the maids, lest they should fail in the same way for lack of finger-grip; with the result that in course of time the cows would "go azew" — that is, dry up. It was not the loss for the moment that made slack milking so serious, but that with the decline of demand there came decline, and ultimately cessation, of supply.

After Tess had settled down to her cow there was for a time no talk in the barton, and not a sound interfered with the purr of the milk-jets into the numerous pails, except a momentary exclamation to one of other of the beasts requesting her to turn round or stand still. The only movements were those of the milkers' hands up and down, and the swing of the cows' tails. Thus they all worked on, encompassed by the vast flat mead which extended to either slope of the valley — a level landscape compounded of old landscapes long forgotten, and, no doubt, differing in character very greatly from the landscape they composed now.

"To my thinking," said the dairyman, rising suddenly from a cow he had just finished off, snatching up his three-legged stool in one hand and the pail in the other, and moving on to the next hard-yielder in his vicinity; "to my thinking, the cows don't gie down their milk to-day as usual. Upon my life, if Winker do begin keeping back like this, she'll not be worth going under by midsummer."

"'Tis because there's a new hand come among us," said Jonathan Kail. "I've noticed such things afore."

"To be sure. It may be so. I didn't think o't."

"I've been told that it goes up into their horns at such times," said a dairymaid.

"Well, as to going up into their horns," replied Dairyman Crick dubiously, as though even witchcraft might be limited by anatomical possibilities, "I couldn't say; I certainly could not. But as nott[213] cows will keep it back as well as the horned ones, I don't quite agree to it. Do ye know that riddle about the nott cows, Jonathan? Why do nott cows give less milk in a year than horned?"

"I don't!" interposed the milkmaid. "Why do they?"

"Because there bain't so many of 'em," said the dairyman. "Howsomever, these gam'sters do certainly keep back their milk to-day. Folks, we must lift up a stave[214] or two — that's the only cure for't."

Songs were often resorted to in dairies hereabout as an enticement to the cows when they showed signs of withholding their usual yield; and the band of milkers at this request burst into melody — in purely business-like tones, it is true, and with no great spontaneity; the result, according to their own belief, being a decided improvement during the song's continuance. When they had gone through fourteen or fifteen verses of a cheerful ballad about a murderer who was afraid to go to bed in the dark because he saw certain brimstone flames around him, one of the male milkers said — "I wish singing on the stoop didn't use up so much of a man's wind! You should get your harp, sir; not but what a fiddle is best."

Tess of the d'Urbervilles

SHEEP

In a letter to Leslie Stephen, the editor of the Cornhill Magazine *who first published* Far from the Madding Crowd *in serial form, Hardy wrote from his parents' Bockhampton home (9 January 1874?): "I have decided to finish it here, which is within a walk of the district in which the incidents are supposed to occur. I find it a great advantage to be actually among the people described at the time of describing them." So great was his knowledge of rural life that Hardy was tempted to overload his instalments with technical descriptions – particularly about sheep – which upset their balance, and which Stephen's mature judgment encouraged him to excise or prune. One such passage, visible as a cancelled draft in the Dorest County Museum, was of more than nine pages which included a long and detailed account of the effects of sheep-rot. The remaining sheep scenes, parts of which appear below, are enough to show Hardy's special knowledge of sheep rearing.*

The disaster:

It was a still, moist, night. Just before dawn he was assisted in waking by the abnormal reverberation of familiar music. To the shepherd, the note of the sheep-bell, like the ticking of the clock to other people, is a chronic sound that only makes itself noticed by ceasing or altering in some unusual manner from the well-known idle tinkle which signifies to the accustomed ear, however distant, that all is well in the fold. In the solemn calm of the awakening morn that note was heard by Gabriel, beating with unusual violence and rapidity. This exceptional ringing may be caused in two ways — by the rapid feeding of the sheep bearing the bell, as when the flock breaks into new pasture, which gives it an intermittent rapidity, or by the sheep starting off in a run, when the sound has a regular palpitation. The experienced ear of Oak knew the sound he now heard to be caused by the running of the flock with great velocity.

He jumped out of bed, dressed, tore down the lane through a foggy dawn, and ascended the hill. The forward ewes were kept apart from those among which the fall of lambs would be later, there being two hundred of the latter class in Gabriel's flock. These two hundred seemed to have absolutely vanished from the hill. There were the fifty with their lambs, enclosed at the other end as he had left them, but the rest, forming the bulk of the flock, were nowhere. Gabriel called at the top of his voice the shepherd's call:

"Ovey, ovey, ovey!"

Not a single bleat. He went to the hedge; a gap had been broken through it, and in the gap were the footprints of the sheep. Rather surprised to find them break fence at this season, yet putting it down instantly to their great fondness for ivy in winter-time, of which a great deal grew in the plantation, he followed through the hedge. They were not in the plantation. He called again: the valleys and furthest hills resounded as when the sailors invoked the lost Hylas[215] on the Mysian shore; but no sheep. He passed through the trees and along the ridge of the hill. On the extreme summit, where the ends of the two converging hedges of which we have spoken were stopped short by meeting the brow of the chalk-pit, he saw the younger dog standing agains the sky — dark and motionless as Napoleon at St Helena.

A horrible conviction darted through Oak. With a sensation of bodily faintness he advanced: at one point the rails were broken through, and there he saw the footprints of his ewes. The dog came up, licked his hand, and made signs implying that he expected some great reward for signal services rendered. Oak looked over the precipice. The ewes lay dead and dying at its foot — a heap of two hundred mangled carcases, representing in their condition just now at least two hundred more.

Oak was an intensely humane man: indeed, his humanity often tore in pieces any politic intentions of his which bordered on strategy, and carried him on as by gravitation. A shadow in his life had always been that his flock ended in mutton — that a day came and found every shepherd an arrant traitor to his defenceless sheep. His first feeling now was one of pity for the untimely fate of these gentle ewes and their unborn lambs.

It was a second to remember another phase of the matter. The sheep were not insured. All the savings of a frugal life had been dispersed at a blow; his hopes of being an independent farmer were laid low — possibly for ever. Gabriel's energies, patience, and industry had been so severely taxed during the years of his life between eighteen and eight-and-twenty, to reach his present stage of progress, that no more seemed to be left in him. He leant down upon a rail, and covered his face with his hands.

Far from the Madding Crowd

Farmer Boldwood decides to call on Bathsheba:

He approached the gate of the meadow. Beyond it the ground was melodious with ripples, and the sky with larks; the low bleating of the flock mingling with both. Mistress and man were engaged in the operation of making a lamb "take", which is performed whenever an ewe has lost her own offspring, one of the twins of another ewe being given her as a substitute. Gabriel had skinned the dead lamb, and was tying the skin over the body of the live lamb in the customary manner, whilst Bathsheba was holding open a little pen of four hurdles, into which the mother and foisted lamb were driven, where they would remain till the old sheep conceived an affection for the young one.

Far from the Madding Crowd

The sheep-washing:

It was the end of May.... The sheep-washing pool was a perfectly circular basin of brick-work in the meadows, full of the clearest water. To birds on the wing its glassy surface, reflecting the light sky, must have been visible for miles around as a glistening Cyclops' eye[216] in a green face. The grass about the margin at this season was a sight to remember long — in a minor sort of way. Its activity in sucking the moisture from the rich damp sod was almost a process observable by the eye. The outskirts of this level water-meadow were diversified by rounded and hollowed pastures, where just now every flower that was not a buttercup was a daisy. The river slid along noiselessly as a shade, the swelling reeds and sedge forming a flexible palisade upon its moist brink.... A tributary of the main stream flowed through the basin of the pool by an inlet and outlet at opposite points of its diameter. Shepherd Oak, Jan Coggan, Moon, Poorgrass, Cain Ball, and several others were assembled here, all dripping wet to the very roots of their hair, and Bathsheba was standing by in a new riding-habit — the most elegant she had ever worn — the reins of her horse being looped over her arm. Flagons of cider were rolling about upon the green. The meek sheep were pushed into the pool by Coggan and Matthew Moon, who stood by the lower hatch, immersed to their waists; then Gabriel, who stood on the brink, thrust them under as they swam along, with an instrument like a crutch, formed for the purpose, and also for assisting the exhausted animals when the wool became saturated and they began to sink. They were let out against the stream, and through the upper opening, all impurities flowing away below. Cainy Ball and Joseph, who performed this latter operation, were if possible wetter than the rest; they resembled dolphins under a fountain, every protuberance and angle of their clothes dribbling forth a small rill.

Far from the Madding Crowd

Grinding the shears:

The next day . . . she found Gabriel Oak at the bottom of her garden, grinding his shears for the sheep-shearing. All the surrounding cottages were more or less scenes of the same operation; the scurr of whetting spread into the sky from all parts of the village as from an armoury previous to a campaign. Peace and war kiss each other at their hours of preparation — sickles, scythes, shears, and pruning-hooks ranking with swords, bayonets, and lances, in their comon necessity for point and edge.

Cainy Ball turned the handle of Gabriel's grindstone, his head performing a melancholy see-saw up and down with each turn of the wheel. Oak stood somewhat as Eros is represented when in the act of sharpening his arrows: his figure slightly bent, the weight of his body thrown over on the shears, and his head balanced sideways, with a critical compression of the lips and contraction of the eyelids to crown the attitude.

His mistress came up and looked upon them in silence for a minute or two; then she said —

"Cain, go to the lower mead and catch the bay mare. I'll turn the winch of the grindstone. I want to speak to you, Gabriel."

Cain departed, and Bathsheba took the handle. Gabriel had glanced up in intense surprise, quelled its expression, and looked down again, Bathsheba turned the winch, and Gabriel applied the shears.

The peculiar motion involved in turning a wheel has a wonderful tendency to benumb the mind. It is a sort of attenuated variety of Ixion's punishment,[217] and contributes a dismal chapter to the history of gaols. The brain gets muddled, the head grows heavy, and the body's centre of gravity seems to settle by degrees in a leaden lump somewhere between the eyebrows and the crown. Bathsheba felt the unpleasant symptoms after two or three dozen turns.

"Will you turn, Gabriel, and let me hold the shears?" she said. "My head is in a whirl, and I can't talk."

Gabriel turned, Bathsheba then began, with some awkwardness, allowing her thoughts to stray occasionally from her story to attend to the shears, which required a little nicety in sharpening.

"I wanted to ask you if the men made any observations on my going behind the sedge with Mr Boldwood yesterday?"

"Yes, they did," said Gabriel. "You don't hold the shears right, miss — I knew you wouldn't know the way — hold like this."

He relinquished the winch, and enclosing her two hands completely in his own (taking each as we sometimes clasp a child's hand in teaching him to write), grasped the shears with her. "Incline the edge so," he said.

Hands and shears were inclined to suit the words, and held thus for a peculiarly long time by the instructor as he spoke.

Far from the Madding Crowd

Diseases of the flock:

"You know, I daresay," [said Knight to Stephen] "that sheep occasionally become giddy — hydatids in the head 'tis called, in which their brains become eaten up, and the animal exhibits the strange peculiarity of walking round and round in a circle continually. I have travelled just in the same way — round and round like a giddy ram."

A Pair of Blue Eyes

Bathsheba's sheep get into a field of young clover, and "be getting blasted":

The majority of the afflicted animals were lying down, and could not be stirred. These were bodily lifted out, and the others driven into the adjoining field. Here, after the lapse of a few minutes, several more fell down, and lay helpless and livid as the rest.

Bathsheba, with a sad, bursting heart, looked at these primest specimens of her prime flock as they rolled there —

> Swoln with wind and the rank mist they drew.[218]

Many of them foamed at the mouth, their breathing being quick and short, whilst the bodies of all were fearfully distended.

"O, what can I do, what can I do!" said Bathsheba, helplessly. "Sheep are such unfortunate animals! — there's always something happening to them! I never knew a flock pass a year without getting into some scrape or other."

"There's only one way of saving them," said Tall.

"What way? Tell me quick!"

"They must be pierced in the side with a thing made on purpose."

"Can you do it? Can I?"

"No, ma'am. We can't, nor you neither. It must be done in a particular spot. If ye go to the right or left but an inch you stab the ewe and kill her. Not even a shepherd can do it, as a rule."

"Then they must die," she said, in a resigned tone.

"Only one man in the neighbourhood knows the way," said Joseph, now just come up. "He could cure 'em all if he were here."

But this is Gabriel Oak, whom Bathsheba has dismissed: and she will not stoop to ask for his help.

"Ah!" she added, brightening, "Farmer Boldwood knows!" "O no, ma'am," said Matthew. "Two of his store ewes got into some vetches t'other day, and were just like these. He sent a man on horseback here post-haste for Gable, and Gable went and saved 'em. Farmer Boldwood hev got the thing they do it with. 'Tis a holler pipe, with a sharp pricker inside. Isn't it, Joseph?"

One of the ewes here contracted its muscles horribly, extended itself and jumped high into the air. The leap was an astonishing one. The ewe fell heavily, and lay still.

Bathsheba went up to it. The sheep was dead.

"O, what shall I do — what shall I do!" she again exclaimed, wringing her hands. "I won't send for him. No, I won't!"

She does.

Gabriel was already among the turgid, prostrate forms. He had flung off his coat, rolled up his shirt-sleeves, and taken from his pocket the instrument of salvation. It was a small tube or trochar,[219] with a lance passing down the inside; and Gabriel began to use it with a dexterity that would have graced a hospital-surgeon. Passing his hand over the sheep's left flank, and selecting the proper point, he punctured the skin and rumen[220] with the lance as it stood in the tube; then he suddenly withdrew the lance, retaining the tube in its place. A current of air rushed up the tube, forcible enough to have extinguished a candle held at the orifice.

It has been said that mere ease after torment is delight for a time; and the countenances of these poor creatures expressed it now. Forty-nine operations were successfully performed. Owing to the great hurry necessitated by the far-gone state of some of the flock, Gabriel missed his aim in one case, and in one only — striking wide of the mark, and inflicting a mortal blow at once upon the suffering ewe. Four had died; three recovered without an operation. The total number of sheep which had thus strayed and injured themselves so dangerously was fifty-seven.

Far from the Madding Crowd

The Great Barn and the sheep-shearing

The passage which follows is one of Hardy's finest, and most characteristic, pieces of writing. From the extraordinary opening description of the countryside in teeming summer, through all the architectural details of the Great Barn, the vivid evocation of its many-centuried past and the time-lag between town and country, to the informed but poetic picture of the sheep-shearing, Hardy reveals many of his lifelong preoccupations and the distinctive quality of his perception.

It was the first day of June, and the sheep-shearing season culminated, the landscape, even to the leanest pasture, being all health and colour. Every green was young, every pore was open, and every stalk was swollen with racing currents of juice. God was palpably present in the country, and the devil had gone with the world to town. Flossy catkins of the later kinds, fern-sprouts like bishops' croziers, the square-headed moschatel, the odd cuckoo-pint, — like an apopletic saint in a niche of malachite, — snow-white ladies'-smocks, the toothwort, approximating to human flesh, the enchanter's night-shade, and the black-petaled doleful-bells,[221] were among the quainter objects of the vegetable world in and about Weatherbury at this teeming time; and of animal, the metamorphosed figures of Mr Jan Coggan, the master-shearer; the second and third shearers, who travelled in the exercise of their calling, and do not require definition by name; Henery Fray the fourth shearer, Susan Tall's husband the fifth, Joseph Poorgrass the sixth, young Cain Ball as assistant-shearer, and Gabrial Oak as general supervisor. None of these were clothed to any extent worth mentioning, each appearing to have hit in the matter of raiment the decent mean between a high and low caste Hindoo. An angularity of lineament, and a fixity of facial machinery in general, proclaimed that serious work was the order of the day.

They sheared in the great barn, called for the nonce the Shearing-barn, which on ground-plan resembled a church with transepts. It not only emulated the form of the neighbouring church of the parish, but vied with it in antiquity. Whether the barn had ever formed one of a group of conventual buildings nobody seemed to be aware; no trace of such surroundings remained. The vast porches at the sides, lofty enough to admit a waggon laden to its highest with corn in the sheaf, were spanned by heavy-pointed arches of stone, broadly and boldly cut, whose very simplicity was the origin of a grandeur not apparent in erections where more ornament has been attempted. The dusky, filmed, chestnut roof, braced and tied in by high collars,[222] curves, and diagonals, was far nobler in design, because more wealthy in material, than nine-tenths of those in our modern churches. Along each side wall was a range of striding buttresses, throwing deep shadows on the spaces between them, which were perforated by lancet openings, combining in their proportions the precise requirements both of beauty and ventilation.

One could say about this barn, what could hardly be said of either the church or the castle, akin to it in age and style, that the purpose which had dictated its original erection was the same with that to which it was still applied. Unlike and superior to either of those two typical remnants of mediævalism, the old barn embodied practices which had suffered no mutilation at the hands of time. Here at least the spirit of the ancient builders was at one with the spirit of the modern beholder. Standing before this abraded pile, the eye regarded its present usage, the mind dwelt upon its past history, with a satisfied sense of functional continuity throughout — a feeling almost of gratitude, and quite of pride, at the permanence of the idea which had heaped it up. The fact that four centuries had neither proved it to be founded on a mistake, inspired any hatred of its purpose, nor given rise to any reaction that had battered it down, invested this simple grey effort of old minds with a repose, if not a grandeur, which a too curious reflection was apt to disturb in its ecclesiastical and military compeers. For once mediævalism and modernism had a common standpoint. The lanceolate[223] windows, the time-eaten arch-stones and chamfers,[224] the orientation of the axis, the misty chestnut work of the rafters, referred to no exploded fortifying art or worn-out religious creed. The defence and salvation of the body by daily bread is still a study, a religion, and a desire.

To-day the large side doors were thrown open towards the sun to admit a bountiful light to the immediate spot of the shearers' operations, which was the wood threshing-floor in the centre, formed of thick oak, black with age and polished by the beating of flails for many generations, till it had grown as slippery and as rich in hue as the state-room floors of an Elizabethan mansion. Here the shearers knelt, the sun slanting in upon their bleached shirts, tanned arms, and the polished shears they flourished, causing these to bristle with a thousand rays strong enough to blind a weak-eyed man. Beneath them a captive sheep lay panting, quickening its pants as misgiving merged in terror, till it quivered like the hot landscape outside.

This picture of to-day in its frame of four hundred years ago did not produce that marked contrast between ancient and modern which is implied by the contrast of date. In comparison with cities, Weatherbury was immutable. The citizen's *Then* is the rustic's *Now*. In London, twenty or thirty years ago are old times; in Paris ten years, or five; in Weatherbury three or four score years were included in the mere present, and nothing less than a century set a mark on its face or tone. Five decades hardly modified the cut of a gaiter, the embroidery of a smock-frock, by the breadth of a hair. Ten generations failed to alter the turn of a single phrase. In these Wessex nooks the busy outsider's ancient times are only old; his old times are still new; his present is futurity.

So the barn was natural to the shearers, and the shearers were in harmony with the barn.

The spacious ends of the building, answering ecclesiastically to nave and chancel extremities, were fenced off with hurdles, the sheep being all collected in a crowd within these two enclosures; and in one angle a catching-pen was formed, in which three or four sheep were continuously kept ready for the shearers to seize without loss of time. In the background, mellowed by tawny shade, were the three women, Maryann Money, and Temperance and Soberness Miller, gathering up the fleeces and twisting ropes of wool with a wimble for tying them round. They were indifferently well assisted by the old maltster, who, when the malting season from October to April had passed, made himself useful upon any of the bordering farmsteads.

Behind all was Bathsheba, carefully watching the men to see that there was no cutting or wounding through carelessness, and that the animals were shorn close. Gabriel, who flitted and hovered under her bright eyes like a moth, did not shear continuously, half his time being spent in attending to the others and selecting the sheep for them. At the present moment he was engaged in handing round a mug of mild liquor, supplied from a barrel in the corner, and cut pieces of bread and cheese.

Bathsheba, after throwing a glance here, a caution there, and lecturing one of the younger operators who had allowed his last finished sheep to go off among the flock without re-stamping it with her initials, came again to Gabriel, as he put down the luncheon to drag a frightened ewe to his shear-station, flinging it over upon its back with a dexterous twist of the arm. He lopped off the tresses about its head, and opened up the neck and collar, his mistress quietly looking on.

"She blushes at the insult," murmured Bathsheba, watching the pink flush which rose and overspread the neck and shoulders of the ewe where they were left bare by the clicking shears — a flush which was enviable, for its delicacy, by many queens of coteries, and would have been creditable, for its promptness, to any woman in the world.

Poor Gabriel's soul was fed with a luxury of content by having her over him, her eyes critically regarding his skilful shears, which apparently were going to gather up a piece of the flesh at every close, and yet never did so....

Full of this dim and temperate bliss he went on to fling the ewe over upon her other side, covering her head with his knee, gradually running the shears line after line round her dewlap, thence about her flank and back, and finishing over the tail.

"Well done, and done quickly!" said Bathsheba, looking at her watch as the last snip resounded.

"How long, miss?" said Gabriel, wiping his brow.

"Three-and-twenty minutes and a half since you took the first lock from its forehead. It is the first time that I have ever seen one done in less than half an hour."

The clean, sleek creature arose from its fleece — how perfectly like Aphrodite rising from the foam should have been seen to be realized — looking startled and shy at the loss of its garment, which lay on the floor in one soft cloud, united throughout, the portion visible being the inner surface only, which, never before exposed, was white as snow, and without flaw or blemish of the minutest kind.

"Cain Ball!"

"Yes, Mister Oak; here I be!"

Cainy now runs forward with the tar-pot. "B.E." is newly stamped upon the shorn skin, and away the simple dam leaps, panting, over the board into the shirtless flock outside. Then up comes Maryann; throws the loose locks into the middle of the fleece, rolls it up, and carries it into the battleground as three-and-a-half pounds of unadulerated warmth for the winter enjoyment of persons unknown and far away, who will, however, never experience the superlative comfort derivable from the wool as it here exists, new and pure — before the unctuousness of its nature whilst in a living state has dried, stiffened, and been washed out — rendering it just now as superior to anything *woollen* as cream is superior to milk-and-water.

But heartless circumstances could not leave entire Gabriel's happiness of this morning. The rams, old ewes, and two-shear ewes had duly undergone their stripping, and the men were proceeding with the shearlings and hogs,[225] when Oak's belief that she was going to stand pleasantly by and time him through another performance was painfully interrupted by Farmer Boldwood's appearance in the extremest corner of the barn.

Far from the Madding Crowd

A Sheep Fair

The day arrives of the autumn fair,
        And torrents fall,
Though sheep in throngs are gathered there,
        Ten thousand all,

Sodden, with hurdles round them reared:
And, lot by lot, the pens are cleared,
And the auctioneer wrings out his beard,
And wipes his book, bedrenched and smeared,
And rakes the rain from his face with the edge of his hand,
As torrents fall.

The wool of the ewes is like a sponge
With the daylong rain:
Jammed tight, to turn, or lie, or lunge,
They strive in vain.
Their horns are soft as finger-nails,
Their shepherds reek against the rails,
The tied dogs soak with tucked-in tails,
The buyers' hat-brims fill like pails,
Which spill small cascades when they shift their stand
In the daylong rain.

POSTSCRIPT

Time has trailed lengthily since met
At Pummery Fair
Those panting thousands in their wet
And woolly wear:
And every flock log since has bled,
And all the dripping buyers have sped,
And the hoarse auctioneer is dead,
Who "Going — going!" so often said,
As he consigned to doom each meek, mewed band
At Pummery Fair.

Human Shows

CIDERMAKING

Shortening Days at the Homestead

The first fire since the summer is lit, and is smoking into the room:
The sun-rays thread it through, like woof-lines in a loom.
Sparrows spurt from the hedge, whom misgivings appal
That winter did not leave last year for ever, after all.
Like shock-headed urchins, spiny-haired,
Stand pollard willows, their twigs just bared.

Who is this coming with pondering pace,
Black and ruddy, with white embossed,
His eyes being black, and ruddy his face,
And the marge of his hair like morning frost?
    It's the cider-maker,
    And appletree-shaker,
And behind him on wheels, in readiness,
His mill, and tubs, and vat, and press.

Human Shows

The apple tree comes to town:

It was his custom during the planting season to carry a specimen apple-tree to market with him as an advertisement of what he dealt in. . . . [Marty] recrossed the market-place. It was impossible to avoid rediscovering Winterborne every time she passed that way, for standing, as he always did at this season of the year, with his specimen apple-tree in the midst, the boughs rose above the heads of the farmers, and brought a delightful suggestion of orchards into the heart of the town.

The Woodlanders

"Under the trees now stood a cider-mill and press. . . ." The best of Hardy's prose writing always stems from his country knowledge. In his first published novel, Desperate Remedies[226] *(1871) there is an evocative description of cider-making — and other aspects of country life — too long to include here. In* The Woodlanders *(1887) he described it afresh:*

In the yard between Grace and the orchards there progressed a scene natural to the locality at this time of year. An apple-mill and press had been erected on the spot, to which some men were bringing fruit from divers points in mawn-baskets,[227] while others were grinding them, and others wringing down the pomace, whose sweet juice gushed forth into tubs and pails. The superintendent of these proceedings had hung his coat to a nail of the outhouse wall, and wore his shirt-sleeves rolled up beyond his elbows, to keep them unstained while he rammed the pomace into the bags of horsehair. Fragments of apple-rind had alighted upon the brim of his hat — probably from the bursting of a bag — while brown pips of the same fruit were sticking among the down upon his fine round arms, and in his beard.

She realized in a moment how he had come there. Down in the heart of the apple-country nearly every farmer kept a cider-making apparatus and wring-house for his own use, building up the pomace in great straw "cheeses", as they were called; but here, on the margin of Pomona's[228] plain, was a debatable land neither orchard nor sylvan exclusively, where the apple-produce was hardly sufficient to warrant each proprietor in keeping a mill of his own. This was the field of the travelling cider-maker. His press and mill were fixed to wheels instead of being set up in a cider-house; and with a couple of horses, buckets, tubs, strainers, and an assistant or two, he wandered from place to place, deriving very satisfactory returns for his trouble in such a prolific season as the present.

The outskirts of the town were just now abounding with apple-gatherings. They stood in the yards in carts, baskets, and loose heaps; and the blue stagnant air of autumn which hung over everything was heavy with a sweet cidery smell. Cakes of pomace lay against the walls in the yellow sun, where they were drying to be used as fuel. Yet it was not the great make of the year as yet; before the standard crop came in there accumulated, in abundant times like this, a large superfluity of early apples, and windfalls from the trees of later harvest, which would not keep long. Thus in the baskets, and quivering in the hopper of the mill, she saw specimens of mixed dates, including the mellow countenances of streaked-jacks, codlins, costards, stubbards, ratheripes, and other well-known friends of her ravenous youth.

The Woodlanders

[Grace] discerned shapes moving up the valley towards her, quite near at hand, though till now hidden by the hedges. Surely they were Giles Winterborne, with two horses and a cider-apparatus, conducted by Robert Creedle. Up, upward they crept, a stray beam of the sun alighting every now and then like a star on the blades of the pomace-shovels, which had been converted to steel mirrors by the action of the malic acid. . . .

He looked and smelt like Autumn's very brother, his face being sunburnt to wheat-colour, his eyes blue as corn-flowers, his sleeves and leggings dyed with fruit-stains, his hands clammy with the sweet juice of apples, his hat sprinkled with pips, and everywhere about him that atmosphere of cider which at its first return each season has such an indescribable fascination for those who have been born and bred among the orchards. Her heart rose from its late sadness like a released bough; her senses revelled in the sudden lapse back to Nature unadorned.

The Woodlanders

Woodcutting and Copsework

A curious kind of partnership existed between Melbury and the younger man — a partnership based upon an unwritten code, by which each acted in the way he thought fair towards the other, on a give-and-take principle. Melbury, with his timber and copse-ware business, found that the weight of his labour came in winter and spring. Winterborne was in the apple and cider trade, and his requirements in cartage and other work came in the autumn of each year. Hence horses, waggons, and in some degree men, were handed over to him when the apples began to fall; he, in return, lending his assistance to Melbury in the busiest woodcutting season, as now.

The Woodlanders

That stiffness about the arm, hip, and knee-joint, which was apparent when [Mr Melbury] walked, was the net product of the divers sprains and over-exertions that had been required of him in handling trees and timber when a young man, for he was of the sort called self-made, and had worked hard. He knew the origin of every one of these cramps; that in his left shoulder had come of carrying a pollard, unassisted, from Tutcombe Bottom home; that in one leg was caused by the crash of an elm against it when they were felling; that in the other was from lifting a bole. On many a morrow, after wearying himself by these prodigious muscular efforts, he had risen from his bed fresh as usual; and confident in the recuperative power of his youth he had repeated the strains anew. But treacherous Time had been only hiding ill-results when they could be guarded against for greater effect when they could not.

The Woodlanders

[Melbury's] principal house-door opened on the square yard or quadrangle towards the road, formerly a regular carriage entrance, though the middle of the area was now made use of for stacking timber, faggots, hurdles, and other products of the wood. . . . The building on the left of the enclosure was a long-backed erection, now used for spar-making, sawing, crib-framing, and copse-ware manufacture in general.

The Woodlanders

Making spars (the sharpened wooden pegs used for fastening down thatch):

In the room from which this cheerful blaze proceeded he beheld a girl seated on a willow chair, and busily working by the light of the fire, which was ample and of wood. With a bill-hook in one hand and a leather glove much too large for her on the other, she was making spars, such as are used by thatchers, with great rapidity. She wore a leather apron for this purpose, which was also much too large for her figure. On her left hand lay a bundle of the straight, smooth hazel rods called spar-gads — the raw material of her manufacture; on her right a heap of chips and ends — the refuse — with which the fire was maintained; in front a pile of the finished articles. To produce them she took up each gad, looked critically at it from end to end, cut it to length, split it into four, and sharpened each of the quarters with dexterous blows, which brought it to a triangular point precisely resembling that of a bayonet.

. . . The young woman laid down the bill-hook for a moment and examined the palm of her right hand which, unlike the other, was ungloved, and showed little hardness or roughness about it. The palm was red and blistering, as if her present occupation were as yet too recent to have subdued it to what it worked in.

The Woodlanders

She laid the spars on the ground within the shed. . . . This erection was the waggon-house of the chief man of business hereabout, Mr George Melbury . . . for whom Marty's father did work of this sort by the piece. . . . The four huge waggons under the shed were built on those ancient lines whose proportions have been ousted by modern patterns, their shapes bulging and curving at the base and ends like Trafalgar line-of-battle ships, with which venerable hulks, indeed, these vehicles evidenced a constructive spirit curiously in harmony. One was laden with sheep-cribs, another with hurdles, another with ash poles, and the fourth, at the foot of which she had placed her thatching-spars, was half full of similar bundles.

The Woodlanders

The woodlanders' year:

It was at the beginning of April. . . . The time was that dull interval in a woodlander's life which coincides with great activity in the life of the woodland itself — a period following the close of the winter tree-cutting and preceding the barking season, when the saps are just beginning to heave with the force of hydraulic lifts inside all the trunks of the forest.

Winterborne's contract was completed, and the plantations were deserted.

The Woodlanders

Bark-ripping:

He heard in the distance a curious sound, something like the quack of ducks, which though it was common enough here about this time was not common to him.

Looking through the trees Fitzpiers soon perceived the origin of the noise. The barking season had just commenced, and what he had heard was the tear of the ripping-tool as it ploughed its way along the sticky parting between the trunk and the rind. Melbury did a large business in bark. . . .

Each tree doomed to the flaying process was first attacked by Upjohn. With a small bill-hook he carefully freed the collar of the tree from twigs and patches of moss which encrusted it to a height of a foot or two above the ground, an operation comparable to the "little toilette" of the executioner's victim. After this it was barked in its erect position to a point as high as a man could reach. If a fine product of vegetable nature could ever be said to look ridiculous it was the case now, when the oak stood naked-legged, and as if ashamed, till the axe-man came and cut a ring round it, and the two Timothys finished the work with the cross-cut saw.

As soon as it had fallen the barkers attacked it like locusts, and in a short time not a particle of rind was left on the trunk and larger limbs. Marty South was an adept at peeling the upper parts; and there she stood encaged amid the mass of twigs and buds like a great bird, running her ripping-tool into the smallest branches, beyond the furthest points to which the skill and patience of the men enabled them to proceed — branches which, in their lifetime, had swayed high above the bulk of the wood, and caught the earliest rays of the sun and moon while the lower part of the forest was still in darkness.

"You seem to have a better instrument than they, Marty," said Fitzpiers.

"No, sir," she said, holding up the tool, a horse's leg-bone fitted into a handle and filed to an edge; "'tis only that they've less patience with the twigs, because their time is worth more than mine."

The Woodlanders

Meanwhile, in the wood they had come from, the men had sat on so long that they were indisposed to begin work again that evening; they were paid by the ton, and their time for labour was as they chose. They placed the last gatherings of bark in rows for the curers,[229] which led them further and further away from the shed; and thus they gradually withdrew homeward as the sun went down.

The Woodlanders

Hurdle-making:

He had been asked to execute a very large order for hurdles and other copse-ware, for which purpose he had been obliged to buy several acres of hazel brushwood standing. He was now engaged in the cutting and manufacture of the same, proceeding with the work daily like an automaton.

The hazel-tree did not belie its name to-day. The whole of the copse-wood where the mist had cleared returned purest tints of that hue, amid which Winterborne himself was in the act of making a hurdle, the stakes being driven firmly into the ground in a row, over which he bent and wove the twigs. Beside him was a square, compact pile like the altar of Cain, formed of hurdles already finished, which bristled on all sides with the sharp points of their stakes. At a little distance the men in his employ were assisting him to carry out his contract. Rows of brushwood lay on the ground as it had fallen under the axe; and a shelter had been constructed near at hand, in front of which burnt the fire whose smoke had attracted Melbury. The air was so dark that the smoke hung heavily, and crept away amid the bushes without rising from the ground. . . .

" 'Twill be up in April before you get it all cleared," said Melbury.

"Yes, there or thereabouts," said Winterborne, a chop of the bill-hook jerking the last word into two pieces.

The Woodlanders

Throwing a Tree

New Forest

The two executioners stalk along over the knolls,
Bearing two axes with heavy heads shining and wide,
And a long limp two-handled saw toothed for cutting great boles,
And so they approach the proud tree that bears the death-mark on its side.

Jackets doffed they swing axes and chop away just above ground,
And the chips fly about and lie white on the moss and fallen leaves;
Till a broad deep gash in the bark is hewn all the way round,
And one of them tries to hook upward a rope, which at last he achieves.

The saw then begins, till the top of the tall giant shivers:
The shivers are seen to grow greater each cut than before;
They edge out the saw, tug the rope; but the tree only quivers,
And kneeling and sawing again, they step back to try pulling once more.

Then, lastly, the living mast sways, further sways: with a shout
Job and Ike rush aside. Reached the end of its long staying powers
The tree crashes downward: it shakes all its neighbours throughout,
And two hundred years' steady growth has been ended in less than two hours.

Winter Words

This poem, first published in a French periodical Commerce, *was accompanied by a French translation by Valéry.*

Postscript:

In respect of the occupations of the characters, the adoption of iron utensils and implements in agriculture, and the discontinuance of thatched roofs for cottages, have almost extinguished the handicrafts classed formerly as "copsework", and the type of men who engaged in them.

1912 Preface to *The Woodlanders*

12 Rural Entertainments

Music and Dancing

"Well, as to father in the corner there," the tranter said, pointing to old William, who was in the act of filling his mouth; "he'd starve to death for music's sake now, as much as when he was a boy-chap of fifteen."

Under the Greenwood Tree

With Hardy, as with Michael Henchard, "music was of regal power". (For the latter, "the merest trumpet or organ tone was enough to move him, and high harmonies transubstantiated him.") Hardy himself records how as a child of four or five music used to make him cry, causing him to dance frenetically to hide his tears; and hymn, psalm, and country-dance tunes remained in his thoughts all his life. But beyond this, his life and writings show that for country people whose days were hard and who lacked other cultural opportunities, music, whether in church or at the dance, could be a most absorbing pursuit and relaxation; and its effects on individuals could be lifelong.

Music recurs in all his writing. The sounds of Nature were "acoustic pictures";[230] *and he often sees things in musical terms. Ethelberta's beautiful features included "the arch of the brows — like a slur in music";*[231] *Thomasin "seemed to belong rightly to a madrigal; — to require viewing through*

rhyme and harmony";[232] *in "Alicia's Diary" the two sisters, expecting an unknown visitor, "waited like two newly-strung harps for the first sounds of the returning wheels".*[233] *Sometimes he could not resist a didactic or reminiscent passage which strikes the reader as forced, as in that from* A Laodicean *quoted below; but always he shows the important place of music in the country community.*

Church Music

The Quire:

The zest of these bygone instrumentalists must have been keen and staying, to take them as it did, on foot every Sunday after a toilsome week through all weathers to the church, which often lay at a distance from their homes. They usually received so little in payment for their performances that their efforts were really a labour of love. In the parish I had in my mind when writing the present tale, the gratuities received yearly by the musicians at Christmas were somewhat as follows: From the manor-house ten shillings and a supper; from the vicar ten shillings; from the farmers five shillings each; from each cottage-household one shilling; amounting altogether to not more than ten shillings a head annually —just enough, as an old executant told me, to pay for their fiddle-strings, repairs, rosin, and music-paper (which they mostly ruled themselves). Their music in those days was all in their own manuscript, copied in the evenings after work, and their music-books were home-bound.

It was customary to inscribe a few jigs, reels, hornpipes, and ballads in the same book, by beginning it at the other end, the insertions being continued from front and back till sacred and secular met together in the middle, often with bizarre effect, the words of some of the songs exhibiting that ancient and broad humour which our grandfathers, and possibly grandmothers, took delight in, and is in these days unquotable.

The aforesaid fiddle-strings, rosin, and music-paper were supplied by a pedlar, who travelled exclusively in such wares from parish to parish, coming to each village about every six months. Tales are told of the consternation once caused among the church fiddlers when, on the occasion of their producing a new Christmas anthem, he did not come to time, owing to being snowed up on the downs, and the straits they were in through having to make shift with whipcord and twine for strings. He was generally a musician himself, and sometimes a composer in a small way, bringing his own new tunes, and tempting each choir to adopt them for a consideration. Some of these compositions which now lie before me, with their repetitions of lines, half-lines, and half-words, their fugues and their intermediate symphonies, are good singing still, though they would hardly be admitted into such hymn-books as are popular in the churches of fashionable society at the present time.

Preface to *Under the Greenwood Tree*

Henchard, in The Three Mariners after morning service, asks the church choir for a tune:

"Not a man among us that have sat in the gallery less than twenty year," said the leader of the band. "As 'tis Sunday, neighbours, suppose we raise the Fourth Psa'am, to Samuel Wakely's tune, as improved by me?"

"Hang Samuel Wakely's tune, as improved by thee!" said Henchard. "Chuck across one of your psalters — old Wiltshire is the only tune worth singing — the psalm-tune that would make my blood ebb and flow like the sea when I was a steady chap. I'll find some words to fit 'en."

The Mayor of Casterbridge

George Somerset ponders on a favourite old hymn-tune:

Thus balanced between believing and not believing in his own future, he was recalled to the scene without by hearing the notes of a familiar hymn, rising in subdued harmonies from a valley below. He listened more heedfully. It was his old friend the "New Sabbath," which he had never once heard since the lisping days of childhood, and whose existence, much as it had then been to him, he had till this moment quite forgotten. Where the "New Sabbath" had kept itself all these years — why that sound and hearty melody had disappeared from all the cathedrals, parish churches, minsters and chapels-of-ease that he had been acquainted with during his apprenticeship of life, and until his ways had become irregular and uncongregational — he could not, at first, say. But then he recollected that the tune appertained to the old west-gallery period of church-music,[234] anterior to the great choral reformation and the rule of Monk[235] — that old time when the repetition of a word, or half-line of a verse, was not considered a disgrace to an ecclesiastical choir.

A Laodicean

Hardy wrote several poems — like "Apostrophe to an old Psalm-tune", too long to include here — where church music plays a part. Others in this anthology are "Afternoon Service at Mellstock" (page 22), "A Church Romance" (page 26), and "To My Father's Violin" (page 26).

On the Tune Called the Old-Hundred-and-Fourth

We never sang together
  Ravenscroft's terse old tune
On Sundays or on weekdays,
In sharp or summer weather,
  At night-time or at noon.

Why did we never sing it,
  Why never so incline

On Sundays or on weekdays,
Even when soft wafts would wing it
   From your far floor to mine?

Shall we that tune, then, never
   Stand voicing side by side
On Sundays or on weekdays?...
Or shall we, when for ever
   In Sheol we abide,

Sing it in desolation,
   As we might long have done
On Sundays or on weekdays
With love and exultation
   Before our sands had run?

Late Lyrics and Earlier

SECULAR MUSIC

An echo of the young Tom Hardy:

The fiddler was a boy of those parts, about twelve years of age, who had a wonderful dexterity in jigs and reels, though his fingers were so small and short as to necessitate a constant shifting for the high notes, from which he scrambled back to the first position with sounds not of unmixed purity of tone. At seven the shrill tweedle-dee of this youngster had begun, accompanied by a booming ground-bass from Elijah New, the parish-clerk, who had thoughtfully brought with him his favourite musical instrument, the serpent. Dancing was instantaneous, Mrs Fennel privately enjoining the players on no account to let the dance exceed the length of a quarter of an hour.

But Elijah and the boy in the excitement of their position quite forgot the injunction. Moreover, Oliver Giles, a man of seventeen, one of the dancers, who was enamoured of his partner, a fair girl of thirty-three rolling years, had recklessly handed a new crown-piece to the musicians, as a bribe to keep going as long as they had muscle and wind. Mrs Fennel, seeing the steam begin to generate on the countenances of her guests, crossed over and touched the fiddler's elbow and put her hand on the serpent's mouth. But they took no notice, and fearing she might lose her character of genial hostess if she were to interfere too markedly, she retired and sat down helpless. And so the dance whizzed on with cumulative fury....

The Three Strangers

In Hardy's writings secular music is usually for dancing. The Dynasts *is full of references to particular tunes (one is quoted in musical notation) and it is interesting to note that some at this date, even at the great Brussels ball on the eve of Waterloo, are still* country *dances with names like*

"Speed the Plough". Hardy had his own views on their origins, as is shown by his correspondence with the English Folk Dance Society:

It is quite natural that my heretical query whether, after all, the country-dance might have been a successor to the true folk-dance should meet with opposition. I hold no strong views, but I ask those who maintain otherwise to explain the following rather formidable facts:

1. Down to the middle of the last century, country villagers were divided into two distinct castes, one being the artisans, traders, "liviers" (owners of freeholds), and the manor-house upper servants; the other the "work-folk", i.e. farm-labourers (these were never called by the latter name by themselves and other country people until about 70 years ago). The two castes rarely intermarried, and did not go to each other's house-gatherings save exceptionally.

2. The work-folk had their own dances, which were reels of all sorts, jigs, a long dance called the "horse-race"; another called "thread-the-needle", etc. These were danced with hops, leg-crossing, and rather boisterous movements.

3. Country-dances were introduced into villages about 1800 onwards by the first group of caste, who had sometimes lived in towns. The work-folk knew nothing of the so-called folk-dances (country-dances), and had to be taught them at mixed gatherings. They would lapse back again to their own dances at their own unmixed merrymakings, where they never voluntarily danced country-dances.

4. That in the London magazines of the eighteenth century, and by music publishers of that date, country-dances were printed, music and figures, as new dances. . . . [*English Folk Dance Society Journal,* 2nd ser., vol. 1(1927), pp. 52–6]

But the boy who had played, with his dashing father, for so many rural festivities was always to remain particularly conscious of the often disastrous effect of dancing and music on susceptible listeners, when "the dancers have grown full of excitement and animal spirits".

"Don't ye play no more, shepherd," said Susan Tall's husband, the young married man who had spoken once before. "I must be moving, and where there's tunes going on I seem as if hung in wires."

Far from the Madding Crowd

Cytherea listens, at their first meeting, to Manston playing the organ:

The tones of the organ . . . moved her to a degree out of proportion to the actual power of the mere notes, practised as was the hand that produced them. The varying strains — now loud, now soft; simple, complicated, weird, touching, grand, boisterous, subdued; each phase distinct, yet modulating into the next with a graceful and easy flow — shook and bent her to themselves, as a gushing brook shakes and bends a shadow cast across its surface. The power of the music did not show itself so much by attracting her attention to the subject of the piece, as by taking up and developing as its libretto the poem of her own life and soul, shifting her deeds and intentions from the hands of her judgment and holding them in its own.

She was swayed into emotional opinions concerning the strange man before her; new impulses of thought came with new harmonies, and entered into her with a gnawing thrill.

Desperate Remedies

Eustacia speculates about the unknown Clym Yeobright:

He was there, of course. Who was she that he danced with? Perhaps some unknown woman, far beneath herself in culture, was by that most subtle of lures sealing his fate this very instant. To dance with a man is to concentrate a twelve month's regulation fire upon him in the fragment of an hour. To pass to courtship without acquaintance, to pass to marriage without courtship, is a skipping of terms reserved for those alone who tread this royal road.

The Return of the Native

But it is in his short story "The Fiddler of the Reels" that Hardy develops to the full his theme about the hypnotic effect of music for the dance . In this "Mop" Ollamoor, a fiddler of extraordinary power – especially over "unsophisticated maidenhood" – virtually ruins the life of Car'line Aspent.

His fiddling possibly had the most to do with the fascination he exercised, for, to speak fairly, it could claim for itself a most peculiar and personal quality, like that in a moving preacher.... There was a certain lingual character in the supplicatory expressions he produced, which would wellnigh have drawn an ache from the heart of a gate-post. He could make any child in the parish, who was at all sensitive to music, burst into tears in a few minutes by simply fiddling one of the old dance-tunes he almost entirely affected — country jigs, reels, and "Favourite Quick Steps" of the last century — some mutilated remains of which even now reappear as nameless phantoms in new quadrilles and gallops, where they are recognized only by the curious, or by such old-fashioned and far-between people as have been thrown with men like Wat Ollamoor in their early life.

[Mop could] play the fiddle so as to draw your soul out of your body like a spider's thread... till you felt as limp as withywind and yearned for something to cling to.

Though she was already engaged to be married before she met him, Car'line, of them all, was the most influenced by Mop Ollamoor's heart-stealing melodies, to her discomfort, nay, positive pain and ultimate injury.

It was not the dance nor the dancers, but the notes of that old violin which thrilled... [her], these having still all the witchery that she had so well known of yore, and under which she had used to lose her power of independent will.... She continued to wend her way through the figure of 8 that was formed by her course, the fiddler introducing into his notes the wild and agonizing sweetness of a living voice in one too highly wrought; its pathos running high and running low in endless variation, projecting through her nerves excruciating spasms, a sort of blissful torture....

For the dénouement the whole story must be read: it is collected in Life's Little Ironies, *and is worth the reading.*

The Fiddler

The fiddler knows what's brewing
    To the lilt of his lyric wiles:
The fiddler knows what rueing
    Will come of this night's smiles!

He sees couples join them for dancing,
    And afterwards joining for life,
He sees them pay high for their prancing
    By a welter of wedded strife.

He twangs: "Music hails from the devil,
    Though vaunted to come from heaven,
For it makes people do at a revel
    What multiplies sins by seven.

"There's many a heart now mangled,
    And waiting its time to go,
Whose tendrils were first entangled
    By my sweet viol and bow!'

Time's Laughingstocks

In the Nuptial Chamber

"O that mastering tune!" And up in the bed
Like a lace-robed phantom springs the bride;
"And why?" asks the man she had that day wed,
With a start, as the band plays on outside.
"It's the townsfolk's cheery compliment
Because of our marriage, my Innocent."

"O but you don't know! 'Tis the passionate air
To which my old Love waltzed with me,
And I swore as we spun that none should share
My home, my kisses, till death, save he!
And he dominates me and thrills me through,
And it's he I embrace while embracing you!"

Satires of Circumstance

Dancing was also enjoyed at most private parties, at "gipsy-parties" — a kind of village picnic like the one Fancy Day so much feared Dick had enjoyed without her, in Under the Greenwood Tree *— and the more sensual "gipsying" on the heath when Eustacia and Wildeve met again so fatefully in* The Return of the Native.[236]

The November bonfires and May Day were also important entertainments which were dancing occasions:

"How dark 'tis now the fire's gone down!" said Christian Cantle, looking behind him with his hare eyes. "Don't ye think we'd better get home-along, neighbours? The heth isn't haunted, I know; but we'd better get home.... Ah, what was that?"

"Only the wind," said the turf-cutter.

"I don't think Fifth-of-November ought to be kept up by night except in towns. It should be by day in outstep,[237] ill-accounted places like this!"

"Nonsense, Christian. Lift up your spirits like a man! Susy, dear, you and I will have a jig — hey, my honey? — before 'tis quite too dark to see how well-favoured you be still, though so many summers have passed since your husband, a son of a witch, snapped you up from me."

This was addressed to Susan Nunsuch; and the next circumstance of which the beholders were conscious was a vision of the matron's broad form whisking off towards the space whereon the fire had been kindled. She was lifted bodily by Mr Fairway's arm, which had been flung round her waist before she had become aware of his intention. The site of the fire was now merely a circle of ashes flecked with red embers and sparks, the furze having burnt completely away. Once within the circle he whirled her round and round in a dance. She was a woman noisily constructed; in addition to her enclosing framework of whalebone and lath, she wore pattens[238] summer and winter, in wet weather and in dry, to preserve her boots from wear; and when Fairway began to jump about with her, the clicking of the pattens, the creaking of the stays, and her screams of surprise, formed a very audible concert.

"I'll crack thy numskull for thee, you mandy[239] chap!" said Mrs Nunsuch, as she helplessly danced round with him, her feet playing like drumsticks among the sparks. "My ankles were all in a fever before, from walking through that prickly furze, and now you must make 'em worse with these vlankers!"[240]

The vagary of Timothy Fairway was infectious. The turf-cutter seized old Olly Dowden, and, somewhat more gently, poussetted[241] with her likewise. The young men were not slow to imitate the example of their elders, and seized the maids; Grandfer Cantle and his stick jiggled in the form of a three-legged object among the rest; and in half a minute all that could be seen on Rainbarrow was a whirling of dark shapes amid a boiling confusion of sparks, which leapt around the dancers as high as their waists. The chief noises were women's shrill cries, men's laughter, Susan's stays and pattens, Olly Dowden's "heu-heu-heu!" and the strumming of the wind upon the furze-bushes, which formed a kind of tune to the demoniac measure they trod. Christian alone stood aloof, uneasily rocking himself as he murmured, "They ought not to do it — how the vlankers do fly! 'tis tempting the Wicked one, 'tis."

The Return of the Native

The Maypole:

It was a lovely May sunset, and the birch trees which grew on this margin of the vast Egdon wilderness had put on their new leaves, delicate as butterflies' wings, and diaphanous as amber. Beside Fairway's dwelling was an open space recessed from the road, and here were now collected all the young people from within a radius of a couple of miles. The pole lay with one end supported on a trestle, and women were engaged in wreathing it from the top downwards with wild-flowers. The instincts of merry England lingered on here with exceptional vitality, and the symbolic customs which tradition has attached to each season of the year were yet a reality on Egdon. . . .[242]

The next morning, when Thomasin withdrew the curtains of her bedroom window, there stood the Maypole in the middle of the green, its top cutting into the sky. It had sprung up in the night, or rather early morning, like Jack's bean-stalk. She opened the casement to get a better view of the garlands and posies that adorned it. The sweet perfume of the flowers had already spread into the surrounding air, which, being free from every taint, conducted to her lips a full measure of the fragrance received from the spire of blossom in its midst. At the top of the pole were crossed hoops decked with small flowers; beneath these came a milk-white zone of Maybloom; then a zone of bluebells, then of cowslips, then of lilacs, then of ragged-robins, daffodils, and so on, till the lowest stage was reached. Thomasin noticed all these, and was delighted that the May-revel was to be so near.

When afternoon came people began to gather on the green. . . . When the enthusiastic brass band arrived and struck up, which it did about five o'clock, with apparently wind enough among its members to blow down his house, [Clym] withdrew. . . . He could not bear to remain in the presence of enjoyment to-day, though he had tried hard.

Nothing was seen of him for four hours. When he came back . . . it was dusk, and the dews were coating every green thing. The boisterous music had ceased. . . .

The Return of the Native

Former Beauties

These market dames, mid-aged, with lips thin drawn,
    And tissues sere,
Are they the ones we loved in years agone,
    And courted here?

Are these the muslined pink young things to whom
    We vowed and swore
In nooks on summer Sundays by the Froom,
    Or Budmouth shore?

Do they remember those gay tunes we trod
Clasped on the green;
Aye, trod till moonlight set on the beaten sod
A satin sheen?

They must forget, forget! They cannot know
What once they were,
Or memory would transfigure them, and show
Them always fair.

Times's Laughingstocks

Postscript:

Letter to Mr Sydney Cockerell from Mrs Florence Hardy:

Max Gate, Dorchester *Jan. 27th, 1918*

Dear Mr Cockerell,
. . . There is great excitement about the play . . . You would have been amused — and delighted — on Friday evening, at a rehearsal, to see T.H. grasp a fiddle and play a dance tune for the dancers. He did not dance, but he was *longing* to I could see, and would have footed it as bravely as any . . .

Viola Meynell, *Friends of a Lifetime*

The play was The Mellstock Choir, *an adaptation of* Under the Greenwood Tree. *Hardy was then in his 78th year.*

PARTIES

The inhabitants of the parish, gentle and simple, said that Steve had made ample amends for the harm he had done; and their good-will was further evidenced by his being invited to no less than nineteen Christmas and New Year's parties . . .

Our Exploits at West Poley

The tranter's party:

During the afternoon unusual activity was seen to prevail about the precincts of tranter Dewy's house. The flagstone floor was swept of dust, and a sprinkling of the finest yellow sand from the innermost stratum of the adjoining sand-pit lightly scattered thereupon. Then were produced large knives and forks, which had been shrouded in darkness and grease since the last occasion of the kind, and bearing upon their sides, "Shear-steel, warranted", in such emphatic letters of assurance, that the warranter's name was not required as further proof, and not given. The key was left in the tap of the cider-barrel instead of being carried in a pocket. And finally the tranter had to stand up in the room and let his wife wheel him round like a turnstile, to see if anything discreditable was visible in his appearance.

... The guests had all assembled, and the tranter's party had reached that degree of development which accords with ten o'clock p.m. in rural assemblies. At that hour the sound of a fiddle in process of tuning was heard from the inner pantry.

"That's Dick," said the tranter. "That lad's crazy for a jig."

"Dick! Now I cannot — really, I cannot have any dancing at all till Christmas-day is out," said old William emphatically. "When the clock ha' done striking twelve, dance as much as ye like."

"Well, I must say there's reason in that, William," said Mrs Penny. "If you do have a party on Christmas-night, 'tis only fair and honourable to the sky-folk to have it a sit-still party. Jigging parties be all very well on the Devil's holidays; but a jigging party looks suspicious now. O yes; stop till the clock strikes, young folk — so say I."

It happened that some warm mead accidentally got into Mr Spink's head about this time.

"Dancing," he said, "is a most strengthening, livening, and courting movement, 'specially with a little beverage added! And dancing is good. But why disturb what is ordained, Richard and Reuben, and the company zhinerally? Why, I ask, as far as that do go?"

"Then nothing till after twelve," said William.

... The hopes of the younger members of the household were therefore relegated to a distance of one hour and three-quarters — a result that took visible shape in them by a remote and listless look about the eyes — the singing of songs being permitted in the interim.

At five minutes to twelve the soft tuning was again heard in the back quarters; and when at length the clock had whizzed forth the last stroke, Dick appeared ready primed, and the instruments were boldly handled; old William very readily taking the bass-viol from its accustomed nail, and touching the strings as irreligiously as could be desired.

The country-dance called the "Triumph, or Follow my Lover", was the figure with which they opened.

... Minute after minute glided by, and the party reached the period when ladies' back-hair begins to look forgotten and dissipated; when a perceptible dampness makes itself apparent upon the faces even of delicate girls — a ghastly dew having for some time rained from the features of their masculine partners; when skirts begin to be torn out of their gathers; when elderly people, who have stood up to please their juniors, begin to feel sundry small tremblings in the region of the knees, and to wish the interminable dance was at Jericho; when (at country parties of the thorough sort) waistcoats begin to be unbuttoned, and when the fiddlers' chairs have been wriggled, by the frantic bowing of their occupiers, to a distance of about two feet from where they originally stood....

And now a further phase of revelry had disclosed itself. It was the time of night when a guest may write his name in the dust upon the tables and chairs, and a bluish mist pervades the atmosphere, becoming a distinct halo round the candles; when people's nostrils, wrinkles, and crevices in general seem to be getting gradually plastered up; when the very fiddlers as well as the dancers get red in the face, the dancers having advanced further still towards incandescence, and entered the cadaverous phase; the fiddlers no longer sit down, but kick back their chairs and saw madly at the strings with legs firmly spread and eyes closed, regardless of the visible world. Again and again did Dick share his Love's hand with another man, and wheel round; then, more delightfully, promenade in a circle with her all to himself, his arm holding her waist more firmly each time, and his elbow getting further and further behind her back, till the distance reached was rather noticeable; and, most blissful, swinging to places shoulder to shoulder, her breath curling round his neck like a summer zephyr that had strayed from its proper date. Threading the couples one by one they reached the bottom, when there arose in Dick's mind a minor misery lest the tune should end before they could work their way to the top again, and have anew the same exciting run down through. Dick's feelings on actually reaching the top in spite of his doubts were supplemented by a mortal fear that the fiddling might even stop at this supreme moment; which prompted him to convey a stealthy whisper to the far-gone musicians to the effect that they were not to leave off till he and his partner had reached the bottom of the dance once more, which remark was replied to by the nearest of those convulsed and quivering men by a private nod to the anxious young man between two semiquavers of the tune, and a simultaneous "All right, ay, ay," without opening the eyes. Fancy was now held so closely that Dick and she were practically one person. The room became to Dick like a picture in a dream; all that he could remember of it afterwards being the look of the fiddlers going to sleep as humming-tops sleep, by increasing their motion and hum, together with the figures of grandfather James and old Simon Crumpler sitting by the chimney-corner talking and nodding in dumb-show, and beating the air to their emphatic sentences like people near a threshing machine.

Under the Greenwood Tree

The wedding party:

"Yes, Tony's was the very best wedding-randy that ever I was at; and I've been at a good many, as you may suppose —... having, as a church-officer, the privilege to attend all christening, wedding, and funeral parties — such being our Wessex custom.

" 'Twas on a frosty night in Christmas week....

"The kitchen was cleared of furniture for dancing, and the old folk played at 'Put' and 'All-fours' in the parlour, though at last they gave that up to join in the dance. The top of the figure was by the large front window of the room, and there were so many couples that the lower part of the figure reached through the door at the back, and into the darkness of the out-house; in fact, you couldn't see the end of the row at all, and 'twas never known exactly how long that dance was, the lowest couples being lost among the faggots and brushwood in the out-house.

"When we had danced a few hours, and the crowns of we taller men were swelling into lumps with bumping the beams of the ceiling, the first fiddler laid down his fiddle-bow, and said he should play no more, for he wished to dance."

The History of the Hardcomes

The Night of the Dance

The cold moon hangs to the sky by its horn,
        And centres its gaze on me;
The stars, like eyes in reverie,
Their westering as for a while forborne,
        Quiz downward curiously.

Old Robert draws the backbrand in,
        The green logs steam and spit;
The half-awakened sparrows flit
From the riddled thatch; and owls begin
        To whoo from the gable-slit.

Yes; far and nigh things seem to know
        Sweet scenes are impending here;
That all is prepared; that the hour is near
For welcomes, fellowships, and flow
        Of sally, song, and cheer;

That spigots are pulled and viols strung;
        That soon will arise the sound
Of measures trod to tunes renowned;
That She will return in Love's low tongue
        My vows as we wheel around.

Time's Laughingtocks

In the Small Hours

I lay in my bed and fiddled
    With a dreamland viol and bow,
And the tunes flew back to my fingers
    I had melodied years ago.
It was two or three in the morning
    When I fancy-fiddled so

Long reels and country-dances,
   And hornpipes swift and slow.

And soon anon came crossing
   The chamber in the gray
Figures of jigging fieldfolk —
   Saviours of corn and hay —
To the air of "Haste to the Wedding",
   As after a wedding-day;
Yea, up and down the middle
   In windless whirls went they!

There danced the bride and bridegroom,
   And couples in a train,
Gay partners time and travail
   Had longwhiles still amain! . . .
It seemed a thing for weeping
   To find, at slumber's wane
And morning's sly increeping,
   That Now, not Then, held reign.

Late Lyrics and Earlier

FOOD AND DRINK

Scattered through the novels and stories are many miscellaneous details about food and eating habits in the country during the nineteenth century — some of which have quite disappeared today. Faith Julian's figure (in The Hand of Ethelberta*) "wrapped up to the top of her head [was seen] cutting into the sky behind them like a sugar-loaf";*[243] *in* Under the Greenwood Tree *we read that at Keeper Day's "the table had been spread for the mixed midday meal of dinner and tea, which was common among frugal countryfolk".*[244] *When Durbeyfield wanted to celebrate his newly-discovered nobility, he ordered what to him was food for an occasion: "Tell 'em at hwome that I should like for supper, — well, lamb's fry if they can get it; and if they can't, black-pot; and if they can't get that, well, chitterlings will do."*

In Old Mrs Chundle *food plays an important part. First the sketching curate, taking time off in the country, shares the old cottager's meal of "taters and cabbage, boiled with a scantling o' bacon" (cost: one penny), the vegetables "well-cooked over a wood fire — the only way to cook a vegetable properly." Then he shares her last meal rather more unwillingly, as the smell of it comes in relays up the long tube which he has installed in the pulpit to help her deafness as he preaches:*

It was a fine frosty morning in the early winter, and he had not got far with his sermon when he became conscious of a steam rising from the bell-mouth of the tube, obviously caused by Mrs Chundle's breathing at the lower end, and it was accompanied by a suggestion of onion stew . . .

"If you carefully analyse the passage I have quoted," he continued in somewhat uncomfortable accents, "you will perceive that it naturally suggests three points for consideration —"

("It's not onions: it's peppermint," he said to himself.)

"Namely, mankind in its unregenerate state —"

("And cider.")

"The incidence of the law, and loving-kindness or grace, which we will now severally consider —"

("And pickled cabbage. What a terrible supper she must have made!")

"Under the twofold aspect of external and internal consciousness."

Old Mrs Chundle

Hardy also gives superb descriptions of food and drink on great occasions.

The wedding feast at the mill:

The cooking for the wedding festivities was on a proportionate scale of thoroughness. They killed the four supernumerary chickens that had just begun to crow, and the little curly-tailed barrow pig,[245] in preference to the sow; not having been put up fattening for more than five weeks it was excellent small meat, and therefore more delicate and likely to suit a town-bred lady's taste than the large one, which, having reached the weight of fourteen score, might have been a little gross to a cultured palate. There were also provided a cold chine, stuffed veal, and two pigeon pies. Also thirty rings of black-pot,[246] a dozen of white-pot,[247] and ten knots of tender and well-washed chitterlings,[248] cooked plain, in case she should like a change.

As additional reserves there were sweetbreads, and five milts,[249] sewed up at one side in the form of a chrysalis, and stuffed with thyme, sage, parsley, mint, groats, rice, milk, chopped egg, and other ingredients. They were afterwards to be roasted before a slow fire, and eaten hot.

The business of chopping so many herbs for the various stuffings was found to be aching work for women; and David, the miller, the grinder, and the grinder's boy being fully occupied in their proper branches, and Bob being very busy painting the gig and touching up the harness, Loveday called in a friendly dragoon of John's regiment who was passing by, and he, being a muscular man, willingly chopped all the afternoon for a quart of strong, judiciously administered, and all other victuals found, taking off his jacket and gloves, rolling up his shirt-sleeves and unfastening his stock in an honourable and energetic way.

All windfalls and maggot-covered codlins were excluded from the apple pies; and as there was no known dish large enough for the purpose, the puddings were stirred up in the milking pail, and boiled in the three-legged bell-metal crock, of great weight and antiquity, which every travelling tinker for the previous thirty years had tapped with his stick, coveted, made a bid for, and often attempted to steal.

In the liquor line Loveday laid in an ample barrel of Casterbridge "strong beer".

This renowned drink — now almost as much a thing of the past as Falstaff's favourite beverage[250] — was not only well calculated to win the hearts of soldiers blown dry and dusty by residence in tents on a hill-top, but of any wayfarer whatever in that land. It was of the most beautiful colour that the eye of an artist in beer could desire; full in body, yet brisk as a volcano; piquant, yet without a twang; luminous as an autumn sunset; free from streakiness of taste; but, finally, rather heady. The masses worshipped it, the minor gentry loved it more than wine, and by the most illustrious county families it was not despised. Anybody brought up for being drunk and disorderly in the streets of its natal borough, had only to prove that he was a stranger to the place and its liquor to be honourably dismissed by the magistrates, as one overtaken in a fault that no man could guard against who entered the town unawares.

In addition, Mr Loveday also tapped a hogshead of fine cider that he had had mellowing in the house for several months, having bought it of an honest down-country man, who did not colour, for any special occasion like the present. It had been pressed from fruit judiciously chosen by an old hand — Horner and Cleeves apple for the body, a few Tom-Putts for colour, and just a dash of Old Five corners for sparkle — a selection originally made to please the palate of a well-known temperate earl who was a regular cider-drinker, and lived to be eighty-eight.

The Trumpet-Major

Preparations are made for the shearing-supper:

"We workfolk shall have some lordly junketing to-night," said Cainy Ball, casting forth his thoughts in a new direction. "This morning I see 'em making the great puddens in the milking-pails — lumps of fat as big as yer thumb, Mister Oak! I've never seed such splendid large knobs of fat before in the days of my life — they never used to be bigger than a horse-bean. And there was a great black crock upon the brandise[251] with his legs a-sticking out, but I don't know what was in within."

"And there's two bushels of biffins[252] for apple-pies," said Maryann.

"Well, I hope to do my duty by it all," said Joseph Poorgrass, in a pleasant, masticating manner of anticipation. "Yes; victuals and drink is a cheerful thing, and gives nerves to the nerveless, if the form of words may be used. 'Tis the gospel of the body, without which we perish, so to speak it."

Far from the Madding Crowd

But Hardy, many of whose relations lived in Puddletown, knew well "that love of fuddling to which the village was at one time notoriously prone",[253] *and how often festive occasions ended in disaster. Such was the harvest-supper, when:*

Sergeant Troy had so strenuously insisted, glass in hand, that drinking should be the bond of their union, that those who wished to refuse hardly liked to be so unmannerly under the circumstances. Having from their youth up been entirely unaccustomed to any liquor stronger than cider or mild ale, it was no wonder that they had succumbed, one and all, with extraordinary uniformity. . . .

Far from the Madding Crowd

In "The Three Strangers" we are told that:

. . . the old mead of those days, brewed of the purest first-year or maiden honey, four pounds to the gallon — with its due complement of white of eggs, cinnamon, ginger, cloves, mace, rosemary, yeast, and processes of working, bottling, and cellaring — tasted remarkably strong; but it did not taste so strong as it actually was.

Wessex Tales

Yet Hardy also recognized drinking as one of the few pleasures the rural poor could sometimes enjoy:

This going to hunt up her shiftless husband at the inn was one of Mrs Durbeyfield's still extant enjoyments in the muck and muddle of rearing children. To discover him at Rolliver's, to sit there for an hour or two by his side and dismiss all thought and care of the children during the interval, made her happy. A sort of halo, an occidental glow, came over life then. Troubles and other realities took on themselves a metaphysical impalpability, sinking to mere mental phenomena for serene contemplation, and no longer stood as pressing concretions which chafed body and soul. The youngsters, not immediately within sight, seemed rather bright and desirable appurtenances than otherwise; the incidents of daily life were not without humourousness and jollity in their aspect there. She felt a little as she had used to feel when she sat by her now wedded husband in the same spot during wooing, shutting her eyes to his defects of character, and regarding him only in his ideal presentation as lover.

Tess of the d'Urbervilles

The multiplying eye: Joseph Poorgrass pauses at the Buck's Head on his lonely journey with Fanny Robin's coffin:

Going down into the kitchen of the inn, the floor of which was a step below the passage, which in its turn was a step below the road outside, what should Joseph see to gladden his eyes but two copper-coloured discs, in the form of the countenances of Mr Jan Coggan and Mr Mark Clark. These owners of the two most appreciative throats in the neighbourhood, within the pale of respectability, were now sitting face to face over a three-legged circular table, having an iron rim to keep cups and pots from being accidentally elbowed off; they might have been said to resemble the setting sun and the full moon shining *vis-à-vis* across the globe.

"Why, 'tis neighbour Poorgrass!" said Mark Clark. "I'm sure your face don't praise our mistress's table, Joseph."

'I've had a very pale companion for the last four miles," said Joseph, indulging in a shudder toned down by resignation. "And to speak the truth, 'twas beginning to tell upon me. I assure ye, I ha'n't seed the colour of victuals or drink since breakfast time this morning, and that was no more than a dew-bit afield."

"Then drink, Joseph, and don't restrain yourself!" said Coggan, handing him a hooped mug three-quarters full.

Joseph drank for a moderately long time, then for a longer time, saying, as he lowered the jug, "'Tis pretty drinking — very pretty drinking, and is more than cheerful on my melancholy errand, so to speak it."

"True, drink is a pleasant delight," said Jan, as one who repeated a truism so familiar to his brain that he hardly noticed its passage over his tongue; and, lifting the cup, Coggan tilted his head gradually backwards, with closed eyes, that his expectant soul might not be diverted for one instant from its bliss by irrelevant surroundings.

"Well, I must be on again," said Poorgrass. "Not but that I should like another nip with ye; but the parish might lose confidence in me if I was seed here."

... "But what's yer hurry, Joseph? The poor woman's dead, and you can't bring her to life, and you may as well sit down comfortable, and finish another with us."

"I don't mind taking just the least thimbleful ye can dream of more with ye, sonnies. But only a few minutes, because 'tis as 'tis."

"Of course, you'll have another drop. A man's twice the man afterwards. You feel so warm and glorious, and you whop and slap at your work without any trouble, and everything goes on like sticks a-breaking. Too much liquor is bad, and leads us to that horned man in the smoky house; but after all, many people haven't the gift of enjoying a wet, and since we be highly favoured with a power that way, we should make the most o't."

"True," said Mark Clark. "'Tis a talent the Lord has mercifully bestowed upon us, and we ought not to neglect it. But, what with the parsons and clerks and school-people and serious tea-parties, the merry old ways of good life have gone to the dogs — upon my carcase, they have!"

"Well, really, I must be onward again now," said Joseph.

"Now, now, Joseph; nonsense! The poor woman is dead, isn't she, and what's your hurry?"

"Well, I hope Providence won't be in a way with me for my doings," said Joseph, again sitting down. "I've been troubled with weak moments lately, 'tis true. I've been drinky once this month already, and I did not go to church a-Sunday, and I dropped a curse or two yesterday; so I don't want to go too far for my safety. Your next world is your next world, and not to be squandered offhand."

The longer Joseph Poorgrass remained, the less his spirit was troubled by the duties which devolved upon him this afternoon. The minutes glided by uncounted, until the evening shades began perceptibly to deepen, and the eyes of the three were but sparkling points on the surface of darkness. Coggan's repeater struck six from his pocket in the usual still small tones.

At that moment hasty steps were heard in the entry, and the door opened to admit the figure of Gabriel Oak, followed by the maid of the inn bearing a candle. He stared sternly at the one lengthy and two round faces of the sitters, which confronted him with the expressions of a fiddle and a couple of warming-pans. Joseph Poorgrass blinked, and shrank several inches into the background.

"Upon my soul, I'm ashamed of you; 'tis disgraceful, Joseph, disgraceful!" said Gabriel indignantly....

"No, Shepherd Oak, no! Listen to reason, shepherd. All that's the matter with me is the affliction called a multiplying eye, and that's how it is I look double to you — I mean, you look double to me."

"A multiplying eye is a very bad thing," said Mark Clark.

"It always comes on when I have been in a public-house a little time," said Joseph Poorgrass meekly. "Yes; I see two of every sort, as if I were some holy man living in the times of King Noah and entering into the ark.... Y-y-y-yes," he added, becoming much affected by the picture of himself as a person thrown away, and shedding tears; "I feel too good for England: I ought to have lived in Genesis by rights, like the other men of sacrifice, and then I shouldn't have b-b-been called a d-d-drunkard in such a way!"

"I wish you'd show yourself a man of spirit, and not sit whining there!"

"Show myself a man of spirit?... Ah, well! let me take the name of drunkard humbly — let me be a man of contrite knees — let it be! I know that I always do say "Please God" afore I do anything, from my getting up to my going down of the same, and I be willing to take as much disgrace as there is in that holy act. Hah, yes!... But not a man of spirit? Have I ever allowed the toe of pride to be lifted against my hinder parts without groaning manfully that I question the right to do so? I inquire that query boldly?"

"We can't say that you have, Hero Poorgrass," admitted Jan.

"Never have I allowed such treatment to pass unquestioned! Yet the shepherd says in the face of that rich testimony that I be not a man of spirit! Well, let it pass by, and death is a kind of friend!"

Far from the Madding Crowd

Postscript: an absentee from Dick and Fancy's wedding:

On the circuitous return walk through the lanes and fields, amid much chattering and laughter, especially when they came to stiles, Dick discerned a brown spot far up a turnip field.

"Why, 'tis Enoch!' he said to Fancy. "I thought I missed him at the house this morning. How is it he's left you?"

"He drank too much cider, and it got into his head, and they put him in Weatherbury stocks for it. Father was obliged to get somebody else for a day or two, and Enoch hasn't had anything to do with the woods since."

... "You mustn't blame en," said Geoffrey; "the man's not hisself now; he's in his morning frame of mind. When he's had a gallon o' cider or ale, or a pint or two of mead, the man's well enough, and his manners be as good as anybody's in the kingdom."

Under the Greenwood Tree

TALK

The talking habit, and the need to discuss events together, were very pronounced in Hardy's rural community: talk was a much-relished entertainment, in which everyone participated.

At Warren's Malthouse:

In the ashpit was a heap of potatoes roasting, and a boiling pipkin of charred bread, called "coffee", for the benefit of whomsoever should call, for Warren's was a sort of clubhouse, used as an alternative to the inn. . . .

"I used to go to his house a-courting my first wife, Charlotte, who was his dairymaid. Well, a very good-hearted man were Farmer Everdene, and I being a respectable young fellow was allowed to call and see her and drink as much ale as I liked, but not to carry away any — outside my skin I mane, of course."

"Ay, ay, Jan Coggan; we know yer maning."

"And so you see 'twas beautiful ale, and I wished to value his kindness as much as I could, and not to be so ill-mannered as to drink only a thimbleful; which would have been insulting the man's generosity —"

"True, Master Coggan, 'twould so," corroborated Mark Clark.

"— And so I used to eat a lot of salt fish afore going, and then by the time I got

there I were as dry as a lime-basket — so thorough dry that that ale would slip down — ah, 'twould slip down sweet! Happy times! heavenly times! Such lovely drunks as I used to have at that house! You can mind, Jacob? You used to go wi' me sometimes."

"I can — I can," said Jacob. "That one, too, that we had at Buck's Head on a White Monday was a pretty tipple."

" 'Twas. But for a wet of the better class, that brought you no nearer to the horned man than you were afore you begun, there was none like those in Farmer Everdene's kitchen. Not a single damn allowed; no, not a bare poor one, even at the most cheerful moment when all were blindest, though the good old word of sin thrown in here and there at such times is a great relief to a merry soul."

"True," said the maltster. "Nater requires her swearing at the regular times, or she's not herself; and unholy exclamations is a necessity of life."

"But Charlotte," continued Coggan — "not a word of the sort would Charlotte allow, nor the smallest item of taking in vain.... Ay, poor Charlotte, I wonder if she had the good fortune to get into Heaven when 'a died! But 'a was never much in luck's way and perhaps 'a went downwards after all, poor soul."

"And did any of you know Miss Everdene's father and mother?" inquired the shepherd....

"Well," said the maltster, "he wasn't much to look at; but she was a lovely woman. He was fond enough of her as his sweetheart."

"Used to kiss her scores and long-hundreds o' times, so 'twas said," observed Coggan....

"Well, now, you'd hardly believe it, but that man — our Miss Everdene's father — was one of the ficklest husbands alive, after a while. Understand, 'a didn't want to be fickle, but he couldn't help it. The poor feller were faithful and true enough to her in his wish, but his heart would rove, do what he would. He spoke to me in real tribulation about it once. 'Coggan,' he said, 'I could never wish for a handsomer woman than I've got, but feeling she's ticketed as my lawful wife, I can't help my wicked heart wandering, do what I will.' But at last I believe he cured it by making her take off her wedding ring and calling her by her maiden name as they sat together after the shop was shut, and so 'a would get to fancy she was only his sweetheart, and not married to him at all. And as soon as he could thoroughly fancy he was doing wrong and committing the seventh, 'a got to like her as well as ever, and they lived on a perfect picture of mutel love."

"Well, 'twas a most ungodly remedy," murmured Joseph Poorgrass; "but we ought to feel deep cheerfulness that a happy Providence kept it from being any worse. You see, he might have gone the bad road and given his eyes to unlawfulness entirely — yes, gross unlawfulness, so to say it."

"You see," said Billy Smallbury, "the man's will was to do right, sure enough, but his heart didn't chime in."

"He got so much better that he was quite godly in his later years, wasn't he, Jan?" said Joseph Poorgrass. "He got himself confirmed over again in a more serious way, took to saying 'Amen' almost as loud as the clerk, and he liked to copy comforting verses from the tombstones. He used, too, to hold the money-plate at Let Your Light so Shine, and stand godfather to poor little come-by-chance children; and he kept a missionary box upon his table to nab folks unawares when they called; yes, and he would box the charity-boys' ears, if they laughed in church, till they could hardly stand upright, and do other deeds of piety natural to the saintly inclined."

"Ay, at that time he thought of nothing but high things," added Billy Smallbury. "One day Parson Thirdly met him and said, 'Good-morning, Mister Everdene; 'tis a fine day!' 'Amen,' said Everdene, quite absent-like, thinking only of religion when he seed a parson. Yes, he was a very Christian man."

Far from the Madding Crowd

"The inn called Peter's Finger was the church of Mixen Lane" – and significant talk, culminating in the plot for the skimmity-ride, happened here, as it happened in other inns.[254] *But the need to compare opinions and retail local events was felt wherever a real community existed, and a few were gathered together.*

When the soldiery encamped upon the down, in The Trumpet-Major, *the whole village was a-buzz; and it was with obviously joyful anticipation that, when she had controlled her excitement "unbecoming in a widow and a mother"*. . . till she was toned down to an ordinary person of forty, Mrs Garland accompanied her daughter downstairs to dine, saying, "Presently we will call on Miller Loveday, and hear what he thinks of it all".

The Trumpet-Major

The details of the accident were then rehearsed by Stephen's father in the dramatic manner common to Martin Cannister, other individuals of the neighbourhood, and the rural world generally. Mrs Smith threw in her sentiments between the acts, as Coryphaeus[255] of the tragedy, to make the description complete. The story at length came to an end, as the longest will. . . .

A Pair of Blue Eyes

As the 5th November bonfires blaze out across the heath, leader and listeners settle down to orchestrate the day's events:

"I not only happened to be there," said Fairway, with a fresh collection of emphasis, "but I was sitting in the same pew as Mis'ess Yeobright. And though you may not see it as such, it fairly made my blood run cold to hear her. Yes, it is a curious thing; but it made my blood run cold, for I was close at her elbow." The speaker looked round upon the bystanders, now drawing closer to hear him, with his lips gathered tighter than ever in the rigorousness of his descriptive moderation.

"'Tis a serious job to have things happen to 'ee there," said a woman behind.

"'Ye are to declare it,' was the parson's words," Fairway continued. "And then up stood a woman at my side — a-touching of me. 'Well, be damned if there isn't Mis'ess Yeobright a-standing up,' I said to myself. Yes, neighbours, though I was in the temple of prayers that's what I said. 'Tis against my conscience to curse and swear in company, and I hope any woman here will overlook it. Still what I did say I did say, and 'twould be a lie if I didn't own it."

"So 'twould, neighbour Fairway."

"'Be damned if there isn't Mis'ess Yeobright a-standing up,' I said," the narrator repeated, giving out the bad word with the same passionless severity of face as before, which proved how entirely necessity and not gusto had to do with the iteration. "And the next thing I heard was, 'I forbid the banns,' from her. 'I'll speak to you after the service,' said the parson, in quite a homely way — yes, turning all at once into a common man no holier than you or I. Ah, her face was pale! Maybe you can call to mind that monument in Weatherbury church — the cross-legged soldier that have had his arm knocked away by the school-children? Well, he would about have matched that woman's face, when she said, 'I forbid the banns.'"

The audience cleared their throats and tossed a few stalks into the fire, not because these deeds were urgent, but to give themselves time to weigh the moral of the story.

"I'm sure when I heard they'd been forbid I felt as glad as if anybody had gied me sixpence," said an earnest voice — that of Olly Dowden, a woman who lived by making heath brooms, or besoms. Her nature was to be civil to enemies as well as to friends, and grateful to all the world for letting her remain alive.

"And now the maid have married him just the same," said Humphrey.

"After that Mis'ess Yeobright came round and was quite agreeable," Fairway resumed, with an unheeding air, to show that his words were no appendage to Humphrey's, but the result of independent reflection.

"Supposing they were ashamed, I don't see why they shouldn't have done it here-right," said a widespread woman whose stays creaked like shoes whenever she stooped or turned. "'Tis well to call the neighbours together and to hae a good racket once now and then; and it may as well be when there's a wedding as at tide-times[256]. . . ."

The Return of the Native

CLUB WALKING

Parish clubs or friendly societies, another form of the self-made entertainment characteristic of Hardy's time and place, used to have an annual walk, or feast, at Whitsun. William Barnes, the Dorset poet who was Hardy's friend, wrote a delightful poem called "Whitsuntide an' Club Walken".

Tranter Dewy describes his wedding-day:

"The long and the short o' the story is that we were married somehow, as I found afterwards. 'Twas on White Tuesday, — Mellstock Club walked the same day, every man two and two, and a fine day 'twas, — hot as fire; how the sun did strike down upon my back going to Church! . . . We new-married folk went a-gaying round the parish behind 'em. Everybody used to wear something white at Whitsuntide in them days. My sonnies, I've got the very white trousers that I wore, at home in box now. Ha'n't I, Ann?"

"You had till I cut 'em up for Jimmy," said Mrs Dewy.

Under the Greenwood Tree

Club-walking with a difference:

It was an interesting event to the younger inhabitants of Marlott, though its real interest was not observed by the participators in the ceremony. Its singularity lay less in the retention of a custom of walking in procession and dancing on each anniversary than in the members being solely women. In men's clubs such celebrations were, though expiring, less uncommon; but neither the natural shyness of the softer sex, or a sarcastic attitude on the part of male relatives, had denuded such women's clubs as remained (if any other did) of this their glory and consummation. The club of Marlott alone lived to uphold the local Cerealia. It had walked for hundreds of years, if not as benefit-club, as votive sisterhood of some sort; and it walked still.

The banded ones were all dressed in white gowns — a gay survival from Old Style days, when cheerfulness and May-time were synonyms — days before the habit of taking long views had reduced emotions to a monotonous average. Their first exhibition of themselves was in a processional march of two and two round the parish.

... In addition to the distinction of a white frock, every woman and girl carried in her right hand a peeled willow wand, and in her left a bunch of white flowers. The peeling of the former, and the selection of the latter, had been an operation of personal care.

There were a few middle-aged and even elderly women in the train, their silver-wiry hair and wrinkled faces, scourged by time and trouble, having almost a grotesque, certainly a pathetic, appearance in such a jaunty situation....

There was to be dancing on the green.... As there were no men in the company the girls danced at first with each other, but when the hour for the close of labour drew on, the masculine inhabitants of the village, together with other idlers and pedestrians, gathered round the spot, and appeared inclined to negotiate for a partner....

Tess of the d'Urbervilles

The Mummers

At this moment the fiddles finished off with a screech, and the serpent emitted a last note that nearly lifted the roof. When, from the comparative quiet within, the mummers judged that the dancers had taken their seats, Father Christmas advanced, lifted the latch, and put his head inside the door.

"Ah, the mummers, the mummers!" cried several guests at once. "Clear a space for the mummers."

Hump-backed Father Christmas then made a complete entry, swinging his huge club, and in a general way clearing the stage for the actors proper, while he informed the company in smart verse that he was come, welcome or welcome not; concluding his speech with

"Make room, make room, my gallant boys,
And give us space to rhyme;
We've come to show Saint George's play,
Upon this Christmas time."

The guests were now arranging themselves at one end of the room, the fiddler was mending a string, the serpent-player was emptying his mouthpiece, and the play began.

The Return of the Native

In 1902 Hardy had the following conversation about his youth with William Archer:

Mr Hardy. The Christmas Mummers flourished well into my recollection — indeed, they have not so long died out.

W.A. I can remember a sort of mummers in Scotland whom we called "guisers"; but they were simply boys wearing masks and begging for half-pence.

Mr Hardy. Oh, our mummers hereabouts gave a regular performance — *The Play of St George* it was called. It contained quite a number of traditional characters: the Valiant Soldier, the Turkish Knight, St. George himself, the Saracen, Father Christmas, the Fair Sabra, and so on. Rude as it was, the thing used to impress me very much — I can clearly recall the odd sort of thrill it would give. The performers used to carry a long staff in one hand and a wooden sword in the other, and pace monotonously round, intoning their parts on one note, and punctuating them by nicking the sword against the staff — something like this: —

"Here come I, the Valiant Soldier (*nick*), Slasher is my name (*nick*)."

W.A. The pacing and rhythmic sing-song suggest kinship with the Chinese acting I have seen in San Francisco and New York. And what was the action of the play?

Mr Hardy. I really don't know, except that it ended in a series of mortal combats in which all the characters but St. George were killed. And then the curious thing was that they were invariably brought to life again. A personage was introduced for the purpose — the Doctor of Physic, wearing a cloak and a broadbrimmed beaver.

W.A. How many actors would there be in a company?

Mr Hardy. Twelve to fifteen, I should think. Sometimes a large village would furnish forth two sets of mummers. They would go to the farmhouse round, between Christmas and Twelfth Night, doing some four or five performances each evening, and getting ale and money at every house. Sometimes the mummers of one village would encroach on the traditional "sphere of influence" of another village, and then there would be a battle in good earnest.

W.A. Did women take part in the performances?

Mr Hardy. I think not — the fair Sabra was always played by a boy. But the character was often omitted.

W.A. And when did the mumming go out?

Mr Hardy. It went on in some neighbourhoods till 1880, or thereabouts. I have heard of a parson here and there trying to revive it; but of course that isn't at all the same thing — the spontaneity is gone.

W. Archer, *Real Conversations*

In his third notebook Hardy records the indictment of some of the Fordington Mummers for assaulting James and William Keats of the Bockhampton Band or "Quire". (William Keats, a tranter, lived directly opposite the Hardys, and he and his family were the models for the Dewys in Under the Greenwood Tree.*) It seems that the Band had become rivals to the mummers, "and plucked from them a portion of their laurels, and profits" — and that "about 100" had attacked William.*

The Famous Tragedy of the Queen of Cornwall[257] *(completed when Hardy was in his eighty-fourth year) is a play in the mumming style; "the costumes are the conventional ones of bright linen fabrics, trimmed with ribbons, as in the old mumming shows." About twenty years earlier, in writing the preface to* The Dynasts, *Hardy had paid tribute to the never-failing influence upon him of those Christmas mummers of his youth:*

In respect of such plays of poesy and dream a practicable compromise may conceivably result, taking the shape of a monotonic delivery of speeches, with dreamy conventional gestures, something in the manner traditionally maintained by the old Christmas mummers, the curiously hypnotizing impressiveness of whose automatic style — that of persons who spoke by no will of their own — may be remembered by all who ever experienced it.

Preface to *The Dynasts*

For more about the mummers' clothes see page 128. Also on page 128 are some delightful drawings of the mummers' staff and smock which Hardy made and sent to the illustrator of his magazine instalments of The Return of the Native.

Postscript:

Max Gate, Dorchester *Dec. 26th, 1920*

Dear Mr Cockerell,

We, contrary to our usual custom, have spent a most exciting Christmas. Yesterday the Mummers (under our beloved Mr Tilley) came and performed in the drawing-room here, to the intense joy of T.H., his brother and sister (whom I had here) and the rest of the household. And friends who accompanied them fiddled to us and sang carols outside — the real old Bockhampton carols. Then they came in, had refreshments in the dining-room and we had a very delightful time with them....

T. is very well. At the party (of the mummers etc.) last night he was so gay — and one of them said to me that he had never seen him so young and happy and excited. He is now — this afternoon — writing a poem with great spirit: always a sign of well-being with him. Needless to say it is an intensely dismal poem.

Our very best wishes to you all,
Yours very sincerely,
Florence Hardy

Viola Meynell, *Friends of a Lifetime*

The Skimmity Ride
A less innocent form of drama

The parcel of love letters from Lucetta, now Mrs Farfrae, to her former lover Michael Henchard are to be delivered by the unreliable Jopp to Lucetta and the safety of destruction. Unknown to her they have been opened on their way and read aloud to the company assembled in Peter's Finger.

"I say, what a good foundation for a skimmity-ride,' said Nance.

"True," said Mrs Cuxsom, reflecting. "'Tis as good a ground for a skimmity-ride as ever I knowed; and it ought not to be wasted. The last one seen in Casterbridge must have been ten years ago, if a day."

A stranger at the inn is listening:

"What do they mean by a 'skimmity-ride'?" he asked.

"O, sir!" said the landlady, swinging her long ear-rings with deprecating modesty; "'tis a' old foolish thing they do in these parts when a man's wife is — well, not too particularly his own. But as a respectable householder I don't encourage it."

"Still, are they going to do it shortly? It is a good sight to see, I suppose?"

"Well, sir!" she simpered. And then, bursting into naturalness, and glancing from the corner of her eye, "'Tis the funniest thing under the sun! And it costs money."

The stranger, intrigued, provides it; and the skimmity is prepared.

On the crucial evening the unsuspecting Lucetta sits alone in her drawing-room awaiting her husband's return. She is joined in haste by Elizabeth-Jane, who tries in vain to keep Lucetta in ignorance of what is happening in the streets outside her window:

The reverie in which these and other subjects mingled was disturbed by a hubbub in the distance, that increased moment by moment.... Her attention was at once riveted to the matter by the voice of a maid-servant next door, who spoke from an upper window across the street to some other maid even more elevated that she.

"Which way be they going now?" inquired the first with interest.

"I can't be sure for a moment," said the second, "because of the malter's chimbley.

O yes — I can see 'em. Well, I declare, I declare!"

"What, what?" from the first, more enthusiastically.

"They are coming up Corn Street after all! They sit back to back!"

"What — two of 'em — are there two figures?"

"Yes. Two images on a donkey, back to back, their elbows tied to one another's! She's facing the head, and he's facing the tail."

"Is it meant for anybody particular?"

"Well — it mid be. The man has got on a blue coat and kerseymere leggings; he has black whispers, and a reddish face. 'Tis a stuffed figure, with a falseface."...

"What's the woman like? Just say, and I can tell in a moment if 'tis meant for one I've in mind."

"My — why — 'tis dressed just as *she* was dressed when she sat in the front seat at the time the play-actors came to the Town Hall!...

"Her neck is uncovered, and her hair in bands, and her back-comb in place; she's got on a puce silk, and white stockings, and coloured shoes."

Again Elizabeth-Jane attempted to close the window, but Lucetta held her by main force.

"'Tis me!" she said, with a face pale as death. "A procession — a scandal — an effigy of me, and him!"... Lucetta's eyes were straight upon the spectacle of the uncanny revel, now advancing rapidly. The numerous lights around the two effigies threw them up into lurid distinctness; it was impossible to mistake the pair for other than the intended victims.

... Meanwhile Mr. Benjamin Grower, that prominent burgess of whom mention has been already made, hearing the din of cleavers, tongs, tambourines, kits,[258] crouds,[259] humstrums,[260] serpents,[261] rams'-horns, and other historical kinds of music as he sat indoors in the High Street, had put on his hat and gone out to learn the cause. He came to the corner above Farfrae's, and soon guessed the nature of the proceedings; for being a native of the town he had witnessed such rough jests before. His first move was to search hither and thither for the constables; there were two in the town, shrivelled men whom he ultimately found in hiding up an alley yet more shrivelled than usual, having some not ungrounded fears that they might be roughly handled if seen.

The Mayor of Casterbridge

FAIRS

Fairs and circuses — one of the few forms of rural entertainment not solely provided by the participants — recur in Hardy's writings. In September 1873, while writing Far from the Madding Crowd, *he walked over to Woodbury-Hill Fair to prepare himself for the scene of "Greenhill Fair" in that novel; after a note about visiting a circus in 1884 he records that he "had something of a craze for circuses in these years and went to all that came to Dorchester."*[262] *In a short story "On the Western Circuit" (1891) — from which the following extract is taken — he calls the hobby-horses with their "equine undulations" "this most delightful holiday-game of our times."*

Charles Raye, a young barrister from London, is drawn one October evening from his study of Melchester Cathedral to visit the fair:

He postponed till the morrow his attempt to examine the deserted edifice, and turned his attention to the noise. It was compounded of steam barrel-organs, the clangings of gongs, the ringing of hand-bells, the clack of rattles, and the undistinguishable shouts of men. A lurid light hung in the air in the direction of the tumult. Thitherward he went, passing under the arched gateway, along a straight street, and into the square.

He might have searched Europe over for a greater contrast between juxtaposed scenes. The spectacle was that of the eighth chasm of the Inferno as to colour and flame, and, as to mirth, a development of the Homeric heaven. A smoky glare, of the complexion of brass-filings, ascended from the fiery tongues of innumerable naphtha lamps affixed to booths, stalls, and other temporary erections which crowded the spacious market square. In front of this irradiation scores of human figures, more or less in profile, were darting athwart and across, up, down, and around, like gnats against a sunset.

Their motions were so rhythmical that they seemed to be moved by machinery. And it presently appeared that they were moved by machinery indeed; the figures being those of the patrons of swings, see-saws, flying-leaps, above all of the three steam roundabouts which occupied the centre of the position. It was from the latter that the din of steam-organs came.

Throbbing humanity in full light was, on second thoughts, better than architecture in the dark.

On the Western Circuit

The sheep fair:

Greenhill was the Nijni Novgorod[263] of South Wessex; and the busiest, merriest, noisiest day of the whole statute number was the day of the sheep fair. . . .

All these bleating, panting, and weary thousands had entered and were penned before the morning had far advanced, the dog belonging to each flock being tied to the corner of the pen containing it. Alleys for pedestrians intersected the pens, which soon became crowded with buyers and sellers from far and near.

In another part of the hill an altogether different scene began to force itself upon the eye towards midday. A circular tent, of exceptional newness and size, was in course of erection here. As the day drew on, the flocks began to change hands, lightening the shepherds' responsibilities; and they turned their attention to this tent and inquired of a man at work there . . . what was going on.

"The Royal Hippodrome Performance of Turpin's Ride to York and the Death of Black Bess," replied the man promptly.

. . . As soon as the tent was completed the band struck up highly stimulating harmonies, and the announcement was publicly made, Black Bess standing in a conspicuous position on the outside, as a living proof, if proof were wanted, of the truth of the oracular utterances from the stage over which the people were to enter. These were so convinced by such genuine appeals to heart and understanding both that they soon began to crowd in abundantly, among the foremost being visible Jan Coggan and Joseph Poorgrass, who were holiday keeping here to-day.

"That's the great ruffen pushing me!" screamed a woman in front of Jan over her shoulder at him when the rush was at its fiercest.

"How can I help pushing ye when the folk behind push me?" said Coggan, in a deprecating tone, turning his head towards the aforesaid folk as far as he could without turning his body, which was jammed as in a vice.

There was a silence; then the drums and trumpets again sent forth their echoing notes. The crowd was again ecstasied, and gave another lurch in which Coggan and Poorgrass were again thrust by those behind upon the women in front.

"O that helpless feymels should be at the mercy of such ruffens!" exclaimed one of these ladies again, as she swayed like a reed shaken by the wind.

"Now," said Coggan, appealing in an earnest voice to the public at large as it stood clustered about his shoulder-blades, "did ye ever hear such a onreasonable woman as that? Upon my carcase, neighbours, if I could only get out of this cheesewring,[264] the damn women might eat the show for me!"

"Don't ye lose yer temper, Jan!" implored Joseph Poorgrass, in a whisper. "They might get their men to murder us, for I think by the shine of their eyes that they be a sinful form of womankind."

Jan held his tongue, as if he had no objection to be pacified to please a friend, and they gradually reached the foot of the ladder, Poorgrass being flattened like a jumping-jack,[265] and the sixpence, for admission, which he had got ready half-an-hour earlier, having become so reeking hot in the tight squeeze of his excited hand that the woman in spangles, brazen rings set with glass diamonds, and with chalked face and shoulders, who took the money from him, hastily dropped it again from a fear that some trick had been played to burn her fingers. So they all entered, and the cloth of the tent, to the eyes of an observer on the outside, became bulged into innumerable pimples such as we observe on a sack of potatoes, caused by the various human heads, backs, and elbows at high pressure within.

... It was now almost dark, and respectable people were getting their carts and gigs ready to go home.

The largest refreshment booth in the fair was provided by an innkeeper from a neighbouring town. This was considered an unexceptionable place for obtaining the necessary food and rest: Host Trencher (as he was jauntily called by the local newspaper) being a substantial man of high repute for catering through all the country round. The tent was divided into first and second-class compartments, and at the end of the first-class division was a yet further enclosure for the most exclusive, fenced off from the body of the tent by a luncheon-bar, behind which the host himself stood, bustling about in white apron and shirt-sleeves, and looking as if he had never lived anywhere but under canvas all his life. In these penetralia were chairs and a table, which, on candles being lighted, made quite a cosy and luxurious show, with an urn, plated tea and coffee pots, china teacups, and plum cakes.

Troy stood at the entrance to the booth, where a gypsy-woman was frying pancakes over a little fire of sticks and selling them at a penny a-piece....

Far from the Madding Crowd

Last Look Round St Martin's Fair

The sun is like an open furnace door,
Whose round revealed retort confines the roar
Of fires beyond terrene;
The moon presents the lustre-lacking face
Of a brass dial gone green,
Whose hours no eye can trace.
The unsold heathcroppers are driven home
To the shades of the Great Forest whence they come
By men with long cord-waistcoats in brown monochrome.
The stars break out, and flicker in the breeze,
It seems, that twitches the trees. —
From its hot idol soon
The fickle unresting earth has turned to a fresh patroon —
The cold, now brighter, moon.

The woman in red, at the nut-stall with the gun,
Lights up, and still goes on:
She's redder in the flare-lamp than the sun
Showed it ere it was gone.
Her hands are black with loading all the day,
And yet she treats her labour as 'twere play,
Tosses her ear-rings, and talks ribaldry
To the young men around as natural gaiety,
And not a weary work she'd readily stay,
And never again nut-shooting see,
Though crying, "Fire away!"

Human Shows

A postscript:

Great Things

Sweet cyder is a great thing,
A great thing to me,
Spinning down to Weymouth town
By Ridgway thirstily,
And maid and mistress summoning

Who tend the hostelry:
O cyder is a great thing,
A great thing to me!

The dance it is a great thing,
A great thing to me,
With candles lit and partners fit
For night-long revelry;
And going home when day-dawning
Peeps pale upon the lea:
O dancing is a great thing,
A great thing to me!

Love is, yea, a great thing,
A great thing to me,
When, having drawn across the lawn
In darkness silently,
A figure flits like one a-wing
Out from the nearest tree:
O love is, yes, a great thing,
A great thing to me!

Will these be always great things,
Great things to me?...
Let it befall that One will call,
"Soul, I have need of thee:"
What then? Joy-jaunts, impassioned flings,
Love, and its ecstasy,
Will always have been great things,
Great things to me!

Moments of Vision

13 Town and Country

The Ruined Maid

"O 'Melia, my dear, this does everything crown!
Who could have supposed I should meet you in Town?
And whence such fair garments, such prosperi-ty?" —
"O didn't you know I'd been ruined?' said she.

— "You left us in tatters, without shoes or socks,
Tired of digging potatoes, and spudding up docks;
And now you've gay brackets and bright feathers three!" —
"Yes: that's how we dress when we're ruined," said she.

— "At home in the barton you said 'thee' and 'thou',
And 'thiks oon', and 'theäs oon', and 't'other', but now
Your talking quite fits 'ee for high compa-ny!" —
"A polish is gained with one's ruin," said she.

— "Your hands were like paws then, your face blue and bleak
But now I'm bewitched by your delicate cheek,
And your little gloves fit as on any la-dy!" —
"We never do work when we're ruined," said she.

— "You used to call home-life a hag-ridden dream,
And you'd sigh, and you'd sock; but at present you seem
To know not of megrims or melancho-ly!" —
"True. One's pretty lively when ruined," said she.

— "I wish I had feathers, a fine sweeping gown,
And a delicate face, and could strut about Town!" —
"My dear — a raw country girl, such as you be,
Cannot quite expect that. You ain't ruined," said she.

Westbourne Park Villas, 1866 *Poems of the Past and Present*

Thus it happened that when the last of Tess's sovereigns had been spent she was unprovided with others to take their place, while on account of the season she found it increasingly difficult to get employment. Not being aware of the rarity of intelligence, energy, health, and willingness in any sphere of life, she refrained from seeking an indoor occupation; fearing towns, large towns, large houses, people of means and social sophistication, and of manners other than rural. From that direction of gentility Black Care had come.

Tess of the d'Urbervilles

Bathsheba's aunt was indoors. "Will you tell Miss Everdene that somebody would be glad to speak to her?" said Mr Oak. (Calling oneself merely Somebody, without giving a name, is not to be taken as an example of the ill-breeding of the rural world: it springs from a refined modesty of which townspeople, with their cards and announcements, have no notion whatever.)

Far from the Madding Crowd

Drudgery in the slums and alley of a city, too long pursued, and accompanied as it too often is by indifferent health, may induce a mood of despondency which is well-nigh permanent; but the same degree of drudgery in the fields results at worst in a mood of painless passivity. A pure atmosphere and a pastoral environment are a very appreciable portion of the sustenance which tends to produce the sound mind and body, and thus much sustenance is, at least, the labourer's birthright.

The Dorsetshire Labourer

Max Gate, 13th April, 1899:

. . . I do not know when we shall go to London: for myself I would rather go into a monastery. . . .

Letter to Mrs Florence Henniker

Apart from sometimes missing the music in London, and occasionally feeling dull in the country, Hardy makes it clear that he thinks life in the country superior to life in the town.

Everything is made worse in London — not only drudgery, but poverty:

"We must not be poor in London. Poverty in the country is a sadness, but poverty in town is a horror. There is something not without grandeur in the thought of starvation on an open mountain or in a wide wood, and your bones lying there to bleach in the pure sun and rain; but a back garret in a rookery, and the other starvers in the room insisting on keeping the window shut — anything to deliver us from that!"

The Hand of Ethelberta

— and Stephen Smith says to Elfride in the wilds of Cornwall that his life in London is more solitary than hers — "as solitary as death".[226]

Life in the country is healthier — Hardy himself almost always had influenza or a sore throat when he was in London.

Hyde Park, 16.5.1901

. . . We have been saying how foolish it seems to have come away from where we were well, and, as you are now, surrounded by birds' songs and young leaves, to make ourselves ill in a city!

Letter to Mrs Florence Henniker

Stephen Smith, who has hitherto been hidden from us by the darkness, was at this time of his life but a youth in appearance, and not a man in years. Judging from his look, London was the last place in the world that one would have imagined to be the scene of his activities: such a face surely could not be nourished amid smoke and mud and fog and dust; such an open countenance could never have seen anything of "the weariness, the fever, and the fret" of Babylon the Second.[267]

A Pair of Blue Eyes

"We will have a change soon," [Ethelberta] said; "we will go out of town for a few days. It will do good in many ways. I am getting so alarmed about the health of the children; their faces are becoming so white and thin and pinched that an old acquaintance would hardly know them; and they were so plump when they came. You are looking as pale as a ghost, and I daresay I am too. A week or two at Knollsea will see us right."

The Hand of Ethelberta

How could it be otherwise, Hardy suggests, when the sycamore tree at Henry Knight's Bede's Inn Chambers has "a thick coat of soot upon the branches, hanging underneath them in flakes";[268] and when, of a morning:

Tall and swarthy columns of smoke were now soaring up from the kitchen chimneys around, spreading horizontally when at a great height, and forming a roof of haze which was turning the sun to a copper colour, and by degrees spoiling the sweetness of the new atmosphere that had rolled in from the country during the night, giving it the usual city smell.

The Hand of Ethelberta

George Somerset visits the London studio of his father, a well-known painter:

Art and vitiated nature were struggling like wrestlers in that apartment, and art was getting the worst of it. The overpowering gloom pervading the clammy air, rendered still more intense by the height of the window from the floor, reduced all the pictures that were standing around to the wizened feebleness of corpses on end. The shadowy parts of the room behind the different easels were veiled in a brown vapour, precluding all estimate of the extent of the studio.... The first thought of an unsophisticated stranger on entering that room could only be the amazed inquiry why a professor of the art of colour, which beyond all other arts requires pure daylight for its exercise, should fix himself on the single square league in habitable Europe to which light is denied at noonday for weeks in succession.

A Laodicean

As far as his own creativity was concerned, Hardy came to feel that town life, with its "fiendish precision and mechanism",[269] *made his writing "mechanical and ordinary".*[270] *Egbert Mayne's reaction to working in London echoes Hardy's own experience:*

Town life had for some time been depressing to him. He began to doubt whether he could ever be happy in the course of existence that he had followed through these later years. The perpetual strain, the lack of that quiet to which he had been accustomed in early life, the absence of all personal interest in things around him, was telling upon his health of body and of mind.

An Indiscretion in the Life of an Heiress

Country quiet was absolutely necessary to Hardy, as he points out in several letters to friends; neither the Max Gate cook's child nor the dog Wessex were allowed to make any noise in the house. Jocelyn Pierston, a native of Portland who had lived for many years in London still notices the noise of the city from his balcony:

Over the opposite square the moon hung, and to the right there stretched a long street, filled with a diminishing array of lamps, some single, some in clusters, among them an occasional blue or red one. From a corner came the notes of a piano-organ strumming out a stirring march of Rossini's. The shadowy black figures of pedestrians moved up, down, and across the embrowned roadway. Above the roofs was a bank of livid mist, and higher a greenish-blue sky, in which stars were visible, though its lower part was still pale with daylight, against which rose chimney-pots in the form of elbows, prongs, and fists.

From the whole scene proceeded a ground rumble, miles in extent, upon which individual rattles, voices, a tin whistle, the bark of a dog, rode like bubbles on a sea. The whole noise impressed him with the sense that no one in its enormous mass ever required rest.

The Well-Beloved

It was not only the noise, the strains, and the smoke, which caused ill-health: at least according to Ethelberta's young page-boy brother Joey, it could be caused by the city's mode of living:

"Indigestion? Much you simple country people can know about that! You should see what devils of indigestions we get in high life — eating 'normous great dinners and suppers that require clever physicians to carry 'em off, or else they'd carry us off with gout next day; and waking in the morning with such a splitting headache, and dry throat, and inward cusses about human nature, that you feel all the world like some great lord. . . ."

The Hand of Ethelberta

This urban way of life brought differences in manners and behaviour, even among children:

Mr Hardy: Have you ever noticed the different relation to nature of the town child and the country child? The town-bred boy will often appreciate nature more than the country boy, but he does not know it in the same sense. He will rush to pick a flower which the country boy does not seem to notice. But it is part of the country boy's life. It grows in his soul — he does not want it in his buttonhole.

W. Archer, *Real Conversations*

Melbury is convinced that his daughter Grace, returning to Little Hintock after her expensive education, "will gradually sink down to our level again, and catch our manners and way of speaking" – and, most unbearable of all, "the regular Hintock shail-and-wamble".[271]

In Oxford Jude could perceive that though [Sue] was a country-girl at bottom, a latter girlhood of some years in London, and a womanhood here, had taken all rawness out of her. . . . She was quite a long way removed from the rusticity that was his. How could one of his cross-grained, unfortunate, almost accursed stock, have contrived to reach this pitch of niceness? London had done it, he supposed.

Jude the Obscure

And at the Hunt Ball at Toneborough:

The room was crowded — too crowded. Every variety of fair one, beauties primary, secondary, and tertiary, appeared among the personages composing the throng. There were suns and moons; also pale planets of little account. Broadly speaking, these daughters of the country fell into two classes: one the pink-faced unsophisticated girls from neighbouring rectories and small country-houses, who knew not town except for an occasional fortnight, and who spent their time from Easter to Lammas Day[272] much as they spent it during the remaining nine months of the year: the other class were the children of the wealthy landowners who migrated each season to the town-house; these were pale and collected, showed less enjoyment in their countenances, and wore in general an approximation to the languid manners of the capital.

A Laodicean

But the difference between town and country behaviour went deeper than mere surface sophistication. Town people suppressed their real feelings – if they had any:

Edward was impatient, and to a certain extent still a country man, who had not, after the manner of city men, subdued the natural impulse to speak out the ruling thought without preface.

Desperate Remedies

Ethelberta never discovered from the Belmaines whether her proposal had been an infliction or a charm, so perfectly were they practised in sustaining that complete divorce between thinking and saying which is the hall-mark of high civilisation.

[Ethelberta's] eye instantly lighted upon her disobedient sister, now looking twice as disobedient as she really was.

"O, you are here, Picotee? I am glad to see you," said the mistress of the house quietly.

This was altogether to Picotee's surprise, for she had expected a round rating at least, in her freshness hardly being aware that this reserve of feeling was an acquired habit of Ethelberta's, and that civility stood in town for as much vexation as a tantrum represented in Wessex.

It impressed Christopher to perceive how, under the estrangement which arose from differences of education, surroundings, experience, and talent, the sympathies of close relationship were perceptible in Ethelberta's bearing towards her brothers and sisters. At a remark upon some simple pleasure wherein she had not participated because absent and occupied by far more comprehensive interests, a gloom as of banishment would cross her face and dim it for a while, showing that the free habits and enthusiasms of country life had still their charm with her, in the face of the subtler gratifications of abridged bodies, candlelight, and no feelings in particular, which prevailed in town.

The Hand of Ethelberta

Freshness and spontaneity might be considered to be country charms; but times were changing, and by 1883 when Hardy wrote "The Dorsetshire Labourer" the effect of the annual removal of the farm labourers was already apparent:

They are also losing their peculiarities as a class; hence the humorous simplicity which formerly characterised the men and the unsophisticated modesty of the women are rapidly disappearing or lessening, under the constant attrition of lives approximating to those of workers in a manufacturing town. It is the common remark of villagers above the labouring class, who know the latter well as personal acquaintances, that "there are no nice homely workfolk now as there used to be." There may be, and is, some exaggeration in this.... [The labourers] vent less often the result of their own observations than what they have heard to be the correct ideas of smart chaps in towns. The women have, in many districts, acquired the rollicking air of factory hands. That seclusion and immutabilty, which was so bad for their pockets, was an unrivalled fosterer of their personal charm in the eyes of those whose experiences had been less limited. But the artistic merit of their old condition is scarcely a reason why they should have continued in it when other communities were marching on so vigorously towards uniformity and mental equality. It is only the old story that progress and picturesqueness do not harmonise. They are losing their individuality, but they are widening the range of their ideas, and gaining in freedom. It is too much to expect them to remain stagnant and old-fashioned for the pleasure of romantic spectators.

The Dorsetshire Labourer

"Old-fashioned" country innocence is a favourite theme with Hardy. Not only are town and country manners different, but, according to him, their moral sense is too. "A town makes a cynic of me," says Adelaide Hinton in Desperate Remedies,[273] *echoing a remark of Edward Springrove's, and foreshadowing some lines in the poem "Wessex Heights" of 1896.*[274]

Arabella discusses with her two friends how to "catch" Jude:

"As he is a romancing, straightfor'ard, honest chap, he's to be had, and as a husband, if you set about catching him in the right way."

Arabella remained thinking awhile. "What med be the right way?" she asked.

"O you don't know — you don't!" said Sarah, the third girl.

"On my word I don't! — No further, that is, than by plain courting, and taking care he don't go too far!"

The third girl looked at the second. "She *don't* know!"

" 'Tis clear she don't!" said Anny.

"And having lived in a town, too, as one may say! Well, we can teach 'ee some'at then, as well as you us."

"Yes. And how do you mean — a sure way to gain a man? Take me for an innocent, and have done wi'it!"

"As a husband."

"As a husband."

"A countryman that's honourable and serious-minded such as he; God forbid that I should say a sojer, or sailor, or commercial gent from the town, or any of them that be slippery with poor women! I'd do no friend that harm!'

Jude the Obscure

Arabella's scheme works — and they marry because Jude thinks her pregnant:

A little chill overspread him at her first unrobing. A long tail of hair, which Arabella wore twisted up in an enormous knob at the back of her head, was deliberately unfastened, stroked out, and hung upon the looking-glass which he had bought her.

"What — it wasn't your own?" he said, with a sudden distaste for her.

"O no — it never is nowadays with the better class."

"Nonsense! Perhaps not in towns. But in the country it is supposed to be different.

Besides, you've enough of your own, surely?"

"Yes, enough as country notions go. But in towns the men expect more, and when I was a barmaid at Aldbrickham —"

"Barmaid at Aldbrickham?"

"Well, not exactly barmaid — I used to draw the drink at a public-house there — just for a little time; that was all. Some people put me up to getting this, and I bought it just for a fancy. The more you have the better in Aldbrickham, which is a finer town than all your Christminsters. Every lady of position wears false hair — the barber's assistant told me so."

Jude thought with a feeling of sickness that though this might be true to some extent, for all that he knew, many unsophisticated girls would and did go to towns and remain there for years without losing their simplicity of life and embellishments. Others, alas, had an instinct towards artificiality in their very blood, and became adepts in counterfeiting at the first glimpse of it.

Jude the Obscure

A man's work was always important to Hardy; and in his view, town and country craftsmen were different. See the description of John Smith on page 198; and within a mere twenty pages of each other he has these two passages on Jude:

His capabilities in [his trade], having been acquired in the country, were of an all-round sort, including monumental stone-cutting, gothic freestone work for the restoration of churches, and carving of a general kind. In London he would probably have become specialized and have made himself a "moulding mason", a "foliage sculptor" — perhaps a "statuary".

He was a handy man at his trade, an all-round man, as artizans in country-towns are apt to be. In London the man who carves the boss or knob of leafage declines to cut the fragment of moulding which merges in that leafage, as if it were a degradation to do the second half of one whole. When there was not much Gothic moulding for Jude to run, or much window tracery on the bankers, he would go out lettering monuments or tombstones, and take a pleasure in the change of handiwork.

Jude the Obscure

Servants, too, were different in town and country. Hardy, no doubt drawing on the experience of Eliza Nicholls and his cousin Martha Sparks (both ladies' maids in London whom at one stage he wished to marry), has some strange things to say about:

. . . the grotesque habits of these men and maids, who were quite unlike the country servants [Picotee] had known, and resembled nothing so much as pixies, elves, or gnomes, peeping up upon human beings from their shady haunts underground, sometimes for good, sometimes for ill . . .

As, to Picotee's consternation, they peer from above at the Doncastles' dinner guests, the principal lady's maid instructs the country girl:

"Now look over the balustrade, and you will see them all in a minute," said Mrs Menlove. "O, you need not be timid; you can look out as far as you like. We are all independent here; no slavery for us; it is not as it is in the country, where servants are considered to be of different blood and bone from their employers, and to have no eyes for anything but their work."

The Hand of Ethelberta

In conclusion:

Though [Bathsheba was] in one sense a woman of the world, it was, after all, that world of daylight coteries and green carpets wherein cattle form the passing crowd and winds the busy hum; where a quiet family of rabbits or hares lives on the other side of your party-wall, where your neighbour is everybody in the tything,[275] and where calculation is confined to market-days. Of the fabricated tastes of good fashionable society she knew but little, and of the formulated self-indulgence of bad, nothing at all.

Far from the Madding Crowd

A Private Man on Public Men

When my contemporaries were driving
Their coach through Life with strain and striving,
And raking riches into heaps,
And ably pleading in the Courts
With smart rejoinders and retorts,
Or where the Senate nightly keeps
Its vigil, till their fames were fanned
By rumour's tongue throughout the land,
I lived in quiet, screened, unknown,
Pondering upon some stick or stone,
Or news of some rare book or bird
Latterly bought, or seen, or heard,
Not wishing ever to set eyes on
The surging crowd beyond the horizon,
Tasting years of moderate gladness
Mellowed by sundry days of sadness,
Shut from the noise of the world without,
Hearing but dimly its rush and rout,
Unenvying those amid its roar,
Little endowed, not wanting more.

Winter Words

14 Love in the Wilds

Solitude, Isolation, and Concentrated Passions

When Charles Morgan wrote of Thomas Hardy's visit to Oxford in 1920, he described his eyes as "so old that age itself seemed to have swung full circle within them — being the eyes of some still young man who had been keeping watch at sea since the beginning of time."[276] *Country dwellers can often be told by their looks in Hardy's writings:*

[Mrs Yeobright] had something of an estranged mien: the solitude exhaled from the heath was concentrated in this face that had risen from it.[277]

[Marty South's] face had the usual fulness of expression which is developed by a life of solitude. Where the eyes of a multitude continuously beat like waves upon a countenance they seem to wear away its mobile power; but in the still water of privacy every feeling and sentiment unfolds in visible luxuriance, to be interpreted as readily as a printed word by an intruder.

The Woodlanders

Solitude of the right kind could bring many advantages – dignity, spontaneity, and individuality.[278] *Eustacia's innate dignity was fortified by her life on the heath:*

Among other things opportunity had of late years been denied her of learning to be undignified, for she lived lonely. Isolation on a heath renders vulgarity well-nigh impossible. It would have been as easy for the heath-ponies, bats, and snakes to be vulgar as for her. A narrow life in Budmouth might have completely demeaned her.

The only way to look queenly without realms or hearts to queen it over is to look as if you had lost them; and Eustacia did that to a triumph. In the captain's cottage she could suggest mansions she had never seen. Perhaps that was because she frequented a vaster mansion than any of them, the open hills. Like the summer condition of the place around her, she was an embodiment of the phrase "a populous solitude"[279] — apparently so listless, void, and quiet, she was really busy and full.

The Return of the Native

Both Hardy and Egbert Mayne[280] *found town life unpalatable after growing up among country silences. So did Angel Clare:*

Early association with country solitudes had bred in him an unconquerable, and almost unreasonable, aversion to modern town life, and shut him out from such success as he might have aspired to by following a mundane calling. . . .

Tess of the d'Urbervilles

Solitude in a town too readily became isolation — "that isolation which is so apt to depress, and harm — sometimes permanently — the lives of country beginners in London," as Hardy wrote in his foreword to the 1907 Yearbook of the Society of Dorset Men in London, of which he was twice President.

But the country's physical isolation can be crippling. Distances manipulate events.[281]

Higher Crowstairs:

Fifty years ago such a lonely cottage stood on such a down, and may possibly be standing there now. In spite of its loneliness, however, the spot, by actual measurement, was not three miles from a country-town. Yet that affected it little. Three miles of irregular upland, during the long inimical seasons, with their sleets, snows, rains, and mists, afford withdrawing space enough to isolate a Timon or a Nebuchadnezzar; much less, in fair weather, to please that less repellent tribe, the poets, philosophers, artists, and others who "conceive and meditate of pleasant things".

The Three Strangers

On the forsaken coach-road south from Bristol:

The spot is lonely, and when the days are darkening the many gay charioteers now perished who have rolled along the way, the blistered soles that have trodden it, and the tears that have wetted it, return upon the mind of the loiterer.

The physiognomy of a deserted highway expresses solitude to a degree that is not reached by mere dales or downs, and bespeaks a tomb-like stillness more emphatic than that of glades and pools. The contrast of what is with what might be, probably accounts for this. To step, for instance, at the place under notice, from the edge of the plantation into the adjoining thoroughfare, and pause amid its emptiness for a moment, was to exchange by the act of a single stride the simple absence of human companionship for an incubus of the forlorn.

The Woodlanders

The effects of isolation in the country are far-reaching. When Elfride, in her father's lonely Cornish rectory, meets Stephen Smith:

Never were conditions more favourable for developing a girl's first passing fancy for a handsome boyish face — a fancy rooted in inexperience and nourished by seclusion — into a wild unreflecting passion fervid enough for anything.

A Pair of Blue Eyes

It is said that about this time the Baron seemed to feel the effects of solitude strongly. Solitude revives the simple instincts of primitive man, and lonely country nooks afford rich soil for wayward emotions. Moreover, idleness waters those unconsidered impulses which a short season of turmoil would stamp out. It is difficult to speak with any exactness of the bearing of such conditions on the mind of the Baron — a man of whom so little was ever truly known — but there is no doubt that his mind ran much on Margery as an individual, without reference to her rank or quality, or to the question whether she would marry Jim Hayward that summer. She was the single lovely human thing within his present horizon, for he lived in absolute seclusion; and her image unduly affected him.

The Romantic Adventures of a Milkmaid

Dr Fitzpiers, like the Baron, was someone from a more urbane setting put down rather incongruously in deep country:

The loneliness of Hintock life was beginning to tell upon his impressionable nature. Winter in a solitary house in the country, without society, is tolerable, nay, even enjoyable and delightful, given certain conditions; but these are not the conditions which attach to the life of a professional man who drops down into such a place by mere accident. They were present to the lives of Winterborne, Melbury, and Grace; but not to the doctor's. They are old association — and almost exhaustive biographical or historical acquaintance with every object, animate and inanimate, within the observer's horizon. He must know all about those invisible ones of the days gone by, whose feet have traversed the fields which look so grey from his windows;

recall whose creaking plough has turned those sods from time to time; whose hands planted the trees that form a crest to the opposite hill; whose horses and hounds have torn through that underwood; what birds affect that particular brake; what bygone domestic dramas of love, jealousy, revenge, or disappointment have been enacted in the cottages, the mansion, the street or on the green. The spot may have beauty, grandeur, salubrity, convenience; but if it lack memories it will ultimately pall upon him who settles there without opportunity of intercourse with his kind.

The Woodlanders

"People living insulated, as I do by the solitude of this place, get charged with emotive fluid like a Leyden jar with electric, for want of some conductor at hand to disperse it. Human love is a subjective thing — the essence itself of man, as that great thinker Spinoza says — *ipsa hominis essentia* — it is joy accompanied by an idea which we project against any suitable object in the line of our vision, just as the rainbow iris is projected against an oak, ash, or elm tree indifferently. So that if any other young lady had appeared instead of the one who did appear, I should have felt just the same interest in her, and have quoted precisely the same lines from Shelley about her, as about this one I saw. Such miserable creatures of circumstance are we all!"

The Woodlanders

Jude also began to "get charged with emotive fluid" as he thought of Sue:

From this moment the emotion which had been accumulating in his breast as the bottled-up effect of solitude and the poetized locality he dwelt in, insensibly began to precipitate itself on this half-visionary form; and he perceived that, whatever his obedient wish in a contrary direction, he would soon be unable to resist the desire to make himself known to her.

Jude the Obscure

This "concentration" of emotion — as a magnifying-glass focuses and concentrates the sun's rays to one spot of intense heat — was a favourite theme of Hardy's when writing of those who lived in lonely country places. "To dance with a man is to concentrate a twelvemonth's regulation fire upon him in the fragment of an hour."[282]

As the mind's eye travels slowly across the elegiac woodlands to the cluster of Little Hintock we are reminded of the depths of tragedy that can lie beneath its gentle exterior:

Thus they rode on, and High-Stoy Hill grew larger ahead. At length could be discerned in the dusk, about half a mile to one side, gardens and orchards sunk in a concave, and, as it were, snipped out of the woodland. From this self-contained place rose in stealthy silence tall stems of smoke, which the eye of imagination could trace downward to their root on quiet hearthstones, festooned overhead with hams and flitches. It was one of the sequestered spots outside the gates of the world where may usually be found more meditation than action, and more listlessness than meditation;

where reasoning proceeds on narrow premises, and results in inferences wildly imaginative; yet where, from time to time, dramas of a grandeur and unity truly Sophoclean are enacted in the real, by virtue of the concentrated passions and closely-knit interdependence of the lives therein.

The Woodlanders

The village gipsying at East Egdon:

The site chosen for the village festivity was one of the lawn-like oases which were occasionally, yet not often, met with on the plateaux of the heath district. The brakes of furze and fern terminated abruptly round the margin, and the grass was unbroken.... The lusty notes of the East Egdon band had directed her unerringly, and she now beheld the musicians themselves, sitting in a blue waggon with red wheels scrubbed as bright as new, and arched with sticks, to which boughs and flowers were tied. In front of this was the grand central dance of fifteen or twenty couples, flanked by minor dances of inferior individuals whose gyrations were not always in strict keeping with the tune.

The young men wore blue and white rosettes, and with a flush on their faces footed it to the girls, who, with the excitement and the exercise, blushed deeper than the pink of their numerous ribbons. Fair ones with long curls, fair ones with short curls, fair ones with love-locks, fair ones with braids, flew round and round; and a beholder might well have wondered how such a prepossessing set of young women of like size, age, and disposition, could have been collected together where there were only one or two villages to choose from.

... By the time she retraced her steps towards the scene of the gipsying, which it was necessary to repass on the way to Alderworth, the sun was going down. The air was now so still that she could hear the band afar off, and it seemed to be playing with more spirit, if that were possible, than when she had come away. On reaching the hill the sun had quite disappeared; but this made little difference either to Eustacia or to the revellers, for a round yellow moon was rising before her, though its rays had not yet outmastered those from the west. The dance was going on just the same, but strangers had arrived and formed a ring around the figure, so that Eustacia could stand among them without a chance of being recognized.

A whole village-full of sensuous emotion, scattered abroad all the year long, surged here in a focus for an hour. The forty hearts of those waving couples were beating as they had not done since, twelve months before, they had come together in similar jollity. For the time Paganism was revived in their hearts, the pride of life was all in all, and they adored none other than themselves.

How many of those impassioned but temporary embraces were destined to become perpetual was possibly the wonder of some of those who indulged in them, as well as of Eustacia who looked on. She began to envy those pirouetters, to hunger for the hope and happiness which the fascination of the dance seemed to engender within them.[283]

The Return of the Native

Intermarriage was almost inevitable:

Winterborne was connected with the Melbury family in various ways. In addition to the sentimental relationship which arose from his father having been the first Mrs Melbury's lover, Winterborne's aunt had married and emigrated with the brother of the timber-merchant many years before — an alliance that was insufficient to place Winterborne, though the poorer, on a footing of social intimacy with the Melburys. As in most villages so secluded as this, intermarriages were of Hapsburgian frequency among the inhabitants, and there were hardly two houses in Little Hintock unrelated by some matrimonial tie or other.

The Woodlanders

The three Avices, the second something like the first, the third a glorification of the first, at all events externally, were the outcome of the immemorial island customs of intermarriage and of prenuptial union, under which conditions the type of feature was almost uniform from parent to child through generations: so that, till quite latterly, to have seen one native man and woman was to have seen the whole population of that isolated rock, so nearly cut off from the mainland.

The Well-Beloved

It has sometimes been conceived of novels that evolve their action on a circumscribed scene — as do many (though not all) of these — that they cannot be so inclusive in their exhibition of human nature as novels wherein the scenes cover large extents of country, in which events figure amid towns and cities, even wander over the four quarters of the globe. I am not concerned to argue this point further than to suggest that the conception is an untrue one in respect of the elementary passions. But I would state that the geographical limits of the stage here trodden were not absolutely forced upon the writer by circumstances; he forced them upon himself from judgment. I considered that our magnificent heritage from the Greeks in dramatic literature found sufficient room for a large proportion of its action in an extent of their country not much larger than the half-dozen countries here reunited under the old name of Wessex, that the domestic emotions have throbbed in Wessex nooks with as much intensity as in the palaces of Europe, and that, anyhow, there was quite enough human nature in Wessex for one man's literary purpose.

General Preface to the Novels and Poems

15 The Past in the Country

The Antiquity of the Countryside

Henry Knight, in pursuit of his hat which a freak air-current has carried over the edge, has slipped above the towering precipice of the dread Cliff-without-a-Name on the Cornish coast. He is hanging by his hands on the face of the escarpment, wondering whether help can come in time:

He reclined hand in hand with the world in its infancy. Not a blade, not an insect, which spoke of the present, was between him and the past. The inveterate antagonism of these black precipices to all strugglers for life is in no way more forcibly suggested than by the paucity of tufts of grass, lichens, or confervae[284] on their outermost ledges....

By one of those familiar conjunctions of things wherewith the inanimate world baits the mind of man when he pauses in moments of suspense, opposite Knight's eyes was an imbedded fossil, standing forth in low relief from the rock. It was a creature with eyes. The eyes, dead and turned to stone, were even now regarding him. It was one of the early crustaceans called Trilobites. Separated by millions of years in their lives, Knight and this underling seemed to have met in their place of death. It was the single instance within reach of his vision of anything that had ever been alive and had had a body to save, as he himself had now.

The creature represented but a low type of animal existence, for never in their vernal years had the plains indicated by those numberless slaty layers been traversed by an intelligence worthy of the name. Zoophytes, mollusca, shell-fish, were the highest developments of those ancient days. The immense lapses of time each formation represented had known nothing of the dignity of man. They were grand times, but they were mean times too, and mean were their relics. He was to be with the small in his death.

Knight was a fair geologist; and such is the supremacy of habit over occasion, as a pioneer of the thoughts of men, that at this dreadful juncture his mind found time to take in, by a momentary sweep, the varied scenes that had had their day between this creature's epoch and his own. There is no place like a cleft landscape for bringing home such imaginings as these.

Time closed up like a fan before him. He saw himself at one extremity of the years, face to face with the beginning of all the intermediate centuries simultaneously. Fierce men, clothed in the hides of beasts, and carrying, for defence and attack, huge clubs and pointed spears, rose from the rock, like the phantoms before the doomed Macbeth. They lived in hollows, woods, and mud huts — perhaps in caves of the neighbouring rocks. Behind them stood an earlier band. No man was there. Huge elephantine forms, the mastodon, the hippopotamus, the tapir, antelopes of monstrous size, the megatherium, and the myledon[285] — all, for the moment, in juxtaposition. Further back, and overlapped by these, were perched huge-billed birds and swinish creatures as large as horses. Still more shadowy were the sinister crocodilian outlines — alligators and other uncouth shapes, culminating in the colossal lizard, the iguanodon. Folded behind were dragon forms and clouds of flying reptiles: still underneath were fishy beings of lower development; and so on, till the lifetime scenes of the fossil confronting him were a present and modern condition of things. These images passed before Knight's inner eye in less than half a minute, and he was again considering the actual present. Was he to die?

A Pair of Blue Eyes

Egdon Heath:

He was in a nest of vivid green. The ferny vegetation round him, though so abundant, was quite uniform: it was a groove of machine-made foliage, a world of green triangles with saw-edges, and not a single flower. The air was warm with a vaporous warmth, and the stillness was unbroken. Lizards, grasshoppers, and ants were the only living things to be beheld. The scene seemed to belong to the ancient world of the carboniferous period,[286] when the forms of plants were few, and of the fern kind; when there was neither bud nor blossom, nothing but a monotonous extent of leafage, amid which no bird sang.

The Return of the Native

At Weatherbury . . . a forking highway . . . skirted the north of Egdon Heath. Into this road they directed the horse's head, and soon were bowling across that ancient country whose surface never had been stirred to a finger's depth, save by the scratching of rabbits, since brushed by the feet of the earliest tribes. The tumuli these had left behind, dun and shagged with heather, jutted roundly into the sky from the uplands, as though they were the full breasts of Diana Multimammia supinely extended there.

The Mayor of Casterbridge

The great inviolate place had an ancient permanence which the sea cannot claim. Who can say of a particular sea that it is old? Distilled by the sun, kneaded by the moon, it is renewed in a year, in a day, or in an hour. The sea changed, the fields changed, the rivers, the villages, and the people changed, yet Egdon remained. Those surfaces were neither so steep as to be destructible by weather, nor so flat as to be the victims of floods and deposits. With the exception of an aged highway, and a still more aged barrow . . . — themselves almost crystalized to natural products by long continuance — even the trifling irregularities were not caused by pickaxe, plough, or spade, but remained as the very finger-touches of the last geological change.

The Return of the Native

The Chase near Trantridge:

Far behind... stretched the soft azure landscape of The Chase — a truly venerable tract of forest land, one of the few remaining woodlands in England of undoubted primaeval date, wherein Druidical mistletoe was still found on aged oaks, and where enormous yew-trees, not planted by the hand of man, grew as they had grown when they were pollarded for bows.

Tess of the d'Urbervilles

The North Wessex downs:

In the afternoon Arabella met and walked with Jude.... They wandered up the slopes till they reached the green track along the ridge, which they followed to the circular British earth-bank adjoining, Jude thinking of the great age of the trackway, and the drovers who had frequented it, probably before the Romans knew the country.

Jude the Obscure

The ancient earthwork:

The peculiar place of which these are some of the features is "Mai-Dun", "The Castle of the Great Hill", said to be the Dunium of Ptolemy, the capital of the Durotriges, which eventually came into Roman occupation, and was finally deserted on their withdrawal from the island....

Impressive by day as this largest Ancient-British work in the kingdom undoubtedly is, its impressiveness is increased now....

Acoustic perceptions multiply to-night. We can almost hear the stream of years that have borne those deeds away from us. Strange articulations seem to float on the air from that point, the gateway, where the animation in past times must frequently have concentrated itself at hours of coming and going, and general excitement. There arises an ineradicable fancy that they are human voices; if so, they must be the lingering airborne vibrations of conversations uttered at least fifteen hundred years ago.

A Tryst at an Ancient Earthwork

THE CONTINUITY OF PAST AND PRESENT

Hardy's particular gift for linking people with places is shown in his constant sense of the presence of past generations wherever he sets foot:

He frequently walked the heath alone, when the past seized upon him with its shadowy hand, and held him there to listen to its tale. His imagination would then people the spot with its ancient inhabitants: forgotten Celtic tribes trod their tracks about him, and he could almost live among them, look in their faces, and see them standing beside the barrows which swelled around, untouched and perfect as at the time of their erection. Those of the dyed barbarians who had chosen the cultivable tracts were, in comparison with those who had left their marks here, as writers on paper beside writers on parchment. Their records had perished long ago by the plough, while the works of these remained. Yet they all had lived and died unconscious of the different fates awaiting their relics. It reminded him that unforeseen factors operate in the evolution of immortality.

The Return of the Native

They were travelling in a direction that was enlivened by no modern current of traffic. . . . The lane was sometimes so narrow that the brambles of the hedge, which hung forward like anglers' rods over a stream, scratched their hats and hooked their whiskers as they passed. Yet this neglected lane had been a highway to Queen Elizabeth's subjects and the cavalcades of the past. Its day was over now, and its history as a national artery done for ever.

Interlopers at the Knap

They hardly spoke to each other, and immediately set out on their climb into the interior of this solemn country, which stood high above the rich alluvial soil they had left half-an-hour before. It was a long walk; thick clouds made the atmosphere dark, though it was as yet only early afternoon; and the wind howled dismally over the slopes of the heath — not improbably the same heath which had witnessed the agony of the Wessex King Ina, presented to after-ages as Lear.

The Withered Arm

Here stretch the downs, high and breezy and green, absolutely unchanged since those eventful days. A plough has never disturbed the turf, and the sod that was uppermost then is uppermost now. Here stood the camp; here are distinct traces of the banks thrown up for the horses of the cavalry, and spots where the midden-heaps lay are still to be observed. At night, when I walk across the lonely place, it is impossible to avoid hearing, amid the scourings of the wind over the grass-bents and thistle, the old trumpet and bugle calls, the rattle of the halters; to help seeing rows of spectral tents and the *impedimenta* of the soldiery. From within the canvases come guttural syllables of foreign tongues, and broken songs of the fatherland; for they were mainly regiments of the King's German Legion that slept round the tent-poles hereabout at that time.

It was nearly ninety years ago.

The Melancholy Hussar of the German Legion

The funeral of the second Avice had happened to be on one of those drenching afternoons of the autumn, when the raw rain flies level as the missiles of the ancient inhabitants across the beaked promontory which has formed the scene of this narrative....

The Well-Beloved

... before him was the sea, the Great Sea, the historical and original Mediterranean; the sea of innumerable characters in history and legend that arranged themselves before him in a long frieze of memories so diverse as to include both Aeneas and St Paul.

A Laodicean

If past inhabitants are there in natural scenes, they are of course there in man-made situations. At Stancy Castle, George Somerset mounts:

... a flight of stone stairs, open to the sky, along whose steps sunburnt Tudor soldiers and other renowned dead men had doubtless many times walked. It led to the principal door on this side. Thence he could observe the walls of the lower court in detail, and the old mosses with which they were padded — mosses that from time immemorial had been burnt brown every summer, and every winter had grown green again.

A Laodicean

At Overcombe:

They crossed the threshold of the mill-house and up the passage, the paving of which was worn into a gutter by the ebb and flow of feet that had been going on there ever since Tudor times....

The Trumpet-Major

At Higher Crowstairs:

The first stranger handed to his neighbour the family mug — a huge vessel of brown ware, having its upper edge worn away like a threshold by the rub of whole generations of thirsty lips that had gone the way of all flesh....

The Three Strangers

Even the cows at Talbothays had ancestors who had left their mark:

Long thatched sheds stretched round the enclosure, their slopes encrusted with vivid green moss, and their eaves supported by wooden posts rubbed to a glossy smoothness by the flanks of infinite cows and calves of bygone years, now passed to an oblivion almost inconceivable in its profundity.

Tess of the d'Urbervilles

— and history repeats itself in the use men make of things and places:

Oak took up the light and went into the porch, followed by Bathsheba with a shawl over her head. The rays fell upon a group of male figures gathered upon the gravel in front, who, when they saw the newly-married couple in the porch, set up a loud "Hurrah!" and at the same moment bang again went the cannon in the background, followed by a hideous clang of music from a drum, tambourine, clarionet, serpent, hautboy, tenor-viol, and double-bass — the only remaining relics of the true and original Weatherbury band — venerable worm-eaten instruments, which had celebrated in their own persons the victories of Marlborough, under the fingers of the forefathers of those who played them now. The performers came forward, and marched up to the front.

Far from the Madding Crowd

Swithin St Cleeve rises on his wedding-day in his little cabin in the fields:

The young rabbits littered during the foregoing summer watched his preparations through the open door from the grey dawn without, as he bustled, half-dressed, in and out under the boughs, and among the blackberries and brambles that grew around.

It was a strange place for a bridegroom to perform his toilet in, but, considering the unconventional nature of the marriage, a not inappropriate one. What events had been enacted in that earthen camp since it was first thrown up, nobody could say; but the primitive simplicity of the young man's preparations accorded well with the prehistoric spot on which they were made. Embedded under his feet were possibly even now rude trinkets that had been worn at bridal ceremonies of the early inhabitants.

Two on a Tower

There were certain early winter days in Casterbridge — days of firmamental exhaustion which followed angry south-westerly tempests — when, if the sun shone, the air was like velvet. [Elizabeth-Jane] seized on these days for her periodical visits to the spot where her mother lay buried — the still-used burial-ground of the old Roman-British city, whose curious feature was this, its continuity as a place of sepulture. Mrs Henchard's dust mingled with the dust of women who lay ornamented with glass hair-pins and amber necklaces, and men who held in their mouth coins of Hadrian, Posthumus, and the Constantines.

The Mayor of Casterbridge

HUMAN ACTIVITIES

Human activities also linked the centuries. Swithin's old grandmother had "seventeenth-century handwriting", just as Mrs Durbeyfield wrote in a "wandering last-century hand" that still retained the old J for I. Much of the regular work of the countryside was still carried out where and as it had been centuries before. Baptista, waiting at Pen-zephyr for her boat to her Isles off Lyonesse:

. . . went to the town gardens, and the Pier, and the Harbour, and looked at the men at work there, loading and unloading as in the time of the Phoenicians.

A Mere Interlude

The magnificent, mellowed:

. . . "old barn embodied practices which had suffered no mutilation at the hands of time. Here at least the spirit of the ancient builders was at one with the spirit of the modern beholder."

This fine passage[287] *is an important statement about the place of the past in the countryman's life — and how slowly change came to the countryside.*

It is about fifty years since the old maltster was at Norcombe (some twenty miles to the north-west of Weatherbury), and the changes there in that time seem to him epoch-making:

"Sit down, Shepherd Oak," continued the ancient man of malt. "And how was the old place at Norcombe, when ye went for your dog? I should like to see the old familiar spot; but faith, I shouldn't know a soul there now."

"I suppose you wouldn't. 'Tis altered very much."

"Is it true that Dicky Hill's wooden cider-house is pulled down?"

'O yes — years ago, and Dicky's cottage just above it."

"Well, to be sure!"

"Yes; and Tompkins's old apple-tree is rooted[288] that used to bear two hogsheads of cider, and no help from other trees."

"Rooted? — you don't say it! Ah! stirring times we live in — stirring times."

"And you can mind the old well that used to be in the middle of the place? That's turned into a solid iron pump with a large stone trough, and all complete."

"Dear, dear — how the face of nations alter, and what we live to see nowadays!"

Far from the Madding Crowd

So the country is always years behind the town: Lucetta's carefully chosen furniture is fifty years ahead of anything to be found in Casterbridge; Bathsheba thinks "samplers are out of date — horribly countrified";[289] *and when the Baron agrees to take milkmaid Margery to the ball as a token of thanks to her, he asks:*

"Bye-the-by, can *you* dance?"

"Yes."

"What?"

"Reels and jigs, and country-dances like the New-Rigged-Ship, and Follow-my-

Lover, and Haste-to-the-Wedding, and the College Hornpipe, and the Favourite Quickstep, and Captain White's dance."

"A very good list — a very good! but unluckily I fear they don't dance any of those now. But if you have the instinct we may soon cure your ignorance. Let me see you dance a moment."

She stood out into the garden-path, the stile being still between them, and seizing a side of the skirt with each hand, performed the movements which are even yet far from uncommon in the dances of the villagers of merry England. But her motions, though graceful, were not precisely those which appear in the figures of a modern ballroom.

"Well, my good friend, it is a very pretty sight," he said, warming up to the proceedings. "But you dance too well — you dance all over your person — and that's too thorough a way for the present day. I should say it was exactly how they danced in the time of your poet Chaucer; but as people don't dance like it now, we must consider. . . ."

The Romantic Adventures of a Milkmaid

Clym Yeobright, desiring to teach his fellow-men on the heath, is too far ahead of them:

Mentally he was in a provincial future, that is, he was in many points abreast with the central town thinkers of his date. Much of this development he may have owed to his studious life in Paris, where he had become acquainted with ethical systems popular at the time.

In consequence of this relatively advanced position, Yeobright might have been called unfortunate. The rural world was not ripe for him. A man should be only partially before his time: to be completely to the vanward in aspirations is fatal to fame.

The Return of the Native

As national government stretched out a hand to order education in the country, the rate of change in this sphere began to accelerate between each generation, as Joan and Tess Durbeyfield found:

Between the mother, with her fast-perishing lumber of superstitions, folklore, dialect, and orally transmitted ballads, and the daughter, with her trained National teachings and Standard knowledge under an infinitely Revised Code,[290] there was a gap of two hundred years as ordinarily understood. When they were together the Jacobean and the Victorian ages were juxtaposed.

Tess of the d'Urbervilles

Hardy indeed paints a Wessex in the turmoil of transition between old and new:

For South Wessex, the year [of the Great Exhibition of 1851] formed in many ways an extraordinary chronological frontier or transit-line, at which there occurred what one might call a precipice in Time. As in a geological "fault", we had presented to us a sudden bringing of ancient and modern into absolute contact, such as probably in no other single year since the Conquest was ever witnessed in this part of the country.

The Fiddler of the Reels

Hardy himself welcomed the modern where it brought real advancement to the countryman. But to be cut off from the past was, for him, utter deprivation. This was what made the little hamlet of Marygreen so depressing:[291]

It was as old-fashioned as it was small, and it rested in the lap of an undulating upland adjoining the North Wessex downs. Old as it was, however, the well-shaft was probably the only relic of the local history that remained absolutely unchanged. Many of the thatched and dormered dwelling-houses had been pulled down of late years, and many trees felled on the green. Above all, the original church, hump-backed, wood-turreted, and quaintly hipped, had been taken down, and either cracked up into heaps of road-metal in the lane, or utilized as pig-sty walls, garden seats, guard-stones to fences, and rockeries in the flower-beds of the neighbourhood. In place of it a tall new building of modern Gothic design, unfamiliar to English eyes, had been erected on a new piece of ground by a certain obliterator of historic records who had run down from London and back in a day. The site whereon so long had stood the ancient temple to the Christian divinities was not even recorded on the green and level grass-plot that had immemorially been the churchyard, the obliterated graves being commemorated by eighteenpenny cast-iron crosses warranted to last five years.

The brown surface of the field went right up towards the sky all round, where it was lost by degrees in the mist that shut out the actual verge and accentuated the solitude. The only marks on the uniformity of the scene were a rick of last year's produce standing in the midst of the arable, the rooks that rose at his approach, and the path athwart the fallow by which he had come, trodden now by he hardly knew whom, though once by many of his own dead family.

"How ugly it is here!" he murmured.

The fresh harrow-lines seemed to stretch like the channellings in a piece of new corduroy, lending a meanly utilitarian air to the expanse, taking away its gradations, and depriving it of all history beyond that of the few recent months, though to every clod and stone there really attached associations enough and to spare — echoes of songs from ancient harvest-days, of spoken words, and of sturdy deeds. Every inch of ground had been the site, first or last, of energy, gaiety, horse-play, bickering, weariness. Groups of gleaners had squatted in the sun on every square yard. Love-matches that had populated the adjoining hamlet had been made up there between reaping and carrying. Under the hedge which divided the field from a distant plantation girls had given themselves to lovers who would not turn their heads to look at them by the next harvest; and in that ancient cornfield many a man had made love-promises to a woman at whose voice he had trembled by the next seed-time after fulfilling them in the church adjoining. But this neither Jude nor the rooks around him considered. For them it was a lonely place, possessing, in the one view, only the quality of a work-ground, and in the other that of a granary good to feed in.

Jude the Obscure

It was characteristic of Sergeant Troy, who was no true countryman, that "with him the past was yesterday; the future, to-morrow; never, the day after".[292] *Hardy, obsessed with the past, often seemed to find it more real than the vanities of the present; and when, at the end of the members' reminiscences at the Field Club about the "group of noble dames" who had figured in their country's history:*

. . . the last member at length departed, the attendant at the museum lowered the fire, the curator locked up the rooms . . . soon there was only a single pirouetting flame on the top of a single coal to make the bones of the ichthyosaurus seem to leap, the stuffed birds to wink, and to draw a smile from the varnished skulls of Vespasian's soldiery.

A Group of Noble Dames

The Clasped Skeletons
Surmised Date 1800B.C.
(In an Ancient British barrow near the writer's house)

O why did we uncover to view
  So closely clasped a pair?
Your chalky bedclothes over you,
    This long time here!

Ere Paris lay with Helena —
  The poets' dearest dear —
Ere David bedded Bathsheba
    You two were bedded here.

Aye, even before the beauteous Jael
  Bade Sisera doff his gear
And lie in her tent; then drove the nail,
    You two lay here.

Wicked Aholah, in her youth,
  Colled loves from far and near
Until they slew her without ruth;
    But you had long colled here.

Aspasia lay with Pericles,
  And Philip's son found cheer

At eves in lying on Thais' knees
      While you lay here.

Cleopatra with Antony,
   Resigned to dalliance sheer,
Lay, fatuous he, insatiate she,
      Long after you'd lain here.

Pilate by Procula his wife
   Lay tossing at her tear
Of pleading for an innocent life;
      You tossed not here.

Ages before Monk Abélard
   Gained tender Héloïse' ear,
And loved and lay with her till scarred,
      Had you lain loving here.

So long, beyond chronology,
   Lovers in death as 'twere.
So long in placid dignity
      Have you lain here!

Yet what is length of time? But dream!
   Once breathed this atmosphere
Those fossils near you, met the gleam
      Of days as you did here;

But so far earlier theirs beside
   Your life-span and career,
That they might style of yestertide
      Your coming here!

Winter Words

16 Country People

In an article in the magazine Theology *of August 1928, a well-known Anglican clergyman wrote:*

If I were asked to advise a priest preparing to become a *village* rector I would suggest first that he should make a good retreat . . . and then that he should make a careful study of Thomas Hardy's novels. . . . From Thomas Hardy he would learn the essential dignity of country people and what deep and often passionate interest belongs to every individual life. You cannot treat them in the mass. . . .

Part of Hardy's success in this field came because he was writing about people he knew. To an interviewer from Black and White *he is recorded as saying:*

"Old Mr Clare was a Dorsetshire parson whose name still lives enshrined in the hearts of thousands. Shepherd Oak, in *Far from the Madding Crowd*, I knew well as a boy; while Bathsheba Everdene is a reminiscence of one of my own aunts. . . . Joseph Poorgrass, Eustacia, and Susan Nunsuch in *The Return of the Native* were all well-known local characters. Girls resembling the three dairymaids in *Tess* used to get me to write their love-letters for them when I was a little boy. I suppose that unconsciously I absorbed a good deal of their mode of life and speech, and so I have been able to produce it in the dairy at Talbothays." (1892)

When he was over sixty, Hardy still remembered the address he was given in a letter from one of these soldier lovers: 'Calcutta, *or Elsewear".*[293]

In his writings Hardy is very much on the side of his country people. His letter to Leslie Stephen about the illustrations for Far from the Madding Crowd *is quoted on page 7; from that early novel to his last, and widely in his poetry, he continued to champion them, portraying them as almost universally likeable and human, shrewd, humorous, stoical, kindly, and solidly loyal to each other. Of all his countrymen, Bailiff Pennyways is the only outstandingly dishonest one; his other villains are almost always people from urban backgrounds or members of the aristocracy, whose clear-souled country goodness may be said to have been corrupted by their wider contacts. (For more on this theme see pages 277–80.)*

Very few of his countrymen are shiftless or idle; even then Hardy shows an understanding of their strains and circumstances.

Parson Tringham's news gives Durbeyfield another excuse to celebrate:

They went home together, Tess holding one arm of her father, and Mrs Durbeyfield the other. He had, in truth, drunk very little — not a fourth of the quantity which a systematic tippler could carry to church on a Sunday afternoon without a hitch in his eastings or genuflections;[294] but the weakness of Sir John's constitution made mountains of his petty sins in this kind. On reaching the fresh air he was sufficiently unsteady to incline the row of three at one moment as if they were marching to London, and at another as if they were marching to Bath — which produced a comical effect, frequent enough in families on nocturnal homegoings; and, like most comical effects, not quite so comic after all. The two women valiantly disguised these forced excursions and countermarches as well as they could from Durbeyfield their cause, and from Abraham, and from themselves; and so they approached by degrees their own door, and the head of the family bursting suddenly into his former refrain as he drew near, as if to fortify his soul at sight of the smallness of his present residence — "I've got a fam-ily vault in Kingsbere!"

But the accident to his horse makes joy short-lived:

The haggling business, which had mainly depended on the horse, became disorganized forthwith. Distress, if not penury, loomed in the distance. Durbeyfield was what was locally called a slack-twisted fellow; he had good strength to work at times; but the times could not be relied on to coincide with the hours of requirement; and having been unaccustomed to the regular toil of the day-labourer, he was not particularly persistent when they did so coincide.

Tess returns home to nurse her sick mother:

It was now the season for planting and sowing; many gardens and allotments of the villagers had already received their spring tillage; but the garden and the allotment of the Durbeyfields were behindhand. She found, to her dismay, that this was owing to their having eaten all the seed potatoes, — that last lapse of the improvident.

Tess of the d'Urbervilles

Alec d'Urberville's Trantridge:

Every village has its idiosyncrasy, its constitution, often its own code of morality. The levity of some of the younger women in and about Trantridge was marked, and was perhaps symptomatic of the choice spirit who ruled The Slopes in that vicinity. The place had also a more abiding defect; it drank hard. The staple conversation on the farms around was on the uselessness of saving money; and smockfrocked arithmeticians, leaning on their ploughs or hoes, would enter into calculations of great nicety to prove that parish relief was a fuller provision for a man in his old age than any which could result from savings out of their wages during a whole lifetime.

After the fair and the drink and the dancing, highlights in their otherwise monotonous lives, the quarrelsome, exalted field folk set out on their homeward walk:

Then these children of the open air, whom even excess of alcohol could scarce injure permanently, betook themselves to the field-path; and as they went there moved onward with them, around the shadows of each one's hand, a circle of opalized light, formed by the moon's rays upon the glistening sheet of dew. Each pedestrian could see no halo but his or her own, which never deserted the head-shadow, whatever its vulgar unsteadiness might be; but adhered to it, and persistently beautified it; till the erratic motions seemed an inherent part of the irradiation, and the fumes of their breathing a component of the night's mist; and the spirit of the scene, and of the moonlight, and of Nature, seemed harmoniously to mingle with the spirit of wine.

Tess of the d'Urbervilles

Hardy's country people are certainly unsophisticated:

Now a great cleaning of window-panes was going on, Hezzy Biles and Sammy Blore being the operators, for which purpose their service must have been borrowed from the neighbouring farmer. Hezzy dashed water at the glass with a force that threatened to break it in, the broad face of Sammy being discernible inside, smiling at the onset.

The parson cut short the practising, and, naming another night for meeting, he withdrew. All the singers assisted him on to his cob, and watched him till he disappeared over the edge of the Bottom.

Two on a Tower

[The first Cytherea] was not so very unlike country girls of that type of beauty, except in one respect. She was perfect in her manner and bearing, and they were not.

Desperate Remedies

[Eustacia] seemed to feel, after a bare look at Diggory Venn . . . that he was not so mean as she had thought him; for her close approach did not cause him to writhe uneasily, or shift his feet, or show any of those little signs which escape an ingenuous rustic at the advent of the uncommon in womankind.

The Return of the Native

Farm-servant Anthony Cripplestraw is too insistent (Corporal Tullidge was badly wounded at Valenciennes in 1793):

"Well, if the young woman don't want to see yer head, maybe she'd like to hear yer arm?" continued Crippleshaw, earnest to please her. . . .

"Your arm hurt too?" cried Anne.

"Knocked to a pummy at the same time as my head," said Tullidge dispassionately.

"Rattle yer arm, corpel, and show her," said Cripplestraw.

"Yes, sure," said the corporal, raising the limb slowly, as if the glory of exhibition had lost some of its novelty, though he was willing to oblige. Twisting it mercilessly about with his right hand he produced a crunching among the bones at every motion. Cripplestraw seemed to derive great satisfaction from the ghastly sound.

"How very shocking!" said Anne, painfully anxious for him to leave off.

"O, it don't hurt him, bless ye. Do it, corpel?" said Cripplestraw.

"Not a bit," said the corporal, still working his arm with great energy.

"There's no life in the bones at all. No life in 'em, I tell her, corpel!"

"None at all."

"They be as loose as a bag of ninepins," explained Cripplestraw in continuation. "You can feel 'em plain, Mis'ess Anne. If ye would like to, he'll undo his sleeve in a minute to oblege ye?"

"O no, no, please not! I quite understand," said the young woman.

"Do she want to hear or see any more, or don't she?" the corporal inquired, with a sense that his time was getting wasted.

Anne explained that she did not on any account; and managed to escape from the corner.

The Trumpet-Major

But the countryman's simplicity is not total:

Jim . . . was a village character, and he had a villager's simplicity: that is, the simplicity which comes from the lack of a complicated experience. But simple by nature he certainly was not. Among the rank and file of rustics he was quite a Talleyrand, or rather had been one, till he lost a good deal of his self-command by falling in love.

"You sent for me, and I have come," she answered humbly, like an obedient familiar in the employ of some great enchanter. Indeed, the Baron's power over this innocent girl was curiously like enchantment, or mesmeric influence. . . .

It was that of Prospero over the gentle Ariel. And yet it was probably only that of the cosmopolite over the recluse, of the experienced man over the simple maid.

The Romantic Adventures of a Milkmaid

To make himself as locally harmonious as possible, Mr Bellston remarked to his companion on the scene —

"It does one's heart good," he said, "to see these simple peasants enjoying themselves."

"O Mr Bellston!" exclaimed Christine; "don't be too sure about that word 'simple'! You little think what they see and meditate! Their reasonings and emotions are as complicated as ours."

The Waiting Supper

"You are mighty sensitive for a cottage girl!" said [d'Urberville].

Tess of the d'Urbervilles

While Mr Belston and Alec d'Urberville were both surprised to find their simple peasants capable of deep feelings, Hardy and another countryman, the poet William Barnes, knew what helped to shape their understanding. In an unsigned review of William Barnes's Poems of Rural Life in the Dorset Dialect *in the* New Quarterly Magazine, *October 1879, Hardy wrote:*

That the life of a modern peasant is not too hopelessly ingrained in prose for poetic treatment he has plainly shown. Farm life as, regulated by the seasons, it varies from day to day through the year, is truthfully reflected; and we are at every step indirectly reminded wherein lies that poetry which, in spite of the occasional sting of poverty, is inseparable from such a condition of life. It lies less in the peasant's residence among fields and trees than in his absolute dependence on the moods of the air, earth, and sky. Sun, rain, wind, snow, dawn, darkness, mist, are to him, now as ever, personal assistants and obstructors, masters and acquaintances, with whom he comes directly into contact, whose varying tempers must be well-considered before he can act with effect.

Nature is a powerful teacher of many things; and Hardy's countryfolk all have their skills. (For their professional skills see Rural Occupations, *pages 180ff.)*

"Weather-wisdom was imbibed with their milk-sops by the children of the Exe Vale"[295] *— Hardy's own brother Henry, a builder, never used a watch but retained to the end of his life his preference for telling the time by natural means.*

..."How truly people who have no clocks will tell the time of day."

"Aye, that they will," said Mr Swancourt corroboratively. "I have known labouring men at Endelstow and other farms who had framed complete systems of observation for that purpose. By means of shadows, winds, clouds, the movements of sheep and oxen, the singing of birds, the crowing of cocks, and a hundred other sights and sounds which people with watches in their pockets never know the existence of, they are able to pronounce within ten minutes of the hour almost at any required instant."

A Pair of Blue Eyes

Hardy's countrymen are common-sense realists:

"Now, Cain Ball," said Gabriel restlessly, "can you swear in the most awful form that the woman you saw was Miss Everdene?"

"Cain Ball, you be no longer a babe and suckling," said Joseph in the sepulchral tone the circumstances demanded, "and you know what taking an oath is. 'Tis a horrible testament mind ye, which you say and seal with your blood-stone, and the prophet Matthew tells us that on whomsoever it shall fall it will grind him to powder. Now, before all the work-folk here assembled, can you swear to your words as the shepherd asks ye?"

"Please no, Mister Oak!" said Cainy, looking from one to the other with great uneasiness at the spiritual magnitude of the position. "I don't mind saying 'tis true, but I don't like to say 'tis damn true, if that's what you mane."

"Cain, Cain, how can you?" asked Joseph sternly. "You be asked to swear in a holy manner, and you swear like wicked Shimei, the son of Gera,[296] who cursed as he came. Young man, fie!"

"No, I don't! 'Tis you want to squander a pore boy's soul, Joseph Poorgrass — that's what 'tis!" said Cain, beginning to cry. "All I mane is that in common truth 'twas Miss Everdene and Sergeant Troy, but in the horrible so-help-me truth that ye want to make of it perhaps 'twas somebody else!"

Far from the Madding Crowd

Giles Winterborne, with the help of his rough and ready manservant Robert Creedle, has given a party for Grace Melbury and her parents; but everything seems to have gone wrong:

"Do you think it went off well, Creedle?" he asked.

"The victuals did; that I know... Not but what that slug might as well have come upon anybody else's plate as hers."

"What slug?"

"Well, maister, there was a little small one upon the edge of her plate when I brought it out, and so it must have been in her few leaves of wintergreen."

"How the deuce did a slug get there?"

"That I don't know no more than the dead; but there my gentleman was."

"But, Robert, of all places, that was where he shouldn't have been!"

"Well, 'twas his native home, come to that; and where else could we expect him to be? I don't care who the man is, slugs and caterpillars always will lurk in close to the stump of cabbages in that tantalizing way."

"He wasn't alive, I suppose?" said Giles, with a shudder on Grace's account.

"O no. He was well boiled. I warrant him well boiled. God forbid that a *live* slug should be seed on any plate of victuals that's served by Robert Creedle.... But Lord, there; I don't mind 'em myself — them green ones; for they were born on cabbage, and they've lived on cabbages, so they must be made of cabbage. But she, the close-mouthed little lady, she didn't say a word about it; though 'twould have made good small conversation as to the nater of such creatures; especially as wit ran short among us sometimes."

The Woodlanders

The death of Susan Henchard:

At the town pump there were gathered when he passed a few old inhabitants, who came there for water whenever they had, as at present, spare time to fetch it, because it was purer from that original fount than from their own wells. Mrs Cuxsom, who had been standing there for an indefinite time with her pitcher, was describing the incidents of Mrs Henchard's death, as she had learnt them from the nurse.

"And she was as white as marble-stone," said Mrs Cuxsom. "And likewise such a thoughtful woman, too — ah, poor soul — that a' minded every little thing that wanted tending. 'Yes', says she, 'when I'm gone, and my last breath's blowed, look in the top drawer o' the chest in the back room by the window, and you'll find all my coffin clothes; a piece of flannel — that's to put under me, and the little piece is to put under my head; and my new stockings for my feet — they are folded alongside, and all my other things. And there's four ounce pennies,[297] the heaviest I could find, a-tied up in bits of linen, for weights — two for my right eye and two for my left,' she said. 'And when you've used 'em, and my eyes don't open no more, bury the pennies, good souls, and don't ye go spending 'em, for I shouldn't like it. And open the windows as soon as I am carried out, and make it as cheerful as you can for Elizabeth-Jane.'"

"Ah, poor heart!"

"Well, and Martha did it, and buried the ounce pennies in the garden. But if ye'll believe words, that man, Christopher Coney, went and dug 'em up, and spent 'em at the Three Mariners. 'Faith,' he said, 'why should death rob life o' fourpence? Death's not of such good report that we should respect 'en to that extent,' said he."

"'Twas a cannibal deed!" deprecated her listeners.

"Gad, then, I won't quite ha'e it," said Solomon Longways. "I say it today, and 'tis a Sunday morning, and I wouldn't speak wrongfully for a zilver zixpence at such a time. I don't see noo harm in it. To respect the dead is sound doxology; and I wouldn't sell skellintons — leastwise respectable skellintons — to be varnished for 'natomies, except I were out o' work. But money is scarce, and throats get dry. Why *should* death rob life o'fourpence? I say there was no treason in it."

"Well, poor soul; she's helpless to hinder that or anything now," answered Mother Cuxsom. "And all her shining keys will be took from her, and her cupboards opened; and little things a' didn't wish seen, anybody will see; and her wishes and ways will all be as nothing!"

The Major of Casterbridge

Hardy's countrymen are as shrewd as any — and shrewder than some.

The workfolk discuss Miss Aldclyffe's new steward:

"The man that the old quean[298] have got is a man you can hardly get upon your tongue to gainsay, by the look o' en," rejoined Clerk Crickett.

"One o' them people that can contrive to be thought no worse of for stealen a horse than another for looken over hedge at en," said a grinder.

Desperate Remedies

When Parson Maybold and Churchwarden Shiner both wish Miss Fancy Day to play the organ, instead of the old string quire, there is more in it than meets the eye:

"Bless ye, my sonnies, 'tisn't the pa'son's move at all. That gentleman over there" (the tranter nodded in the direction of Shiner's farm) "is at the root of the mischty."

"What! Shiner?"

"Ay; and I see what the pa'son don't see. Why, Shiner is for putting forward that young woman that only last night I was saying was our Dick's sweetheart, but I suppose can't be, and making much of her in the sight of the congregation, and thinking he'll win her by showing her off. Well, perhaps 'a woll."

"Then the music is second to the woman, the other churchwarden is second to Shiner, the pa'son is second to the churchwardens, and God A'mighty is nowhere at all."

Under the Greenwood Tree

In A Pair of Blue Eyes, *with countrymen called by names like Lickpan and Worm — the latter constantly asserting that he is "only a poor wambling man" — Hardy comes perilously near ridiculing his rustic characters. (Still an inexperienced writer, just at this time he may particularly have wished, involved as he was with middle-class Emma Gifford, to dissociate himself from them.)*

But Worm, in spite of the noises like fish frying in his head, still had the measure of his master, Parson Swancourt, as he took the architect Smith round the church:

"Look there," said Mr Swancourt. "What do you think of my roofing?" He pointed with his walking-stick at the chancel roof.

"Did you do that, sir?"

"Yes, I worked in short sleeves all the time that was going on. I pulled down the old rafters, fixed the new ones, put on the battens, slated the roof, all with my own hands, Worm being my assistant. We worked like slaves, didn't we, Worm?"

"Ay, sure, we did; harder than some here and there — hee, hee!" said William Worm, cropping up from somewhere. "Like slaves, 'a b'lieve — hee, hee! And weren't ye foaming mad, sir, when the nails wouldn't go straight? Mighty I![299] There, 'tisn't so bad to cuss and keep it in as to cuss and let it out, is it, sir?"

"Well — why?"

"Because you, sir, when ye were a-putting on the roof, only used to cuss in your mind, which is, I suppose, no harm at all."

"I don't think you know what goes on in my mind, Worm."

"O doan't I, sir — hee, hee! Maybe I'm but a poor wambling thing, sir, and can't read much; but I can spell as well as some here and there. Doan't ye mind, sir, that blustrous night when ye asked me to hold the candle to ye in yer workshop, when you were making a new chair for the chancel?"

"Yes, what of that?"

"I stood with the candle, and you said you liked company, if 'twas only a dog or cat — maning me; and the chair wouldn't do nohow."

"Ah, I remember."

"No; the chair wouldn't do nohow. 'A was very well to look at but, Lord! —"

"Worm, how often have I corrected you for irrelevant speaking!"

" — 'A was very well to look at, but you couldn't sit in the chair nohow. 'Twas all a-twist wi' the chair, like the letter Z, directly you sat down upon the chair. 'Get up, Worm,' says you, when you seed the chair go all a-sway wi' me. Up you took the chair, and flung en like fire and brimstone to t'other end of your shop — all in a passion. 'Damn the chair!' says I. 'Just what I was thinking,' says you, sir. 'I could see it in your face, sir,' says I, 'and I hope you and God will forgi'e me for saying what you wouldn't.' To save your life you couldn't help laughing, sir, at a poor wambler reading your thoughts so plain. Ay, I'm as wise as one here and there."

A Pair of Blue Eyes

Hardy's country folk are usually independent-minded — even if their roof depends upon another[300] *they have an innate sense of their own worth as individuals. Ethelberta as a child often refused to curtsey — "She was always one of the independent sort — you never saw such a maid as she was!"*[301] *Stephen Smith's mother shows her mettle over his attachment to Elfride Swancourt:*

"She's a pretty piece enough," Mrs Smith continued, "and very lady-like and clever too. But though she's very well fit for you as far as that is, why, mercy 'pon me, what ever do you want any woman at all for yet?"

John made his naturally short mouth a long one, and wrinkled his forehead. "That's the way the wind d'blow, is it?" he said.

"Mother," exclaimed Stephen, "how absurdly you speak! Criticizing whether she's fit for me or no, as if there were room for doubt on the matter! Why, to marry her would be the great blessing of my life — socially and practically, as well as in other respects. No such good fortune as that, I'm afraid; she's too far above me. Her family doesn't want such country lads as I in it."

"Then if they don't want you, I'd see them dead corpses before I'd want them, and go to families who do want you."

"Ah, yes; but I could never put up with the distaste of being welcomed among such people as you mean, whilst I could get indifference among such people as hers."

"What crazy twist of thinking will enter your head next?" said his mother. "And come to that, she's not a bit too high for you, or you too low for her. See how careful I am to keep myself up. I'm sure I never stop for more than a minute together to talk to any journeymen people; and I never invite anybody to our party o' Christmases who are not in business for themselves. And I talk to several carriage people that come to my lord's without saying ma'am or sit to 'em, and they take it as quiet as lambs."

"You curtseyed to the rector, mother; and I wish you hadn't."

"But it was before he called me by my Christian name, or he would have got very little curtseying from me!" said Mrs Smith, bridling and sparkling with vexation. "You go on at me, Stephen, as if I were your worst enemy! What else could I do with the man to get rid of him, banging it into me and your father by sidė and by seam about his greatness, and what happened when he was a young fellow at college, and I don't know what-all; the tongue o' en flopping round his mouth like a mop-rag round a dairy, didn't it, John?"

"That's about the size o't," replied her husband.

A Pair of Blue Eyes

"Worm!" the rector shouted.

A minute or two after a voice was heard round the corner of the building, mumbling, "Ah, I used to bė strong enough, but 'tis altered now! Well, there, I'm as independent as one here and there, even if they do write 'squire' after their names"....

A Pair of Blue Eyes

... *Independent, but also well-mannered and tolerant:*

Down in the Luxellian vault the masons are preparing the tomb for the newly-dead Lady Luxellian:

"Better move Lord George first, I suppose, Simeon?"

He pointed with his foot to a heavy coffin, covered with what had originally been red velvet, the colour of which could only just be distinguished now.

"Just as ye think best, Master John," replied the shrivelled mason. "Ah, poor Lord George!" he continued, looking contemplatively at the huge coffin; "he and I were as bitter enemies once as any could be when one is a lord and t'other only a creeping man. Poor fellow! He'd clap his hand upon my shoulder and cuss me as familiar and neighbourly as if he'd been a common chap. Ay, 'a cussed me up hill and 'a cussed me down; and then 'a would rave out again, and the goold clamps of his fine new teeth would glisten in the sun like fetters of brass, while I, being a small man and poor, was fain to say nothing at all. Such a strappen fine gentleman as he was too! Yes, I rather liked en sometimes. But once now and then, when I looked at his towering height, I'd think in my inside, 'What a weight you'll be, my lord, for our arms to lower under the aisle of Endelstow Church some day!'"

"And was he?" inquired a young labourer.

"He was. He was five hundredweight if 'a were a pound. What with his lead, and his oak, and his handles, and his one thing and t'other" — here the ancient man slapped his hand upon the cover with a force that caused a rattle among the bones inside — "he half broke my back when I took his feet to lower him down the steps there. 'Ah, 'saith I to John there — didn't I, John? — 'that ever one man's glory should be such a weight upon another man!' But there, I liked my lord George sometimes."

A Pair of Blue Eyes

At the shepherd's christening-party at Higher Crowstairs:

Nineteen persons were gathered here . . . Enjoyment was pretty general, and so much the more prevailed in being unhampered by conventional restrictions. Absolute confidence in each other's good opinion begat perfect ease, while the finishing stroke of manner, amounting to a truly princely serenity, was lent to the majority by the absence of any expression or trait denoting that they wished to get on in the world, enlarge their minds, or do any eclipsing thing whatever — which nowadays so generally nips the bloom and *bonhomie* of all except the two extremes of the social scale.

The Three Strangers

The serenity Hardy describes as springing from a freely-chosen lack of worldly ambition is also shown in most of his characters in a stoical acceptance of the harsh realities of injustice, poverty, or illness.[302]

"Yes," Worm groaned to Stephen, "I've got such a noise in my head that there's no living night or day. 'Tis just for all the world like people frying fish: fry, fry, fry, all day long in my poor head, till I don't know whe'r I'm here or yonder. There, God A'mighty will find it out sooner or later, I hope, and relieve me."

A Pair of Blue Eyes

This passage also shows the religious orientation, the God-ward reference, of Hardy's country folk. Hardy himself quotes more from the Bible than any other book; Liddy Smallbury finds it natural as the workfolk line up to be paid to say to her mistress, "The Philistines be upon us"; and Joseph Poorgrass (who when laid up with a bad leg took the opportunity to read The Pilgrim's Progress *— an interesting sidelight on nineteenth-century country literacy) spends most of his time "beginning to feel like a man in the Bible":*

"The very thing I said this morning," observed Joseph. "'Justice is come to weigh him in the balances,' I said in my reflectious way, 'and if he's found wanting, so be it unto him,' and a bystander said 'Hear,hear! A man who can talk like that ought to be heard.' But I don't like dwelling upon it, for my few words are my few words, and not much; though the speech of some men is rumoured abroad as though by nature formed for such."[303]

Far from the Madding Crowd

Hardy's truly rural characters are distinguished from their urban counterparts by their strong moral sense.[304] *Some of this is conventional:*

The topic at present handled was a highly popular and frequent one — the personal character of Mrs Charmond, the owner of the surrounding glades and groves.

"My brother-in-law told me, and I have no reason to doubt it," said Creedle, "that she'll sit down to her dinner with a gown hardly higher than her elbows. 'O, you wicked woman!' he said to hisself when he first see her, 'you go to the Table o' Sundays, and kneel, as if your knee-jints were greased with very saint's anointment, and tell off your hear-us-good-Lords as pat as a business-man counting money; and yet you can eat your victuals a-stript to such a wanton figure as that!' Whether she's a reformed character by this time I can't say; but I don't care who the man is, that's how she went on when my brother-in-law lived there."

"Did she do it in her husband's time?"

"That I don't know — hardly, I should think, considering his temper. Ah — !" Here Creedle threw grieved resemblances into physical form by resigning his head to obliquity and letting his eyes water. "That man! 'Not if the angels of heaven come down, Creedle,' he said, 'shall you do another day's work for me!' Yes — he would as soon take a winged angel's name in vain as yours or mine! Well, now I must get these spars home-along, and to-morrow, thank God, I must see about using 'em."

The Woodlanders

Some goes much deeper. Grace Fitzpiers still believes she may be able to divorce her adulterous husband and marry her lifelong friend Giles Winterborne; he has just heard privately that it cannot be:

"Don't you think you will ever be happy, Giles?"

He did not reply for some instants. "When the sun shines flat on the north front of Sherton Abbey — that's when my happiness will come to me!" said he, staring as it were into the earth.

"But — then that means that there is something more than my offending you in not liking the Sherton tavern? If it is because I — did not like to let you kiss me in the Abbey — well, you know, Giles, that it was not on account of my cold feelings, but because I did certainly, just then, think it was rather premature, in spite of my poor father. That was the true reason — the sole one. But I do not want to be hard — God knows I do not!" she said, her voice fluctuating. "And perhaps — as I am on the verge of freedom — I am not right, after all, in thinking there is any harm in your kissing me."

"O Heaven!' groaned Winterborne to himself. His head was turned askance as he still resolutely regarded the ground. For the last several minutes he had seen this great temptation approaching him in regular siege; and now it had come. The wrong, the social sin, of now taking advantage of the offer of her lips, had a magnitude in the eyes of one whose life had been so primitive, so ruled by household laws as Giles's, which can hardly be explained.

"Did you say anything?" she asked timidly.

"O no — only that —"

"You mean that it must *be already* settled, since my father is coming home?" she said gladly.

"Ah — yes."

"Then why don't you do what you want to?" She was almost pouting at his hesitation.

Winterborne, though fighting valiantly against himself all this while — though he would have protected Grace's good repute as the apple of his eye, was a man; and, as Desdemona said, men are not gods. In face of the agonizing seductiveness shown by her, in her unenlightened school-girl simplicity about the laws and ordinances, he betrayed a man's weakness. Since it was so — since it had come to this, that Grace, deeming herself free to do it, was virtually asking him to demonstrate that he loved her — since he could demonstrate it only too truly — since life was short and love was strong — he gave way to the temptation, notwithstanding that he perfectly well knew her to be wedded irrevocably to Fitzpiers. Indeed, he cared for nothing past or future, simply accepting the present and what it brought, deciding once in his life to clasp in his arms her he had watched over and loved so long.

She looked up suddenly from his long embrace and passionate kiss, influenced by a sort of inspiration. "O, I suppose," she stammered, "that I am really free? — that this is right? Is there *really* a new law? Father cannot have been too sanguine in saying —"

He did not answer, and a moment afterwards Grace burst into tears in spite of herself. "O, why does not my father come home and explain!" she sobbed upon his breast, "and let me know clearly what I am! It is too trying, this, to ask me to — and then to leave me so long in so vague a state that I do not know what to do, and perhaps do wrong!"

Winterborne felt like a very Cain, over and above his previous sorrow. How he had sinned against her in not telling her himself only knew. He lifted her up and turned aside: the feeling of his cruelty mounted higher and higher. How could he have dreamt of kissing her? He could hardly refrain from tears. Surely nothing more pitiable had ever been known than the condition of this poor young thing, now as heretofore the victim of her father's well-meant but blundering policy.

The Woodlanders.

But what distinguishes Hardy's countryfolk above all else is their exceptionally strong sense of community. Their loyalty, support, and sympathy for each other, and their genuine interest in each other is in striking contrast to the relationships of much of twentieth-century western urban society. This is reflected in their characteristic mode of address, calling each other "Neighbour", in the way they care for their simple-minded ones,[305] and in, for example, the readiness of Tess's friends to finish her work for her when she collapses with exhaustion.

The peace at Warren's Malthouse is threatened – but preserved by converted action (Henery claims to be "a strange old piece"...):

"A strange old piece, ye say!" interposed the maltster, in a querulous voice. "At the same time ye be no old man worth naming — no old man at all. Yer teeth bain't half gone yet; and what's a old man's standing if so be his teeth bain't gone? Weren't I stale in wedlock afore ye were out of arms? 'Tis a poor thing to be sixty, when there's people far past four-score — a boast weak as water."

It was the unvarying custom in Weatherbury to sink minor differences when the maltster had to be pacified.

"Weak as water! yes," said Jan Coggan. "Malter, we feel ye to be a wonderful veteran man, and nobody can gainsay it."

"Nobody," said Joseph Poorgrass. "Ye be a very rare old spectacle, malter, and we all admire ye for that gift."

"Ay, and as a young man, when my senses were in prosperity, I was likewise liked by a good-few who knowed me,' said the maltster.

"'Ithout doubt you was — 'ithout doubt."

The bent and hoary man was satisfied, and so apparently was Henery Fray. That matters should continue pleasant Maryann spoke, who, what with her brown complexion, and the working wrapper of rusty linsey,[306] had at present the mellow hue of an old sketch in oils — notably some of Nicholas Poussin's:—

"Do anybody know of a crooked man, or a lame, or any second-hand fellow at all that would do for poor me?" said Maryann. "A perfect one I don't expect to get at my time of life. If I could hear of such a thing 'twould do me more good than toast and ale."

Far from the Madding Crowd

Mrs Worm knows how to be neighbourly even in little things:

"Take your things off, Mrs Worm," said Mrs Smith. "We are rather in a muddle, to tell the truth, for my son is just dropped in from Indy a day sooner than we expected, and the pig-killer is coming presently to cut up."

Mrs Barbara Worm, not wishing to take any mean advantage of persons in a muddle by observing them, removed her bonnet and mantle with eyes fixed upon the flowers in the plot outside the door.

"What beautiful tiger-lilies!" said Mrs Worm.

A Pair of Blue Eyes

The Chalk-Newton band act in sympathy with a dead man. (On their carol-singing rounds on Christmas Eve, the band meets a group of gravediggers from Sidlinch village burying old Sergeant Holway, a suicide, with no ceremony — or coffin — at a lonely cross-roads.):[307]

When their tread had died away from the ear, and the wind swept over the isolated grave with its customary siffle of indifference, Lot Swanhills turned and spoke to old Robert Toller, the hautboy player.

"'Tis hard upon a man, and he a wold sojer, to serve en so, Richard. Not that the sergeant was ever in a battle bigger than would go into a half-acre paddock, that's true. Still, his soul ought to hae as good a chance as another man's, all the same, hey?"

Richard replied that he was quite of the same opinion. "What d'ye say to lifting up a carrel over his grave, as 'tis Christmas, and no hurry to begin down in parish, and 'twouldn't take up ten minutes, and not a soul up here to say us nay, or know anything about it?"

Lot nodded assent. "The man ought to hae his chances," he repeated.

"Ye may as well spet upon his grave, for all the good we shall do en by what we lift up, now he's got so far," said Notton, the clarionet man and professed sceptic of the choir. "But I'm agreed if the rest be."

They thereupon placed themselves in a semicircle by the newly-stirred earth, and roused the dull air with the well-known Number Sixteen of their collection, which Lot gave out as being the one he thought best suited to the occasion and the mood:—

He comes′ the pri′-soners to′ re-lease′,
In Sa′tan's bon′dage held′.

"Jown it — we've never played to a dead man afore," said Ezra Cattstock, when, having concluded the last verse, they stood reflecting for a breath or two. "But it do seem more merciful than to go away and leave en, as they t'other fellers have done."

The Grave by the Handpost

Abel Whittle forgets his injuries but remembers a debt of gratitude. (One of Farfrae's labourers, Abel Whittle, has been gone from work without a word for three weeks. Searching for Henchard, whom they fear ill, Farfrae and Elizabeth-Jane come to a ruined cottage on the heath some twenty miles from Casterbridge.):

The door was ajar; Farfrae knocked; and he who stood before them was Whittle, as they had conjectured.

His face showed marks of deep sadness, his eyes lighting on them with an unfocused gaze.... As soon as he recognized them he started.

"What, Abel Whittle; is it that ye are heere?" said Farfrae.

"Ay, yes, sir! You see he was kind-like to mother when she wer here below, though 'a was rough to me."

"Who are you talking of?"

"O sir — Mr Henchet! Didn't ye know it? He's just gone — about half-an-hour ago, by the sun; for I've got no watch to my name."

"Not — dead?" faltered Elizabeth-Jane.

"Yes, ma'am, he's gone! He was kind-like to mother when she wer here below, sending her the best ship-coal, and hardly any ashes from it at all; and taties, and such-like that were very needful to her. I seed en go down street on the night of your worshipful's wedding to the lady at yer side, and I thought he looked low and faltering. And I followed en over Grey's Bridge, and he turned and zeed me, and said, 'You go back!' But I followed, and he turned again, and said, 'Do you hear, sir? Go back!' But I zeed that he was low, and I followed on still. Then 'a said, 'Whittle, what do ye follow me for when I've told ye to go back all these times?' And I said, 'Because, sir, I see things be bad with 'ee, and ye wer kind-like to mother if ye were rough to me, and I would fain be kind-like to you.' Then he walked on, and I followed; and he never complained at me no more. We walked on like that all night; and in the blue o' the morning, when 'twas hardly day, I looked ahead o' me, and I zeed that he wambled, and could hardly drag along. By that time we had got past here, but I had seen that this house was empty as I went by, and I got him to come back; and I took down the boards from the windows, and helped him inside. 'What, Whittle,' he said, 'and can ye really be such a poor fond fool as to care for such a wretch as I!' Then I went on further, and some neighbourly woodmen lent me a bed, and a chair, and a few other traps, and we brought 'em here, and made him as comfortable as we could. But he didn't gain strength, for you see, ma'am, he couldn't eat — no, no appetite at all — and he got weaker; and to-day he died. One of the neighbours have gone to get a man to measure him."

The Mayor of Casterbridge

Solidarity at Talbothays dairy farm:

After supper, when she reached her bedroom, they were all present. A light was burning, and each damsel was sitting up whitely in her bed, awaiting Tess, the whole like a row of avenging ghosts.

But she saw in a few moments that there was no malice in their mood. They could scarcely feel as a loss what they had never expected to have. Their condition was objective, contemplative.

"He's going to marry her!" murmured Retty, never taking her eyes off Tess. "How her face do show it!"...

"Yes — going to *marry* him — a gentleman!" repeated Izz Huett.

And by a sort of fascination the three girls, one after another, crept out of their beds, and came and stood barefooted round Tess. Retty put her hands upon Tess's shoulders, as if to realize her friend's corporeality after such a miracle, and the other two laid their arms round her waist, all looking into her face.

"How it do seem! Almost more than I can think of!" said Izz Huett.

Marian kissed Tess. "Yes," she murmured as she withdrew her lips.

"Was that because of love for her, or because other lips have touched there by now?" continued Izz drily to Marian.

"I wasn't thinking o' that," said Marian simply. "I was on'y feeling all the strangeness o't— that she is to be his wife, and nobody else. I don't say nay to it, nor either of us, because we did not think of it — only loved him. Still, nobody else is to marry'n in the world — no fine lady, nobody in silks and satins; but she who do live like we."

"Are you sure you don't dislike me for it?" said Tess in a low voice.

They hung about her in their white nightgowns before replying, as if they considered their answer might lie in her look.

"I don't know — I don't know," murmured Retty Priddle. "I want to hate 'ee; but I cannot!"

"That's how I feel," echoed Izz and Marian. "I can't hate her. Somehow she hinders me!"

"He ought to marry one of you," murmured Tess.

"Why?"

"You are all better than I."

"We better than you?" said the girls in a low, slow whisper. "No, no, dear Tess!"

"You are!" she contradicted impetuously. And suddenly tearing away from their clinging arms she burst into a hysterical fit of tears, bowing herself on the chest of drawers and repeating incessantly, "O yes, yes, yes!"

Having once given way she could not stop her weeping.

"He ought to have had one of you!" she cried. "I think I ought to make him even now! You would be better for him than — I don't know what I'm saying! O! O!"

They went up to her and clasped her round, but still her sobs tore her.

"Get some water," said Marian. "She's upset by us, poor thing, poor thing!"

They gently led her back to the side of the bed, where they kissed her warmly.

"You are best for'n," said Marian. "More ladylike, and a better scholar than we, especially since he has taught 'ee so much. But even you ought to be proud. You *be* proud, I'm sure."

"Yes, I am," she said; "and I am ashamed at so breaking down!"

When they were all in bed, and the light was out, Marian whispered across to her —

"You will think of us when you be his wife, Tess, and of how we told 'ee that we loved him, and how we tried not to hate you, and did not hate you, and could not hate you, because you were his choice, and we never hoped to be chose by him."

They were not aware that, at these words, salt, stinging tears prickled down upon Tess's pillow anew, and how she resolved, with a bursting heart, to tell all her history to Angel Clare, despite her mother's command — to let him for whom she lived and breathed despise her if he would and her mother regard her as a fool, rather than preserve a silence which might be deemed a treachery to him, and which somehow seemed a wrong to these.

Tess of the d'Urbervilles

After Hardy's friend Mrs Florence Henniker had moved to Shoreham in Kent (the same countryside that so inspired the painter Samuel Palmer nearly a century earlier), Hardy wrote to her:

Max Gate, 17 July, 1914

... Your neighbours are probably like most country folk — rather stolid. Yet that sort of person does really feel a sincerer regard for one's welfare than town people, I consider.

The neighbours at Warren's Malthouse show their genuine interest in each other:

"Why, Joseph Poorgrass, ye han't had a drop!" said Mr Coggan to a self-conscious man in the background, thrusting the cup towards him.

"Such a modest man as he is!" said Jacob Smallbury. "Why, ye've hardly had strength of eye enough to look in our young mis'ess's face, so I hear, Joseph?"

All looked at Joseph Poorgrass with pitying reproach.

"No — I've hardly looked at her at all," simpered Joseph, reducing his body smaller whilst talking, apparently from a meek sense of undue prominence. "And when I seed her, 'twas nothing but blushes with me!"

"Poor feller," said Mr Clark.

"'Tis a curious nature for a man," said Jan Coggan.

"Yes," continued Joseph Poorgrass — his shyness, which was so painful as a defect, filling him with a mild complacency now that it was regarded as an interesting study. "'Twere blush, blush, blush with me every minute of the time, when she was speaking to me."

"I believe ye, Joseph Poorgrass, for we all know ye to be a very bashful man."

"'Tis a' awkward gift for a man, poor soul," said the maltster. "And ye have suffered from it a long time, we know."

"Ay, ever since I was a boy. Yes — mother was concerned to her heart about it — yes. But 'twas all nought."

"Did ye ever go into the world to try and stop it, Joseph Poorgrass?"

"O ay, tried all sorts o' company. They took me to Greenhill Fair, and into a great gay jerry-go-nimble show,[308] where there were women-folk riding around — standing upon horses, with hardly anything on but their smocks; but it didn't cure me a morsel. And then I was put errand-man at the Women's Skittle Alley at the back of the Tailor's Arms in Casterbridge. 'Twas a horrible sinful situation, and a very curious place for a good man. I had to stand and look ba'dy[309] people in the face from morning till night; but 'twas no use — I was just as bad as ever after all. Blushes hev been in the family for generations. There, 'tis a happy providence that I be no worse."

"True," said Jacob Smallbury, deepening his thoughts to a profounder view of the subject. "'Tis a thought to look at, that ye might have been worse; but even as you be, 'tis a very bad affliction for 'ee, Joseph. For ye see, shepherd, though 'tis very well for a woman, dang it all, 'tis awkward for a man like him, poor feller?"

"'Tis — 'tis," said Gabriel, recovering from a meditation. "Yes, very awkward for the man."

"Ay, and he's very timid, too," observed Jan Coggan. "Once he had been working late at Yalbury Bottom, and had had a drap of drink, and lost his way as he was coming home-along through Yalbury Wood, didn't ye, Master Poorgrass?"

"No, no, no; not that story!" expostulated the modest man, forcing a laugh to bury his concern.

"— And so 'a lost himself quite," continued Mr Coggan, with an impassive face, implying that a true narrative, like time and tide, must run its course and would respect no man. "And as he was coming along in the middle of the night, much afeared, and not able to find his way out of the tree nohow, 'a cried out. 'Man-a-lost!

man-a-lost!' A owl in a tree happened to be crying 'Whoo-whoo-whoo!' as owls do, you know, shepherd" (Gabriel nodded), "and Joseph, all in a tremble, said, 'Joseph Poorgrass, of Weatherbury, sir!'"

"No, no, now — that's too much!" said the timid man, becoming a man of brazen courage all of a sudden. "I didn't say *sir*. I'll take my oath I didn't say 'Joseph Poorgrass o' Weatherbury, sir.' No, no; what's right is right, and I never said sir to the bird, knowing very well that no man of a gentleman's rank would be hollering there at that time o' night. 'Joseph Poorgrass of Weatherbury,' — that's every word I said, and I shouldn't ha' said that if 't hadn't been for Keeper Day's metheglin.[310] . . . There, 'twas a merciful thing it ended where it did."

The question of which was right being tacitly waived by the company, Jan went on meditatively:—

"And he's the fearfullest man, bain't ye, Joseph? Ay, another time ye were lost by Lambing-Down Gate, weren't ye, Joseph?"

"I was," replied Poorgrass, as if there were some conditions too serious even for modesty to remember itself under, this being one.

"Yes; that were the middle of the night, too. The gate would not open, try how he would, and knowing there was the Devil's hand in it, he kneeled down."

"Ay," said Joseph, acquiring confidence from the warmth of the fire, the cider, and a perception of the narrative capabilities of the experience alluded to. "My heart died within me, that time; but I kneeled down and said the Lord's Prayer, and then the Belief right through, and then the Ten Commandments, in earnest prayer. But no, the gate wouldn't open; and then I went on with Dearly Beloved Brethren, and, thinks I, this makes four, and 'tis all I know out of the book,[311] and if this doesn't do it nothing will, and I'm a lost man. Well, when I got to Saying After Me, I rose from my knees and found the gate would open — yes, neighbours, the gate opened the same as ever."

A meditation on the obvious inference was indulged in by all. . . .

Far from the Madding Crowd

Talk like this is the almost universal vehicle for Hardy's portrayal of country humour (which is singularly lacking in his last novel, Jude the Obscure, *where much of the action takes place in towns, and where Hardy's bitter theme and aim are all-engulfing).*

Dairyman Crick tells how once the churn was damaged:

"Jack Dollop, a 'hore's-bird[312] of a fellow we had here as milker at one time, sir, courted a young woman over at Mellstock, and deceived her as he had deceived many afore. But he had another sort o' woman to reckon wi' this time, and it was not the girl herself. One Holy Thursday, of all days in the almanack, we was here as we mid be now, only there was no churning in hand, when we zid the girls's mother coming up to the door, wi' a great brass-mounted umbrella in her hand that would ha' felled an ox; and saying 'Do Jack Dollop work here? — because I want him! I have a big bone to pick with he, I can assure 'n!' And some way behind her mother walked Jack's young woman, crying bitterly into her handkerchief. 'O Lard, here's a time!' said Jack, looking out o' winder at 'em. 'She'll murder me! where shall I get — where shall I —? Don't tell her where I be!' And with that he scrambled into the churn through the trap-door, and shut himself inside, just as the young woman's mother busted into the milk-house. 'The villain — where is he?' says she, 'I'll claw his face for'n, let me only catch him!' Well, she hunted about everywhere, ballyragging Jack by side and by seam, Jack lying a'most stifled inside the churn, and the poor maid — or young woman rather — standing at the door crying her eyes out. I shall never forget it, never! 'Twould have melted a marble stone! But she couldn't find him nowhere at all." . . .

"Well, how the old woman should have had the wit to guess it I could never tell, but she found out that he was inside that there churn. Without saying a word she took hold of the winch (it was turned by handpower then), and round she swung him, and Jack began to flop about inside. 'O Lard! stop the churn! let me out!' says he, popping out his head, 'I shall be churned into a pummy!'[313] (He was a cowardly chap in his heart, as such men mostly be.) 'Not till ye make amends for ravaging her virgin innocence!' says the old woman. 'Stop the churn, you old witch!' screams he. 'You call me old witch, do ye, you deceiver!' says she, 'when ye ought to ha' been calling me mother-in-law these last five months.' And on went the churn, and Jack's bones rattled round again. Well, none of us ventured to interfere; and at last 'a promised to make it right wi' her."

Tess of the d'Urbervilles

Fate and two women:

"Clerk Crickett, I fancy you know everything about everybody," said Gad.

"Well, so's," said the clerk modestly. 'I do know a little. It comes to me."

"And I know where from."

"Ah."

"That wife o' thine. She's an entertainen woman, not to speak disrespectful."

"She is: and a winnen one. Look at the husbands she've had — God bless her!"

"I wonder you could stand third in that list, Clerk Crickett," said Mr Springrove.

"Well, 't has been a power o' marvel to myself oftentimes. Yes, matrimony do begun wi' 'Dearly beloved', and ends wi' 'Amazement', as the prayer-book says. But what could I do, neighbour Springrove? 'Twas ordained to be. Well do I call to mind what your poor lady said to me when I had just married. 'Ah, Mr Crickett,' says she, 'your wife will soon settle you as she did her other two: here's a glass o' rum, for I shan't see your poor face this time next year.' I swallowed the rum, called again next year, and said, 'Mrs Springrove, you gave me a glass o' rum last year because I was going to die — here I be alive still, you see.' 'Well thought of, clerk! Here's two glasses for you now, then,' says she. 'Thank you, mem,' I said, and swallered the rum. Well, dang my old sides, next year I thought I'd call again and get three. An call I did.

But she wouldn't give me a drop o' the commonest. 'No, clerk,' says she, 'you are too tough for a woman's pity.'... Ah, poor soul, 'twas true enough! Here be I, that was expected to die, alive and hard as a nail, you see, and there's she moulderen in her grave."

"I used to think 'twas your wife's fate not to have a liven husband when I zid 'em die off so," said Gad.

"Fate? Bless thy simplicity, so 'twas her fate; but she struggled to have one, and would, and did. Fate's nothing beside a woman's schemen!'

"I suppose, then, that Fate is a He, like us, and the Lord, and the rest o' 'em up above there," said Gad, lifting his eyes to the sky.

Desperate Remedies

Dairyman Crick has another story to tell – an echo from the Hardy family's past?

"Once there was a old aged man over at Mellstock — William Dewy[314] by name — one of the family that used to do a good deal of business as tranters over there, Jonathan, do ye mind? — I knowed the man by sight as well as I know my own brother, in a manner of speaking. Well, this man was a-coming home-along from a wedding where he had been playing his fiddle, one fine moonlight night, and for shortness' sake he took a cut across Forty-acres, a field lying that way, where a bull was out to grass. The bull seed William, and took after him, horns aground, begad; and though William runned his best, and hadn't *much* drink in him (considering 'twas a wedding, and the folks well off), he found he'd never reach the fence and get over in time to save himself. Well, as a last thought, he pulled out his fiddle as he runned, and struck up a jig, turning to the bull, and backing towards the corner. The bull softened down, and stood still, looking hard at William Dewy, who fiddled on and on; till a sort of a smile stole over the bull's face. But no sooner did William stop his playing and turn to get over hedge than the bull would stop his smiling and lower his horns towards the seat of William's breeches. Well, William had to turn about and play on, willy-nilly; and 'twas only three o'clock in the world, and 'a knowed that nobody would come that way for hours, and he so leery[315] and tired that 'a didn't know what to do. When he had scraped till about four o'clock he felt that he verily would have to give over soon, and he said to himself, 'There's only this last tune between me and eternal welfare! Heaven save me, or I'm a done man.' Well, then he called to mind how he'd seen the cattle kneel o' Christmas Eves in the dead o' night. It was not Christmas Eve then, but it came into his head to play a trick upon the bull. So he broke into the 'Tivity Hymn, just as at Christmas carol-singing; when, lo and behold, down went the bull on his bended knees, in his ignorance, just as if 'twere the true 'Tivity night and hour. As soon as his horned friend were down, William turned, clinked off like a long-dog, and jumped safe over hedge, before the praying bull had got on his feet again to take after him. William used to say that he'd seen a man look a fool a good many times, but never such a fool as that bull looked when he found his pious feelings had been played upon, and 'twas not Christmas Eve.... Yes, William

Dewy, that was the man's name; and I can tell you to a foot where's he a-lying in Mellstock Churchyard at this very moment — just between the second yew-tree and the north aisle."

Tess of the d'Urbervilles

(For this legend in verse, see The Oxen *on page 67.)*

The countryman's colourful talk – besides his humour – is exemplified in these extracts, but never so vividly as with Haymoss:

The brown person was a labouring man known to the world of Welland as Haymoss (the encrusted form of the word Amos, to adopt the phrase of philologists). The reason of the halt had been some inquiries addressed to him by Lady Constantine.

"Who is that — Amos Fry, I think?" she had asked.

"Yes, my lady," said Haymoss; "a homely barley driller, born under the eaves of your ladyship's outbuildings, in a manner of speaking — though your ladyship was neither born nor 'tempted[316] at that time."

"Who lives in the old house behind the plantation?"

"Old Gammer Martin, my lady, and her grandson."

"He has neither father nor mother, then?"

"Not a single one, my lady."

"Where was he educated?"

"At Warborne, — a place where they draw up young gam'sters' brains like rhubarb under a ninepenny pan, my lady, excusing my common way. They hit so much learning into en that 'a could talk like the day of Pentecost; which is a wonderful thing for a simple boy, and his mother only the plainest ciphering woman in the world. Warborne Grammar School — that's where 'twas 'a went to. His father, the reverent Pa'son St Cleeve, made a terrible bruckle hit[317] in 's marrying, in the sight of the high. He were the curate here, my lady, for a length 'o time."

"Oh, curate," said Lady Constantine. "It was before I knew the village."

"Ay, long and merry ago! And he married Farmer Martin's daughter — Giles Martin, a limberish[318] man, who used to go rather bad upon his legs, if you can mind? I knowed the man well enough; who should know en better! The maid was a poor windling[319] thing, and, though a playward[320] piece o' flesh when he married her, she socked and sighed, and went out like a snoff![321] Yes, my lady. Well, when Pa'son St Cleeve married this homespun woman the toppermost folk wouldn't speak to his wife. Then he dropped a cuss or two, and said he'd no longer gets his living by curing their twopenny souls o' such d— nonsense as that (excusing my common way), and he took to farming straightway, and then 'a dropped down dead in a nor'-west thunderstorm; it being said — hee-hee! — that Master God was in tantrums wi'en for leaving his service, — hee-hee! I give the story as I heard it, my lady, but be dazed if I believe in such trumpery about folks in the sky, nor anything else that's said on 'em, good or bad."

Two on a Tower

The rustic Hodge – or a real human being? The last word about country people must come direct from Hardy himself. In Tess of the d'Urbervilles *he reproduces almost identically a passage he had used in "The Dorsetshire Labourer" in 1883: it was a subject he deeply cared about.*

It seldom happens that a nickname which affects to portray a class is honestly indicative of the individuals composing that class. . . . When we arrive at the farm-labouring community we find it to be seriously personified by the pitiable picture known as Hodge. . . . This supposed real but highly conventional Hodge is a degraded being of uncouth manner and aspect, stolid understanding, and snail-like movement. . . . Hodge hangs his head or looks sheepish when spoken to, and thinks Lunnon a place paved with gold. Misery and fever lurk in his cottage . . . He hardly dares to think at all.

The Dorsetshire Labourer

But when Angel Clare came to live among farm-folk, he found that after a short time of adjustment to a "contrasting society":

. . . the typical and unvarying Hodge ceased to exist. He had been disintegrated into a number of varied fellow-creatures — beings of many minds, beings infinite in difference; some happy, many serene, a few depressed, one here and there bright even to genius, some stupid, others wanton, others austere; some mutely Miltonic, some potentially Cromwellian;[322] into men who had private views of each other, as he had of his friends; who could applaud or condemn each other, amuse or sadden themselves by the contemplation of each other's foibles or vices; men every one of whom walked in his own individual way the road to dusty death.[323]

Tess of the d'Urbervilles

Friends Beyond[324]

William Dewy, Tranter Reuben, Farmer Ledlow late at plough,
    Robert's kin, and John's, and Ned's,
And the Squire, and Lady Susan, lie in Mellstock churchyard now!

"Gone," I call them, gone for good, that group of local hearts and heads;
    Yet at mothy curfew-tide,
And at midnight when the noon-heat breathes it back from walls and leads,

They've a way of whispering to me — fellow-wight who yet abide —
    In the muted, measured note
Of a ripple under archways, or a lone cave's stillicide:

"We have triumphed: this achievement turns the bane to antidote,
    Unsuccesses to success,
Many thought-worn eves and morrows to a morrow free of thought.

"No more need we corn and clothing, feel of old terrestrial stress;
Chill detraction stirs no sigh;
Fear of death has even bygone us: death gave all that we possess."

W.D. — "Ye mid burn the old bass-viol that I set such value by."
Squire. — "You may hold the manse in fee,
You may wed my spouse, may let my children's memory of me die."

Lady S. — "You may have my rich brocades, my laces; take each household key;
Ransack coffer, desk, bureau;
Quiz the few poor treasures hid there, con the letters kept by me."

Far. — 'Ye mid zell my favourite heifer, ye mid let the charlock grow,
Foul the grinterns,[325] give up thirst."
Far. Wife — "If ye break my best blue china, children, I shan't care or ho."[326]

All — "We've no wish to hear the tidings, how the people's fortune shift;
What your daily doings are;
Who are wedded, born, divided; if your lives beat slow or swift.

"Curious not the least are we if our intents you make or mar,
If you quire to our old tune,
If the City stage still passes, if the weirs still roar afar."

— Thus, with very gods' composure, freed those crosses late and soon
Which, in life, the Trine allow
(Why, none witteth), and ignoring all that haps beneath the moon,

William Dewy, Tranter Reuben, Farmer Ledlow late at plough,
Robert's kin, and John's, and Ned's,
And the Squire, and Lady Susan, murmur mildly to me now.

Wessex Poems

Notes

Many passages appear under one heading (eg Folklore) when they are also good examples of another (eg Medicine). The index has been used to gather all these cross-references: with each section heading in these notes an asterisk shows the index entries where other relevant passages may be found.

ABBREVIATIONS USED IN THE NOTES
Life: *The Life of Thomas Hardy*, by F. E. Hardy (London 1962)
Orel: *Personal Writings of Thomas Hardy*, ed. Harold Orel (Kansas 1966, London 1967)
Archer: *Real Conversations*, by William Archer (London 1904)

INTRODUCTION

1 *Life*, p 62
2 ibid, pp 246–7
3 David Cecil, *Hardy the Novelist*, ch IV
4 "Afterwards" (*Moments of Vision*)
5 Life, p 202
6 p 30
7 p 13
8 *Life*, p 336
9 p 24
10 Interview with Raymond Plathwayt for *Black & White*, 1892
11 *Dorset County Chronicle*, 24 November 1910
12 General Preface to the Wessex edition of Hardy's works, 1912
13 "The Withered Arm" (*Wessex Tales*), p 73
14 *The Return of the Native*, Book First, ch 1
15 ibid, Book Fourth, ch 2
16 *Life*, p 96
17 ibid, p 405
18 Alexander Somerville, *The Whistler at the Plough*, Manchester 1852, p 380
19 *Life*, p 165
20 *Tess of the d'Urbervilles*, ch 51, quoted here p 178
21 Preface to *Far from the Madding Crowd*, quoted here p 70
22 *The Mayor of Casterbridge*, ch 14
23 *Life*, p 312
24 *The Woodlanders*, ch 2, quoted here p 282
25 *Far from the Madding Crowd*, ch 2
26 *Life*, p 167
27 "Wessex Heights" (*Satires of Circumstance*)
28 *Life*, p 165
29 ibid
30 *The Return of the Native*, Book First, ch 7, quoted here p 283
31 *The Woodlanders*, ch 4, quoted here p 287
32 *The Return of the Native*, Book Fourth, ch 3, quoted here p 286
33 ibid, quoted here p 286
34 *The Woodlanders*, ch 1, quoted here p 286
35 p 162
36 See *Humour in the index
37 *Life*, p 97
38 p 322
39 Interview with Hardy, *Pall Mall Gazette*, 2 January 1892, quoted in Blunden's *Thomas Hardy*, p 78 (London, 1962 edition). I am indebted for this identification to Dr James Gibson
40 "The Ghost of the Past" (*Satires of Circumstance*)
41 "Interlopers at the Knap" (*Wessex Tales*), quoted here p 291
42 *The Woodlanders*, ch 1, quoted here p 284
43 *Jude the Obscure*, p 33

44 "The Dorsetshire Labourer", quoted Orel, p 169
45 *Far from the Madding Crowd*, ch 44, quoted here p 293
46 *The Return of the Native,* Book Third, ch 2, quoted here p 295
47 *Far from the Madding Crowd,* ch 22, quoted here p 230
48 ibid, quoted here p 232
49 "Interlopers at the Knap" (*Wessex Tales*), pt IV
50 *The Return of the Native*, Book Second, ch 6, quoted here p 104
51 *The Woodlanders,* ch 1
52 *The Return of the Native,* Book First, ch 1
53 "Interlopers at the Knap" (*Wessex Tales*), pt I

HARDY'S PLACES

54 Archer, p 33
55 *Life*, p 21
56 ibid
57 In successive editions of *Under the Greenwood Tree* Hardy gradually altered his descriptions of the tranter's house to a close picture of his own birthplace (see C. J. P. Beatty, "Notes and Queries", vol 208, pp 26–7).
58 Beetle: a kind of hammer with a heavy wooden handle and head
59 Water-cider: made by adding water to the apples that have already been pressed
60 Fourteens: candles of the size where fourteen made up a pound

HARDY'S PEOPLE

61 *Life*, p 215
62 The Three Hardys were Thomas I and his two sons James and Thomas II (the poet's father). See also *Clothes
63 p 164
64 *Life*, p 206
65 Variorum edition of the *Life*, ed R Taylor, p 217
66 p 3
67 *Life,* pp 19 and 102
68 This poem is quoted in full on p 322

FOLKLORE
(see also *Superstitions, *Paganism, *Fatalism, * Legends and traditions, *Customs)

69 See also pp 141, 143, 164–6, 310
70 *Life*, p 158
71 British Library, Ashley Library, catalogue vol 10
72 Emma Lavinia Hardy, *Some Recollections* (ed E. Hardy & R. Gittings, OUP 1961), pp 40–4
73 p 87
74 I Samuel IX, verses 18–21
75 Scrofula, known as the King's Evil (see p 87)
76 *Life*, p 370
77 For the rest of this passage see p 249; see also p 286
78 The festival celebrations in honour of Ceres, the Roman goddess of Harvest
79 *Tess of the d'Urbervilles*, ch 23
80 See also p 89
81 Old Style: before the calendar was reformed in 1752; the old dating was still frequently used in country districts
82 Hardy to Miss Tomson, 22 February 1898 (?). (Christie's sale catalogue, recorded in Gittings, *Young Thomas Hardy,* note to p 148)
83 Maenades: the Bacchantes, or priestesses of Bacchus, Roman god of wine
84 Thor and Woden (or Odin): the ancient Norse gods after whom our Thursday and Wednesday are named. Thor was god of war and thunder, Woden the god of the underworld and also of wisdom
85 For another funeral custom — the burial of a suicide — see pp 77, 144, 313

*THE LAW
(see also *Constables, *Hanging, *Stocks, *Suicides, *Transportation)

86 pp 144, 313
87 *Life*, p 213
88 ibid, p 153
89 More of this story appears on pp 51–3
90 Other comic constables appear with the skimmity-ride on p 268

MEDICINE AND DISEASE
(see also *Death, *Sickness)

91 Scrofula: see note 75. It was once held to be curable by the king's touch. For more about such folk cures and superstitions see pp 51–5.
92 *Life,* p 154
93 ibid, p 231

94 For a note about the lack of a doctor on Portland Bill, see p 164
95 Death in childbirth is the subject of the poem *Julie-Jane* on p 75
96 The sequel to this story is on p 78
97 Hermaphrodite
98 The Register of Baptisms
99 August 1st, formerly kept as a kind of Harvest Festival, when the first bread from the new corn was consecrated
100 Skeleton (dialect)
101 Castrated rams
102 For other superstitious beliefs see pp 45–56

*DIALECT

103 Fess: pleased
104 Mommet: scarecrow
105 Plim: swell
106 Vlee: fly (a small carriage)
107 Mampus: mass, crowd
108 Leery: empty (cf German: leer)
109 Three-cunning: knowing, secretive
110 Skimmer your pate: hit you about the head with a skimming ladle
111 Daddlen, etc: idling round, clearing his throat, and spitting
112 Deedy: serious
113 Or'nary: inferior, insignificant
114 Sprawl: energy
115 Kimberlin: a stranger from the Wessex mainland
116 Shail: shuffle
117 Wamble: totter, walk unsteadily
118 *Life*, p 344
119 ibid, p 170

BUILDINGS
(see also *Chimney-corners, *Church, *Inns)

120 For another reference to the "Beelzebub kind of fork" see p 138
121 A machine for turning a spit by using the draught of air up a chimney
122 A kind of plaster made from lead oxide and olive oil
123 From which the weights of a grandfather clock are hung
124 Presumably shaken in order to clean off encrusted lime etc
125 Likely to be Hardy's birthplace at Higher Bockhampton
126 A pink-flowered herb growing on walls and roofs
127 p 153
128 p 262
129 p 257
130 p 260
131 ie a long clay pipe
132 The strength of beer, measured by the amount of malt per barrel
133 Person in authority
134 The crest of a hill
135 ie don't take offence

*CLOTHES

136 Millgate, *Thomas Hardy*, pp 84 and 587, n 37
137 The furthest limit (the most northerly part of the world in *Greek and *Roman thought)
138 Hobnailed boots
139 A twilled fine woollen cloth
140 For more about the mummers see pp 264–6

SCHOOLING
(see also *Education)

141 *The Mayor of Casterbridge*, ch 41
142 p 94
143 p 161
144 p 321
145 The fee paid by an apprentice. Hardy's mother bargained for a reduction in his premium from £50 to £40 for ready cash, though the fee Mr Hicks usually asked was £100 (Gittings, *Young Thomas Hardy*, ch 3).
146 An apprentice or learner, still working for a low wage
147 pp 156–8, 164

*CHURCH
(see also *Anglican, *Biblical allusions, *Christian, *Common Prayer, *Dissenters, *God, etc)

148 *Life*, p 145
149 p 109
150 This year
151 This refers to a controversy as to which way the priest should stand when celebrating Communion.
152 p 86
153 *Tess of the d'Urbervilles*, ch 44
154 I Kings chapter XIX

*NEWS, *COMMUNICATIONS, AND DISTANCES
(see also *Railways, *Transport)

155 A spark in the candle-flame was believed to mean a letter for the person to whom it pointed; for other superstitious beliefs see pp 45ff
156 *Twelfth Night*, Act I, scene 1
157 *The Merchant of Venice,* Act V, scene 1
158 *A Pair of Blue Eyes*, ch 29
159 ibid, ch 25
160 The red-cloaked evil spirit of the Faust legend
161 Lerret: a coracle-type boat peculiar to Portland Bill, particularly adapted to the difficulties of landing on the Chesil Beach
162 See also "The Milkmaid" on p 121
163 pp 142, 283
164 *The Return of the Native*, Book Sixth, ch 4; see also p 191

*CLASS, *POWER, *POVERTY — AND ESCAPE
(see also *Emigration, *Workhouse)

165 Dorset County Library, Lock Collection A1
166 p 164
167 ie where his cider-press was housed
168 p 194
169 Orel, p 174

RURAL *OCCUPATIONS

*Weirs and Waterways (see also pp 73, 78, 101, 167)
170 *The Return of the Native*, p 205
171 For a typically grotesque use of a weir see *The Mayor of Casterbridge*, ch 41

*Fires
172 p 100
173 A stone platform or pillar under a rick
174 Reed-drawing: pulling rough straw through a press to comb it (see p 221)

*Smuggling
175 To warn the smugglers, by a furze fire, to land elsewhere
176 p 17
177 p 42

*POACHING
*Postilions and Mail-coaches
178 Felloes: wheel-rims
179 Usually two couples
180 Hardy's wife Emma and his sister Kate

*Carters, Waggoners, *Carriers, and Road Traffic
181 Skid: brake
182 Gittings, *Young Thomas Hardy*, ch 16
183 Dumpy level: a surveyor's spirit-level with an attached telescope
184 Tilt: a wagon-awning
185 See also "Life and Death at Sunrise" on p 162, and the waggons on p 237

*Mason
186 See also p 280

*Tranter
187 ie at around £25

*Barber
188 See also Timothy Fairway's claim to be a barber on p 71

*Postman
189 For more about postal conditions as Hardy wrote about them see p 148

*Furze-cutter

*Reddleman
190 See also the children's bogey on pp 67 and 152

*Lime-burner

*Mills and milling
191 Bolting: sifting bran etc from the flour
192 Hopper: the container which feeds grain to the milling machinery

*Shoemaker
193 Moroni: a sixteenth-century Italian painter whose work Hardy had probably seen in the National Gallery in London
194 Bradded: fastened with shoemaker's brads (thin flat nails)
195 Pomace: mass of crushed apples (as in cider-making)
196 Unray'd: undressed
197 Teaving: twisting about

*Sexton

*Hiring-fairs and Working Conditions (see also *agricultural)

198 The canvas covering of a waggon
199 Dan: an old word for "master"; for other instances of hardship because of distance see pp 156ff
200 Collected in *Old Mrs Chundle and Other Stories* (New Wessex edition, vol 3)

*Farming and the *Agricultural Community
201 The Yahoos were the brutes in human form in *Gulliver's Travels*
202 Toys popular earlier in the century which showed objects and views three-dimensionally
203 Gurth, the serf in *Ivanhoe*, had a named brass collar welded round his neck
204 Alastor: an avenger (Greek); also the name of a poem by Shelley, a favourite poet of Hardy's
205 Seed-lip: a sower's basket
206 Heptarchy: the seven kingdoms of Britain in Anglo-Saxon times (Northumbria, Mercia, East Anglia, Essex, Kent, Sussex, Wessex)
207 By chewing it (dialect)
208 The projecting beam, armed with a pulley and tackle, through which goods could be hauled up to each level
209 A weighing machine
210 See also *Farmers

*Field-women

*Dairying
211 Advanced: near the birth of their calves
212 Men paid by the day
213 Nott: without horns (dialect)
214 Stave: stanza or verse of a song

*Sheep
215 Hylas, who journeyed with Hercules on the voyage of the Argonauts, was carried off by nymphs at Cios on the Mysian coast. Every year the inhabitants of Cios cried his name over their countryside.
216 Cyclops' eye: in Greek and Latin literature the Cyclope were man-eating giants from Sicily who had only one eye in the centre of the forehead
217 Ixion, King of Thessaly, in Greek mythology was chained to a perpetually-revolving wheel of fire for his attempt to seduce Hera, queen of the gods of Olympus
218 Swoln with wind: from Milton's *Lycidas*
219 Trochar (usually spelt trocar): an instrument used for drawing fluid from the body and relieving pressure in diseases of flatulence, such as "blast" or "bloat" in ruminant animals
220 Rumen: the first of the four stomachs of ruminants
221 Doleful-bells: Fritillaria meleagris, sometimes known as the Snake's Head, with dark drooping flowers ranging from purple to brown
222 Collars: horizontal beams which collect together sloping rafters above their spring
223 Lanceolate: in the shape of a spearhead
224 Chamfers: channels or fluting
225 Shearlings: sheep that have only once been shorn; hogs: sheep that have not yet been shorn

Cidermaking (see also *Cider)
226 ch 8, pt 3
227 Mawm-baskets: large round wicker baskets (dialect)
228 Pomona: the Roman goddess of fruit trees

*Woodcutting and Copsework
229 The bark would be sold for tanning

RURAL ENTERTAINMENTS

*Music and Dancing (see also *Dance, *Quire)
230 *The Return of the Native*, Book First, ch 9
231 *The Hand of Ethelberta*, ch 33
232 *The Return of the Native,* Book First, ch 4
233 "Alicia's Diary" (*A Changed Man*)
234 The west-gallery period: ie when "Quires" like the Mellstock one provided the music
235 The two brothers Edwin and William Monk edited hymn-books and played an active part in the Victorian revival of church music
236 p 286
237 Outsept: remote, out of the way (dialect)
238 Pattens: overshoes (see p 131)
239 Mandy: insolent (dialect)
240 Vlankers: fire sparks (dialect)
241 Poussetted: swung round by the hands
242 The few lines omitted here are quoted on p 61

*Parties

*Food and Drinks (see also *Cider, *Liquor)
243 *The Hand of Ethelberta*, ch 4
244 *Under the Greenwood Tree,* pt II, ch 6
245 Barrow pig: a castrated boar
246 Black pot: black pudding
247 White pot: a kind of milk pudding, with eggs, flour, spices, etc
248 Chitterlings: the smaller intestines of the pig, often fried
249 Milts: spleens
250 Falstaff's favourite beverage: sack, a white wine, formerly imported from Spain and the Canaries
251 Brandise: brandiron (a tripod for holding cooking-pots etc over the fire)
252 Biffins: large red apples
253 *Far from the Madding Crowd*, Preface

*Talk
254 p 267
255 Coryphaeus: in *Greek drama the leader of the chorus
256 Tide-times: times of religious festival (such as Easter-tide)

*Club-walking

*The Mummers
257 Collected in *Old Mrs Chundle and Other Stories*

The *Skimmity-Ride
258 Kit: a small fiddle
259 Croud: a kind of makeshift violin, derived from an ancient Celtic stringed instrument
260 Humstrum: a kind of primitive Jew's harp played with the fingers and held in the mouth
261 Serpent: an old deep-toned wind instrument about 8ft long, made of wood covered with leather, in three coils

*Fairs
262 *Life*, p 166
263 Nijni Novgorod: a Russian town (in 1932 renamed Gorki after its distinguished native), where from 1817 to the Revolution an annual fair was held which drew custom from all over Europe and Asia
264 Cheesewring: dialect word for the apparatus used for pressing curds in cheese-making
265 The name for two kinds of toy, but probably here used for a jack-in-the-box

*TOWN AND COUNTRY

266 *A Pair of Blue Eyes*, ch 3
267 A reference to Disraeli's *Tancred* (1847) in which he calls London "a modern Babylon"
268 *A Pair of Blue Eyes*, ch 13
269 *Life*, p 207
270 ibid, p 149
271 *The Woodlanders*, ch 11; see p 96
272 Lammas Day: August 1st
273 *Desperate Remedies*, pt II, ch 8
274 Partly quoted on p 6
275 Tything (commonly spelt tithing): a rural division of ten householders. In the old English system of "frithborh" or "peace-pledge" they were each responsible for the others' good conduct.

*LOVE IN THE WILDS
(see also *Isolation, *Solitude)

276 *Life*, p 400
277 *The Return of the Native*, Part the First, ch 3
278 pp 308ff
279 Byron, *Childe Harold*, canto III
280 p 276
281 pp 156–8
282 *The Return of the Native*, Part the Second, ch 5: see p 246
283 For more about paganism see pp 61–4

*THE PAST IN THE COUNTRY

284 Confervae: green algae
285 Megatherium, myledon (usually spelt mylodon): huge extinct sloth-like animals
286 Carboniferous: the geological period roughly 300 million years ago
287 p 230
288 Rooted: uprooted
289 *Far from the Madding Crowd,* ch 44
290 An educational measure of 1862 under which a system of "payment [of grants] by results" (obtained in each school) was introduced
291 See also Dr Fitzpiers' similar situation on p 284
292 *Far from the Madding Crowd*, ch 25

*COUNTRY PEOPLE

293 Archer, p 32
294 Eastings, etc: in church, turning to the east and kneeling
285 "The Romantic Adventures of a Milk-maid" (*A Changed Man*)
296 Gera: see II Samuel XVI, verses 5–14
297 Coins rather heavier than those of the realm, which were sometimes minted for private trade
298 Quean: an impudent hussy, a jade
299 Mighty I!: God Almighty! (dialect)
300 pp 5 and 174–8
301 *The Hand of Ethelberta*, ch 14
302 See also pp 46, 88, and 165ff
303 For more of Joseph Poorgrass's delicious speech see pp 256–9, 261, 305, etc
304 p 279
305 pp 90–2
306 Linsey: a coarse material of wool and flax
307 See also p 144
308 A circus (dialect)
309 Bawdy
310 Metheglin: a spiced kind of mead
311 The Book of *Common Prayer (he is referring to parts of the Anglican service)
312 Hore's-bird: a term of abuse like whoreson, sometimes spelt "husbird" (see "The Bride-Night Fire" on p 100)
313 Pummy: pomace, the crushed apple pulp for making cider
314 *Dewy: see *Under the Greenwood Tree*
315 Leery: empty, hungry (dialect)
316 'Tempted: attempted (cf "before you were even thought of")
317 Bruckle hit: mistake (dialect)
318 Limberish: rather frail (dialect)
319 Windling: fragile
320 Playward: lively
321 Snoff: snuffed out like a candle
322 Miltonic, Cromwellian: Gray's "Elegy in a Country Churchyard", stanza 15
323 Dusty death: *Macbeth*, Act V, scene 5
324 William *Dewy; Tranter Reuben (*Dewy); Farmer *Ledlow; Squire (*Grey); Lady Susan (*O'Brien)
325 Grinterns: granary compartments
326 Ho: grieve, pine

List of Hardy's Works

referred to or quoted from in this book

ARTICLES (collected in *Thomas Hardy's Personal Writings*, ed. H. Orel, Macmillan 1967)

William Barnes: Obituary
Preface to his poems
Review of his poems

The Dorsetshire Labourer

Memories of Church Restoration

General Preface to the Wessex edition, 1912 (others detailed with title of work)

The Preservation of Ancient Cottages

AUTOBIOGRAPHY

F. E. Hardy: *The Life of Thomas Hardy* (two volumes combined, Macmillan 1962)

ed. R. H. Taylor: Variorum of the *Life* in *Personal Notebooks of Thomas Hardy* (Macmillan 1978)

CONVERSATIONS

recorded by:
William Archer: *Real Conversations* (Heinemann 1904)

Vere Collins: *Talks with Thomas Hardy at Max Gate* (Duckworth 1928)

DRAMA

The Dynasts

The Famous Tragedy of the Queen of Cornwall (vol. III, New Wessex edition)

LETTERS

From various sources e.g. the *Life,* British Library, etc.

Friends of a lifetime: Letters to S. Cockerell, ed. V. Meynell (Cape 1940)

One Rare Fair Woman: Hardy's letters to Florence Henniker, ed. E. Hardy & F. B. Pinion (Macmillan 1972)

Collected Letters of Thomas Hardy, ed. Purdy & Millgate (Oxford 1978–1987)

NOTEBOOKS

Originals in the Dorset County Museum; now published in

Personal Notebooks of Thomas Hardy, ed. R. H. Taylor (Macmillan 1978)

NOVELS

Desperate Remedies
Far from the Madding Crowd
The Hand of Ethelberta
Jude the Obscure
A Laodicean
The Mayor of Casterbridge
A Pair of Blue Eyes
The Poor Man and the Lady (unpublished)
The Return of the Native
Tess of the d'Urbervilles
The Trumpet-Major
Two on a Tower
Under the Greenwood Tree
The Well-Beloved
The Woodlanders

POEMS

The Complete Poetical Works of Thomas Hardy: 3 vol. edition, ed. S. Hynes (O.U.P. 1982–85)

The Complete Poems of Thomas Hardy: 1 vol. edition, ed. James Gibson (Macmillan 1976)

(All poems are listed under Thomas Hardy, Works, in the index.)

STORIES (New Wessex edition in 3 volumes)

Vol. I WESSEX TALES & A GROUP OF NOBLE DAMES

The Distracted Preacher
Fellow-Townsmen
Interlopers at the Knap
The Melancholy Hussar of the German Legion
The Three Strangers
A Tradition of 1804
The Withered Arm
Preface to Wessex Tales

Preface to A Group of Noble Dames
The First Countess of Wessex

Vol. II LIFE'S LITTLE IRONIES & A CHANGED MAN

Absentmindedness in a Parish Choir
Andrey Satchel and the Parson and Clerk
A Few Crusted Characters
The Fiddler of the Reels
The History of the Hardcomes
Netty Sargent's Copyhold
Old Andrey's Experience as a Musician

On the Western Circuit
The Superstitious Man's Story
A Tragedy of Two Ambitions
The Winters & the Palmleys
Preface to Life's Little Ironies

Alicia's Diary
A Changed Man
The Duke's Reappearance
Enter a Dragoon
The Grave by the Handpost
Master John Horseleigh, Knight
A Mere Interlude
The Romantic Adventures of a Milkmaid
A Tryst at an Ancient Earthwork
The Waiting Supper
What the Shepherd saw

Vol. III OLD MRS. CHUNDLE & OTHER STORIES

Destiny and a Blue Cloak
The Doctor's Legend
An Indiscretion in the Life of an Heiress
Old Mrs Chundle
Our Exploits at West Poley

Index